Design of Multistory Reinforced Concrete Buildings
for Earthquake Motions

Design of **Multistory**

Published by PORTLAND CEMENT ASSOCIATION

Reinforced Concrete Buildings

for Earthquake Motions

JOHN A. BLUME

President, John A. Blume & Associates, Engineers
San Francisco, California

NATHAN M. NEWMARK

Head, Department of Civil Engineering, University of Illinois
Urbana, Illinois

LEO H. CORNING

Chief Consulting Structural Engineer, Portland Cement Association
Chicago, Illinois

West Grand Avenue, Chicago 10, Illinois

The activities of the Portland Cement Association, a national organization, are limited to scientific research, the development of new or improved products and methods, technical service, promotion and educational effort (including safety work), and are primarily designed to improve and extend the uses of portland cement and concrete. The manifold program of the Association and its varied services to cement users are made possible by the financial support of over 70 member companies in the United States and Canada, engaged in the manufacture and sale of a very large proportion of all portland cement used in these two countries. A current list of member companies will be furnished on request.

Preface

CONSIDERABLE knowledge has been gained in the last three decades about the phenomena of ground motion, the characteristics of structures, and their behavior in earthquakes. In addition, much has been learned about the response of various vibrating systems to such motion. Despite this progress and coincidental development of earthquake design criteria and codes, the unknowns and the complexities are still so great that earthquake-resistant design is not yet capable of complete and rigorous execution solely by means of mathematical analysis, design codes, specifications, or rules of procedure. It is an art as well as a science, and requires experience and judgment on the part of the engineer, as well as sensitivity to the true nature of the problem including the behavior of materials and structures subject to various types and degrees of motion. Above all it is necessary to have an understanding of the manner in which a structure absorbs the energy transmitted to it by an earthquake and the maximum amount of motion or energy the structure can sustain.

It is intended that this manual will furnish current information pertaining to these topics and specifically to the earthquake-resistant design of multistory reinforced concrete buildings. The authors and the Portland Cement Association emphasize, however, that neither this manual nor any earthquake code, spectral analysis, or other procedure can supplant the sound professional judgment of engineers familiar with the earthquake problem.

Earthquakes can be expected in presently active earthquake areas of the world, and probably in many of the apparently dormant areas as well. Engineers have learned from experience how to design and to construct buildings to resist the effects of earthquake motions, but the relatively simple empirical rules that have been developed as a result of experience may not always be the most satisfactory and may not result in the most economical construction.

The objective is to proportion a structure in such a way that it can survive without damage in a moderate earthquake and without major structural damage as the result of the most severe earthquake reasonably predictable during the anticipated life of the structure. Furthermore, the structure should not collapse even when subjected to the motions of an earthquake of abnormal intensity. It is assumed, of course, that no structure would be located directly over an active known fault.

The problem involves more than merely achieving an adequate design. The objectives of the design must be attained in the actual construction of the building. The development of design specifications and construction procedures for earthquake-resistant structures has been and, in fact, still is an evolutionary process. Although most design specifications involve the concept of a statically equivalent lateral design force, the appropriate choice of the equivalent static force is governed by the dynamic behavior of the structure. The design of earthquake-resistant structures is basically a dynamic and not a static problem. For a working understanding of the problem, one must consider inelastic deformation and energy absorption and must take into account the periods of vibration of the structure and the nature of the resistance of the structure under all conditions to which it is likely to be subjected. Many of these factors can be taken into account implicitly rather than explicitly. An advantage of having a code or design specification to follow is that it helps to remind the designer of some important aspects of the behavior of the structure that he might otherwise overlook.

Many materials can be used for earthquake-resistant construction. Whatever the material, there are ways of using it that are most efficient and economical in resisting the motions and forces produced by earthquakes. The purpose of this manual is to present basic principles of earthquake-resistant design, with particular application to the design of multistory reinforced concrete buildings. Consideration is given to the dynamic behavior of reinforced concrete members and to methods of design that provide the necessary strength and ductility to resist earthquake effects. Recommendations are given not only for design but for construction procedures and inspection to ensure, to the greatest possible degree, the achievement of the aims of the designer.

The underlying principles in the development of modern codes for seismic design are discussed. In particular, recommendations for normal design procedures are based on the 1959 report, *Recommended Lateral Force Requirements*, prepared by the Seismology Committee of the Structural Engineers Association of California, because the recommendations are the most recent and are considered to present the most rational code-type design requirements developed to date. In order to emphasize the true nature of the problem, however, considerable space in this manual is devoted to matters of dynamic movement, inelastic resistance, and energy absorption. The general procedures described, which are basic in the subject of structural dynamics, may be used in the analysis of very tall, slender, or unusual reinforced concrete buildings to supplement the design specifications.

The reader will find in Chapter 1 a general description of earthquake ground motion and the effects of such motion on the dynamic behavior of simple spring-mass systems having one degree of freedom. The concept of the response spectrum is introduced, and general predictions of earthquake response spectra are given for single-degree-of-freedom systems. Also considered in this chapter are the behavior of simple inelastic systems and the response spectra characterizing their action for certain earthquake motions.

The more complex behavior of systems having many degrees of freedom is considered in Chapter 2. An illustrative example is given in Chapter 2 of the behavior of a three-story structure to indicate the general characteristics of the response of a complex system as compared with that of a simple system. The behavior of multi-degree-of-freedom systems in the inelastic range is considered, as well as the effects of foundation and soil conditions and other factors. Methods are given in this chapter for computation of the natural periods of vibration of a building.

In Chapter 3, the principles of earthquake-resistant design, as distinct from analysis, are considered. The significance of design specifications and in particular of the SEAOC design code is discussed, and guidance is given for estimating the period of vibration and the required ductility of a proposed structure in order that it will have the appropriate characteristics to resist earthquake motions.

A detailed discussion of design codes and specifications is given in Chapter 4, with particular emphasis on the SEAOC recommendations. The method of using these to obtain an adequate design of a reinforced concrete building is described. Consideration is given to the way in which the various elements of a building can absorb energy, and general concepts are presented to permit the designer to take account of the ways in which the structure may be designed so as to resist earthquake motions and forces.

In Chapter 5, consideration is given to the behavior of reinforced concrete members under both static and dynamic loads. The strength, the stress-strain relationships, and the ductility or energy-absorbing capacity of members of different types are considered in detail with a view toward developing the criteria that the designer must adopt in order to assure the appropriate energy-absorbing capacity and ductility in his design. Consideration is given to members subjected primarily to flexure or to combined flexure and axial load. The effects of reversed loading on a building are considered to enable the designer to make necessary provision to prevent damage from the reversal of motion.

The ways in which the principles developed in Chapter 5 are applied in the design of reinforced concrete frames are described in Chapter 6. Recommendations are given to enable the designer to provide the necessary ductility in reinforced concrete buildings. These recommendations involve the selection of the strength of concrete and type of reinforcement, the amount and arrangement of the reinforcing steel, and special details that are desirable at joints and connections, in shear walls, and in other aspects of reinforced concrete buildings.

Throughout the manual and particularly in Chapters 5 and 6, it is the intention of the authors that the provisions of the Building Code Requirements for Reinforced Concrete (ACI 318-56) of the American Concrete Institute are generally applicable to buildings constructed in seismic as well as nonseismic areas. However, because of the unique conditions to which structures may be subjected in severe earthquakes, certain more stringent design requirements and details are recommended.

In order to demonstrate the procedures and principles described, an illustrative design example is given in Chapter 7. This example, pertaining to a 24-story reinforced concrete frame building, illustrates the steps to be taken in estimating the period to be used, the determination of the seismic forces according to the SEAOC code, and the design of typical columns, beams, and connections.

Because of the importance of construction procedures and the inspection necessary to ensure that the appropriate procedures are being carried out, Chapter 8 presents recommendations for construction and inspection of reinforced concrete in buildings. Recommendations are given to assure adequate control of the quality of concrete and placement of steel, and methods are described to enable the inspector to carry out his responsibilities systematically and effectively.

A description of some of the steps involved in a dynamic review of a typical design, with particular reference to the design example given in Chapter 7, is presented in Appendix A. Appendix B is a description of the reserve energy technique for the design and rating of structures in the inelastic range. Its application is illustrated by a review of the design example of Chapter 7. A verbatim reprint of the SEAOC Seismology Committee *Recommended Lateral Force Requirements*, July 1959, with subsequent changes and corrections, is included as Appendix C. For the convenience of the reader, all references cited in the manual have been numbered consecutively and are listed in Appendix D.

A summary of the notation used repeatedly in the body of the manual is given in Appendix E. The notation used conforms to generally accepted symbols to the extent possible. Because of the scope of the manual, it has been necessary to assign meanings to certain symbols which commonly have distinctly different meanings in different areas of science or engineering. The transcription of the SEAOC *Recommended Lateral Force Requirements* in Appendix C is a verbatim copy; therefore any notation used in the body of the manual which differs from that in the SEAOC code is indicated in the list of notation in Appendix D.

Acknowledgment

This manual was prepared for the Portland Cement Association by the authors with the help of Alfred L. Parme, principal engineer, and John A. Sbarounis, structural engineer, Advanced Engineering Group of the Portland Cement Association.

The authors wish to express their appreciation to their associates for their valued assistance in the studies leading to the preparation of the manual, and for their help in writing. Grateful acknowledgment is made to Dr. Chester P. Siess, professor of civil engineering, and Dr. Mete A. Sozen, associate professor of civil engineering, University of Illinois, Urbana, and to H. J. Sexton, vice president and chief engineer, and Roland L. Sharpe, vice president, of John A. Blume & Associates, Engineers, San Francisco. The detailed review and constructive criticism of the manuscript by Stephenson B. Barnes, consulting structural engineer, Los Angeles, and John F. Meehan, supervising structural engineer, California State Division of Architecture, Sacramento, are also gratefully acknowledged.

The work of many authors, investigators, and committees of technical organizations has been drawn upon in writing the manual. It has been the authors' intention to give full credit by references throughout the text to the bibliography in which are listed the sources of all data, charts, and information cited or reproduced. It is hoped that all to whom credit is due have been included. Any omissions are inadvertent.

JOHN A. BLUME
NATHAN M. NEWMARK
LEO H. CORNING

Contents

Chapter 1   Earthquake Ground Motion and Its Effects   1
  1.1   Description of Earthquake Motions   1
  1.2   Dynamic Response of Simple Systems   3
  1.3   Dynamic Response Spectrum for Simple Elastic Systems   7
  1.4   Predictions of General Response Spectra for Simple Elastic
      Systems   10
  1.5   Dynamic Response Spectrum for Simple Inelastic Systems   11
  1.6   Design Spectra for Simple Elasto-Plastic Systems   14
  1.7   Ductility Factors for Structures   15

Chapter 2   Earthquake Response of Multi-Degree-of-Freedom Systems   17
  2.1   Elastic Response of Multi-Degree-of-Freedom Systems   17
  2.2   Computation of Period of Vibration—Fundamental Mode   19
  2.3   Computation of Period of Vibration—Higher Modes   25
  2.4   Illustrative Example—Three-Degree-of-Freedom System   30
  2.5   Behavior of Multi-Degree-of-Freedom Systems in the Inelastic
      Range   37
  2.6   Effects of Foundations, Soil Conditions, and Other Factors 38

Contents

Chapter 3   Principles of Earthquake-Resistant Design   40
    3.1   Details of Basis for Rational Design   40
    3.2   Dependence of Behavior of Structure on Design Basis   41
    3.3   Comparison of Design Recommendations   42
    3.4   Estimate of Period of Vibration   44
    3.5   Summary of General Concepts   45

Chapter 4   Design Considerations and Code Requirements   47
    4.1   General Considerations   47
    4.2   Working Stresses and Loading Combinations   49
    4.3   Lateral Force Coefficient for Total Shear   51
    4.4   Variation of Seismic Force with Height   54
    4.5   Period of Vibration   58
    4.6   Required Building Separation and Earthquake Deflection   60
    4.7   Overturning   62
    4.8   Flexibility and Stiffness or Rigidity   64
    4.9   Torsion   71
    4.10 Framing, Ductility, and Energy Absorption   73
    4.11 Limit Design of Frames   86
    4.12 Parts of Buildings   88
    4.13 Reserve Energy Technique for Inelastic Design   90

Chapter 5   Strength, Ductility, and Energy Absorption
            of Reinforced Concrete Members   92
    5.1   Introduction   92
    5.2   Stress-Strain Relationships   93
    5.3   Reinforced Concrete Sections Subjected to Bending Only   101
    5.4   Reinforced Concrete Sections Subjected to Combined
          Bending and Axial Load   113
    5.5   Behavior of Reinforced Concrete Members Subjected to
          Combined Bending, Axial Load, and Shear   117
    5.6   Bending Deformation of Reinforced Concrete Members   121
    5.7   Strength and Behavior of Reinforced Concrete Shear Walls   131
    5.8   Energy-Absorbing Capacity   137
    5.9   Reversed Loading   141

Chapter 6   Design of Reinforced Concrete Frames   145
    6.1   General Principles   145
    6.2   Working Stress and Ultimate-Strength Design   146
    6.3   Strength of Concrete and Reinforcement   147
    6.4   Arrangement of Reinforcement for Beams and Slabs   148
    6.5   Arrangement of Reinforcement for Columns   156
    6.6   Recommended Arrangement of Reinforcement in Walls   163
    6.7   Expansion and Construction Joints   166

Chapter 7   Design of a 24-Story Building   168
  7.1   Introduction   168
  7.2   Seismic Shear and Overturning Moment   170
  7.3   Frame Analysis   173
  7.4   Column Loads Due to Overturning Moment   183
  7.5   Wind Analysis   186
  7.6   Vertical Loads   186
  7.7   Proportioning of Sections   187
  7.8   Detailing for Ductility   194
  7.9   Frame Displacement or Drift   200

Chapter 8   Construction and Inspection   203
  8.1   Codes and Standards   203
  8.2   Responsibility for Quality   204
  8.3   Concrete   206
  8.4   Forms   234
  8.5   Placing Reinforcement   236
  8.6   Building Separations   240

Appendix A   Elastic Modal Analysis of a 24-Story Building   241
  A.1   Modal Frequencies and Displacements   241
  A.2   Response Spectra   244
  A.3   Modal Shears   244
  A.4   Maximum Elastic Shears   246
  A.5   Comparison with Code Design Shears   247

Appendix B   Energy-Absorption Considerations   250
  B.1   Reserve Energy Technique   250
  B.2   Reserve Energy Analysis of a 24-Story Building   271

Appendix C   Recommended Lateral Force Requirements, SEAOC   286

Appendix D   References   296

Appendix E   Notation   306

Index   315

CHAPTER 1

Earthquake Ground Motion and Its Effects

1.1 Description of Earthquake Motions

In an earthquake the ground moves in a random fashion in all directions. Measurements have been made in recent decades[1]* of the "strong motion" accelerations, as a function of time, corresponding to the motions in two horizontal components; there are also records available of vertical accelerations and displacements. From these accelerations, there have been obtained the ground velocities and ground displacements as a function of time. The measured ground accelerations obtained from a strong-motion earthquake record are shown in Fig. 1-1. This figure shows the north-south component of the motions in the El Centro earthquake of May 18, 1940, and gives the intensity of ground acceleration, ground velocity, and ground displacement plotted as functions of time. It can be seen that the maximum recorded ground acceleration is about $0.33g$, the maximum ground velocity about 13.7 in. per second, and the maximum ground displacement (from the initial position) about 8.3 in. This is the most severe earthquake motion for which accurate records are now available; it may be considered as an earthquake to be expected in a specific location in California with an estimated frequency of once in 50 years, or more often if the region is close to more than one active fault. Somewhat larger motions would no doubt be experienced close to an epicenter.

---

*Numbers refer to correspondingly numbered items in the list of references (Appendix D).

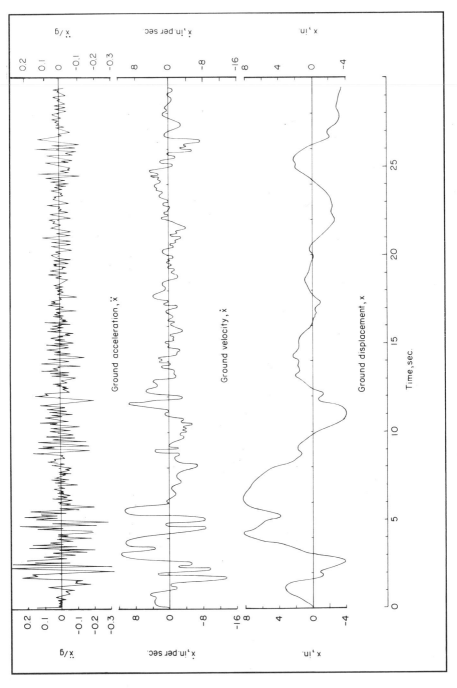

Fig. 1-1. Ground acceleration, velocity, and displacement, El Centro, Calif., earthquake of May 18, 1940, N-S component.

Similar diagrams are obtained from other earthquakes, but in general most of them indicate lower intensities of acceleration, velocity, and displacement. The 1940 El Centro earthquake is characterized by a relatively long duration of intense motion. The random character of this motion is evident, as is the fact that the displacements, velocities, and accelerations are large in only the first 12 seconds of motion.

A similar record is obtained for the east-west component of motion of the same earthquake, but the maximum values are not reached at precisely the same time. The horizontal resultant of the instantaneous motions varies in direction. Because of the random nature of the motions, any horizontal component for almost any earthquake has about the same general characteristics as for any other earthquake of about the same intensity. Similar records, with slightly smaller intensity, are obtained for the vertical motions.

1.2 Dynamic Response of Simple Systems

If a simple structure such as that shown in Fig. 1-2 is subjected to ground motion of the type given in Fig. 1-1, it will be excited into motion and will respond in a vibratory fashion. In the structure shown, let the displacement of the ground

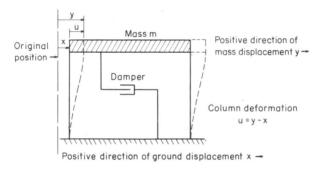

Fig. 1-2. Single-degree-of-freedom structure.

from the original position be designated by x, the displacement of the mass m by y, and define the displacement of the mass relative to the ground by the quantity u where

$$u = y - x \qquad (1\text{-}1)$$

The columns in the structure exert a lateral force or shear on the mass and on the ground of magnitude V, where V is a function of u. The relation between V and u may often be simplified as shown in Fig. 1-3, which is an elasto-plastic relationship in which the elastic range is expressed by a linear relationship

$$V = \lambda u \qquad (1\text{-}2)$$

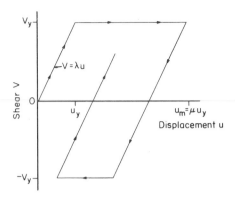

Fig. 1-3. Elasto-plastic shear-displacement relationship.

When yielding occurs, at a displacement u_y, the resistance remains constant at a magnitude V_y. If the displacement is not reversed, the displacement may reach a maximum value u_m. If, however, the displacement is reversed, the elastic recovery follows along a line parallel to the initial line, and the recovery proceeds elastically until a negative yield value, $-V_y$, is reached in the opposite direction.

Velocity damping of the motion is considered, in which the damping force is equal to a damping coefficient times the velocity of the mass relative to the ground, $\dot{u}$. Consider a damping force of magnitude

$$\eta\dot{u}$$

The equation of motion for the system can be written

$$m\ddot{y} + \eta\dot{u} + \lambda u = 0 \tag{1-3}$$

This equation can be transformed into the following form by subtracting $m\ddot{x}$ from both sides and noting that $\ddot{u} = \ddot{y} - \ddot{x}$

$$m\ddot{u} + \eta\dot{u} + \lambda u = -m\ddot{x} \tag{1-4}$$

This equation can be solved in various ways [2, 3, 4, 5, 6]. When the ground motion is zero, equation (1-4) corresponds to a damped free vibration. That value of the coefficient η which corresponds to the limiting case for periodic motion is called the critical damping coefficient, and has a magnitude which can be written as

$$\text{critical value of } \eta = 2m\omega \tag{1-5}$$

in which ω is the circular frequency of undamped vibration, given by the equation

$$\omega^2 = \frac{\lambda}{m} \text{ or } \omega = \sqrt{\frac{\lambda}{m}} \tag{1-6}$$

The natural frequency f and the period T are readily determined from the relations

$$f = \frac{\omega}{2\pi} \qquad\qquad T = \frac{1}{f} = \frac{2\pi}{\omega}$$

It is convenient to define the proportion of critical damping, β, as the ratio between η and its critical value, as in equation (1-7)

$$\beta = \frac{\eta}{2m\omega} \qquad (1\text{-}7)$$

Although the dynamic response as a function of time of a system having particular characteristics is a tedious matter to compute, the calculations can be performed. For a ground motion corresponding to the 1940 El Centro earthquake, the results obtained by numerical integration[7] of the equations of motion are shown in Fig. 1-4 for an elastic system in the upper part of the figure and for an elasto-plastic system in the lower part. The calculations plotted are for a system having a period of vibration T of 1.0 second, with a damping coefficient β equal to 10 per cent of the critical value. Merely for illustration in this example, for the elasto-plastic system, the yield displacement was taken as one-half the maximum displacement. This gives a ductility factor μ of 2 where the ductility factor is defined as the ratio between the maximum displacement and the yield displacement of the simple system.

It happens in this particular instance that the maximum displacement is the same for the elastic and for the elasto-plastic structures. It will be shown later that they are generally nearly the same unless the ductility factor is extremely large.

It is of interest to note that plastic action occurs only for several brief intervals during the history of the motion in the particular case shown in Fig. 1-4. This is indicated by the bars showing the duration of yielding. Only five yield intervals are noted during the particular response that is shown. Calculations have been reported [6, 8, 9, 10] for a number of simple structures subjected to various earthquake motions corresponding both to simple ground disturbances and to recorded accelerograms from several different earthquakes. The results are substantially the same and are discussed in detail in Section 1.5.

It is apparent from the form of equation (1-4) that for a given transient ground motion x as a function of time, the response of an elastic system depends only on the magnitude of damping and on the circular frequency of vibration of the system or, what amounts to the same thing, on the percentage of critical damping and on the natural period of the system. In other words, the magnitudes of the mass and of the spring stiffness of the structure do not independently affect the response to a ground motion. However, because the structure is subjected to a base motion and not to a force, the maximum stress that the structure experiences is a function of its stiffness as well as of its period of vibration. In general, the stiffer the spring in the structure, the greater will be the stress in the spring and the smaller its relative deflection or displacement for a given ground motion.

The most significant feature of plots such as shown in Fig. 1-4 is the maximum relative displacement or strain of the system. If the maximum relative displacement is known, the maximum spring force in the columns or the maximum shear

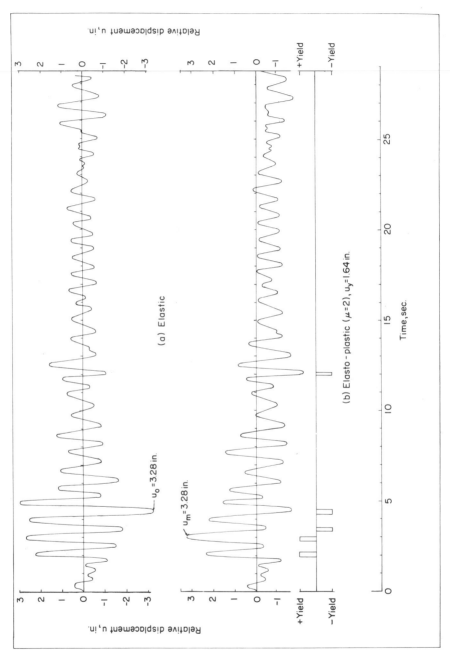

Fig. 1-4. Response of a system with $T = 1.0$ second, $\beta = 0.10$; 1940 El Centro, Calif., earthquake, N-S component.

can be determined immediately, as can also the maximum acceleration of the mass m. These values are useful directly in design.

1.3 Dynamic Response Spectrum for Simple Elastic Systems

For a specific excitation of a simple system having a particular percentage of critical damping, the maximum response is a function of the natural period of vibration of the system. A plot of the maximum response (for example, of relative displacement u, absolute displacement y, acceleration $\ddot{y}$, or spring force V) against the period of vibration T, or against the natural frequency of vibration f, or the circular frequency of vibration ω, is called a "response spectrum." The most useful response spectra are those for acceleration $\ddot{y}$, velocity $\dot{u}$, and displacement u. It is not common to plot the absolute displacement y. Since the response spectra give the maximum values of these quantities for each frequency considered, it is desirable to use a different symbol to indicate the spectral value. Consequently, in the following, the spectral value of the displacement relative to ground will be designated by the symbol S, the spectral value of the velocity relative to ground will be denoted by the symbol S_v, and the spectral value of the absolute acceleration of the mass will be denoted by the symbol S_a. To be precise, the maximum values of velocity and acceleration are not actually plotted as the spectral values because it is more convenient and sufficiently accurate to use something that approximates the maximum velocities and accelerations and which is more simply related to the displacements. The quantities used are the following:

$$S_v = \omega S = 2\pi f S \qquad (1\text{-}8)$$

$$S_a = \omega^2 S = 4\pi^2 f^2 S \qquad (1\text{-}9)$$

The quantity designated by spectral acceleration is actually the maximum acceleration for a system without damping, and is very nearly equal to the maximum acceleration for a system with damping.

The quantity used instead of the actual relative velocity is also very nearly equal to the maximum relative velocity except for very low frequency systems. It is precisely equal to the maximum velocity if the latter occurs after the ground motion ceases. It is a measure of the elastic energy in the spring elements of the system [3]. This can be shown by the following transformation that follows directly from the definition of stored energy U as the area under the shear-displacement diagram:

$$\frac{U}{m} = \frac{1}{2} V \frac{u}{m} = \frac{1}{2} \frac{\lambda}{m} u^2 = \frac{1}{2} \omega^2 u^2 \qquad (1\text{-}10)$$

U becomes maximum, U_m, when u equals S.

$$\frac{U_m}{m} = \frac{1}{2}\omega^2 S^2 = \frac{1}{2} S_v^2 \qquad (1\text{-}11)$$

It will be noted from equations (1-8) and (1-9) that if the spectral displacement is stated in inches, the spectral velocity will be in inches per second and the spectral acceleration in inches per second squared. In order for the spectral acceleration to be stated in gravity units, the right-hand side of equation (1-9) should be divided by the gravity acceleration.

Dynamic response spectra for single-degree-of-freedom elastic systems have been computed for a number of input motions [5, 6, 8, 9, 11, 12, 13, 14, 15, 16]. Typical of the results are the spectra shown in Figs. 1-5 and 1-6. Fig. 1-5 shows the response acceleration spectra for elastic systems with various degrees of damping, from no damping to 20 per cent critical damping. In Fig. 1-6, the same data are plotted in terms of the spectral velocity, with the difference that the ordinates are plotted on a logarithmic scale for period. In this sort of plot, because of the relations in equations (1-8) and (1-9), it is possible to draw diagonal scales—for acceleration sloping down to the right, and for displacement sloping down to the left—so that one can read values of spectral acceleration, spectral velocity, and spectral displacement all from the same plot. As a guide in evaluating the numerical values in Fig. 1-6, there is shown in the same

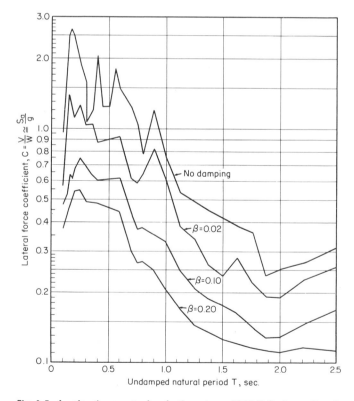

Fig. 1-5. Acceleration spectra for elastic systems, 1940 El Centro earthquake.

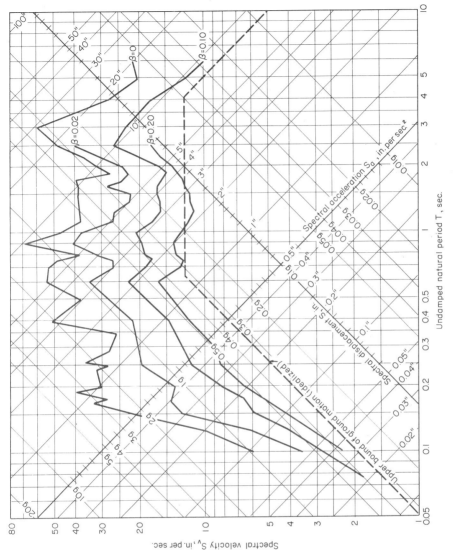

Fig. 1-6. **Response spectra for elastic systems, 1940 El Centro earthquake.**

figure a polygon made up of three bounds: the line on the left is the maximum ground acceleration of 0.33g, the line on the top is the maximum ground velocity of 13.7 in. per second, and the line on the right is the maximum ground displacement of 8.3 in.

Although there are minor differences among spectra plotted for different input data, they all show roughly the same general characteristics as follows:

1. The spectra for zero damping show rather marked oscillations with very irregular sharp peaks.

2. The oscillations generally decrease as the damping increases.
3. For extremely short periods (or for very high frequency structures), the spectral acceleration values approach magnitudes equal to the maximum ground acceleration [8, 16]. For moderately short periods, of the order of 0.1 to 0.3 seconds with a damping factor β of about 0.05 to 0.10, the spectral accelerations are about twice as great as the maximum ground accelerations.
4. For very long periods or for very low frequencies, the maximum spectral displacements approach the maximum ground displacement.
5. For intermediate frequencies, the maximum spectral velocity has a magnitude of several times the input velocity for no damping, ranging down to values about equal to the input maximum ground velocity for about 20 per cent critical damping.
6. For damping in the range of 5 to 10 per cent critical, the maximum spectral acceleration is of the order of twice the maximum ground acceleration, the maximum spectral velocity is of the order of 1.5 times the maximum ground velocity, and the maximum spectral displacement is of the same order as the maximum ground displacement.

1.4 Predictions of General Response Spectra for Simple Elastic Systems

The foregoing broad generalizations about the spectral values give an indication of a way in which spectra can be estimated for other earthquakes where records are not available or for predicted future earthquakes. For elastic systems with degrees of damping of 5 to 10 per cent critical, the spectrum on a log-log plot (see Fig. 1-6) can be considered as being bounded by three lines:
1. an acceleration line having a magnitude equal to twice the maximum ground acceleration,
2. a velocity line having a magnitude equal to 1.5 times the maximum ground velocity,
3. a displacement line having a magnitude equal to the maximum ground displacement.

For very small amounts of damping, less than 2 per cent, the numerical coefficients of 2, 1.5, and 1.0, respectively, for ground acceleration, ground velocity, and ground displacement become more nearly 4, 3, and 2, or very nearly doubled in each case, if one considers the bounding value for the upper limit of the individual fluctuations. However, the means of the fluctuations are not too far from the bounding values summarized above and are probably more significant quantities.

Other methods of prediction are to use average spectral values from several earthquakes [5], or to adjust average "smoothed" spectra, as shown in Appendix B, Figs. B-5 and B-6, to allow for possible variations in epicentral distance and magnitude of future earthquakes [17, 18].

1.5 Dynamic Response Spectrum for Simple Inelastic Systems

The calculation of the response of inelastic systems is more difficult than that for elastic systems. However, calculations have been made for several kinds of input based on the relatively simple elasto-plastic load-deformation curve in which deformation is proportional to load up to the yield point and thereafter deformation increases without further increase in load as illustrated in Fig. 1-3, until strain hardening begins [6, 8, 9, 10, 19]. Other types of inelastic systems are illustrated in Fig. B-4 in Appendix B. Such systems would show somewhat

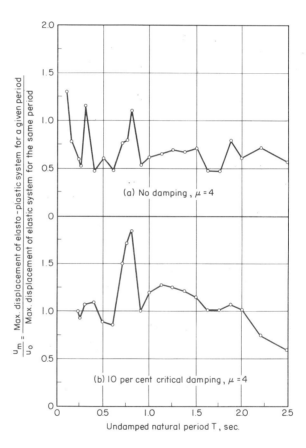

Fig. 1-7. Comparison of maximum relative displacements of elasto-plastic and elastic systems as a function of their natural periods, 1940 El Centro earthquake.

greater energy absorption capacity for the same degree of ductility. Results of calculations of systems other than elasto-plastic are available [16, 17, 20]. The results of the various calculations are reasonably consistent.

Fig. 1-7 shows a comparison of the maximum relative displacements of elasto-plastic and elastic systems as a function of the natural period of vibration, for systems with no damping and 10 per cent critical damping, in which the elasto-plastic systems all have the same ductility factor, namely, $\mu = 4$. It can be seen that there is some difference but not a systematic one in the displacements of the two systems for the same period. The displacements never differ by more than a factor of 2 and are generally less for the elasto-plastic system than for the elastic system when the amount of damping is small. Similar results have been reported elsewhere [9]. Considerably larger displacements for elasto-plastic systems than for elastic systems having the same period are reported [9] for conditions that

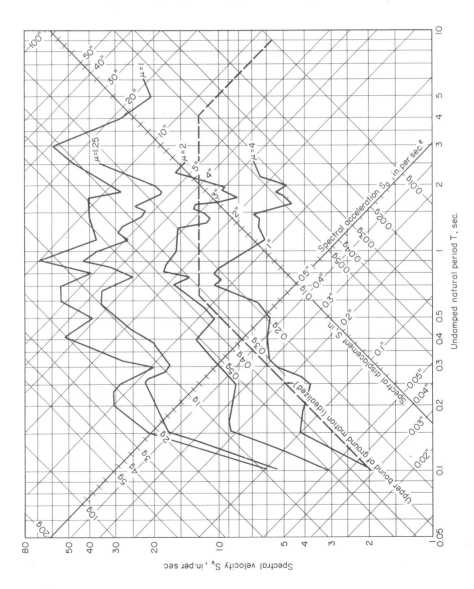

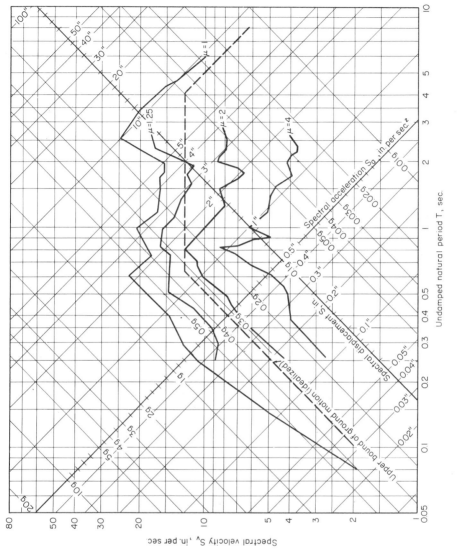

Fig. 1-9. Response spectra for elasto-plastic systems with 10 per cent critical damping, 1940 El Centro earthquake.

correspond to nearly rigid-plastic systems, far beyond any practical range (corresponding to values of ductility factor of 100 to 200 or more), but for values of the order of 20 or less the results are of the same general nature as those shown in Fig. 1-7.

In reference 8, calculations were made using the procedures developed in reference 7, and making use of a high-speed digital computer, from which the response spectra shown in Figs. 1-8 and 1-9 were prepared. The response spectra plotted here are for the elastic component of the response of the elasto-plastic system. Plotted in this way, one can use the same type of plot as in Fig. 1-6. To obtain the true maximum displacement, however, one must multiply the values read from the plots by the ductility factor. The accelerations and velocity are correct as read directly from the plots.

These spectra for the elasto-plastic systems have the same general characteristics as spectra for elastic systems, but in general the spectrum plots appear to be displaced downward, at each frequency, by an amount that is dependent on the ductility factor. It also appears, by comparison between Figs. 1-8 and 1-9, that the two sources of energy absorption—viscous damping and plastic behavior—both affect the response in about the same way and are roughly additive in their effects. However, the influence of viscous damping seems to diminish as the ductility ratio increases or as the energy absorption in plastic behavior increases. This is indicated by the fact that on Figs. 1-8 and 1-9, the data for a ductility factor of 4 lie much closer together than the data for a ductility factor of 1. Similar plots have been obtained for earthquakes other than the 1940 El Centro.

As an example of the use of the elastic response spectrum shown in Fig. 1-6, one can read from it, for the motions corresponding to the 1940 El Centro earthquake and for a structure with a period of 1 second and 10 per cent of critical damping, values of a spectral velocity of 20 in. per second, a spectral acceleration of $0.33g$, and a spectral displacement of 3.2 in. For the same period and damping factor, an elasto-plastic system having a ductility factor of 4 will have an acceleration of only $0.1g$ and an elastic displacement of about 1.0 in. or a total displacement of about 4 in., from Fig. 1-9.

If the same elastic structure has a period of 2 seconds in the elastic range, it will have a spectral acceleration of $0.13g$ and a spectral displacement of about 5 in. For an elasto-plastic system with a ductility factor of 4, these quantities become about $0.04g$ and 1.5 in. for elastic displacement or 6 in. for total displacement.

1.6 Design Spectra for Simple Elasto-Plastic Systems

From the above data, and within the limits of predictability of the characteristics of future earthquakes, one can conclude that a reasonable design spectrum for an elasto-plastic system can be derived merely by taking account of the fact that the spectral displacement of the elasto-plastic system is practically the same as that for an elastic system having the same period of vibration. Consequently, one could obtain a design spectrum for the elasto-plastic system by dividing the ordinates of the spectrum response for the elastic system, at each period, by the ductility factor for which it is desired to design. For example, with a ductility factor of 4, which is a reasonable design value, one would divide the elastic spectrum values by 4 to obtain the elasto-plastic values. It is noted that a factor of roughly this magnitude appears to be consistent with the relationship between the computed El Centro spectrum and most design codes.

Slightly different approaches to the design of inelastic systems were proposed by Housner [14] and Blume [17, 20, 21]. These procedures, one of which is also described in reference 8, consider that instead of the spectral displacement being the same for a given frequency, the energy absorbed is the same for the elasto-plastic system and the elastic system. It was also suggested [21] that period and damping could be ignored in reducing elastic coefficients for elasto-plastic values. This energy criterion leads to a slightly different formulation that corresponds also to a shifting down of the spectra by a ratio which, instead of being obtainable by dividing the elastic spectrum by μ, is obtained by dividing the elastic spectrum by the quantity

$$\sqrt{2\mu - 1}$$

The difference in results between these two approaches for the useful values of μ less than about 5 is not great in view of the uncertainties of the calculations.

It is normally not desirable to design directly for ductility factors greater than 4 or 5 or for ratios of critical damping greater than 5 to 10 per cent irrespective of the materials or type of structure involved. It should be noted, however, that the energy absorption value of composite materials and complex structures such as buildings may be greater than indicated by the idealized elasto-plastic relationship assumed above.

1.7 Ductility Factors for Structures

The magnitude of the ductility factor that can be achieved in a structure depends on the material, the structural complexity and configuration, the speed of loading, the temperature, the tendency of some materials to fail with a brittle fracture, and other factors, including joints, connections, and any stress concentrations. Therefore, the ductility of the material used is not a direct indication of the ductility of the structure as a whole.

Although it is recognized that the effects of nuclear blasts on structures are not strictly comparable with the effects of earthquake motions, laboratory and field tests and data from operational use of nuclear weapons [22] are of some significance in the consideration of the ductility of structures. Indications are that structures of practical configuration having frames of ductile materials, or a combination of ductile materials, generally have ductility factors under blast loading from a minimum of about 3 to a maximum of 8. Simple elements, as distinguished from an entire structure, occasionally exhibit substantially higher values.

In order to arrive at a basis for selection of a design ductility factor, consideration was given to the magnitude of the ductility implicitly assumed in standard and accepted seismic design procedures. If one takes into account the feedback of energy from a massive building to the ground and other attenuating factors,

15

a minimum ductility ratio in the order of 4 to 6 becomes a reasonable criterion in view of SEAOC code requirements, El Centro type and intensity earthquake records, and the results of theoretical analyses of elastic and elasto-plastic structures. Additional ductility or consideration of all available energy absorption capacity may be indicated for special structures, more severe earthquake risks, or the upper stories of slender buildings.

For those who wish to consider this problem on the basis of total resistance (including the contribution of walls or other elements), other earthquake exposure, and on the basis of energy reconciliation, the reserve energy technique described in Appendix B may be used. This procedure also provides for changes in stiffness and period under the severe lurches of earthquake motion.

As indicated in the first paragraph of this section, the determination of the ductility and energy capacity required for a specific structure depends upon many factors and is, therefore, beyond the scope of this manual. In view of this, a minimum criterion is adopted: that reinforced concrete structures for earthquake resistance must be designed, detailed, and constructed in such a manner that the ductility factor will be at least 4 up to the point of beginning of visible damage, and even greater to the point of beginning of structural damage.

CHAPTER **2**

Earthquake Response
of Multi-Degree-of-Freedom Systems

2.1 Elastic Response of Multi-Degree-of-Freedom Systems

In a system such as shown in Fig. 2-1, there are a number of masses and springs
in series connected to a base, rather than just one mass and spring. This system
behaves in a much more complex manner than the simple system considered in
Fig. 1-2. Such a multi-degree-of-freedom system has "modes" of vibration, and
can oscillate in any of these modes at the particular frequency of that mode. The
fundamental frequency of the system corresponds, in general, to a motion that
involves displacement of all of the masses toward the same side, but the higher
modes correspond to reversals in the directions of motion of the various masses,
with inflection points in the system between the base and the top.

So long as the structure remains elastic, and is undamped, or when the damping forces satisfy certain requirements, it is possible to analyze it [11, 12, 20, 23, 24, 25,
26] as if it were a system of simple single-degree-of-freedom elements. Each element is considered to have its particular frequency, and to be excited by the
ground motion in a manner determined by a "participation" coefficient and
the spectrum response quantity desired—acceleration, displacement, or velocity. An example of such an analysis is given in Section 2.4.

The procedure outlined gives the maximum response for each of the modes.
The actual responses are nearly independent functions of time, and the maximums in the different modes do not necessarily occur at the same time. Although
it is possible to obtain the time history of the motion in each of the modes, this
is an extremely complex and tedious calculation and has been done only rarely.

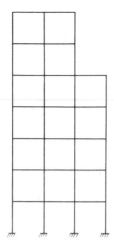

Fig. 2-1. Multi-degree-of-freedom structure.

Maximum responses of multistory buildings for several earthquakes, as distinct from the sum of the modal maximums, have been determined by numerical methods and are reported in the literature [19, 25, 26].

For the most general types of damping, even including viscous damping, modal vibrations in independent uncoupled modes cannot exist. Among the types of viscous damping for which modal analysis is possible are linear combinations of (1) damping proportional to relative velocity between the masses, where the damping coefficient is proportional to the spring constant coupling the same masses, and (2) damping proportional to the velocity of each mass relative to the ground, with each damping coefficient proportional to the magnitude of the attached mass. For these kinds of damping, and for certain other restricted damping arrangements, modal vibrations are possible; where they are possible, the modes have the same shape as for the undamped system [27, 28]. In these cases, the maximum possible response of the system (stress, deformation, displacement, velocity, etc.) is given by the sum of the maximum modal responses without regard to sign. This is an absolute upper limit to the response. This upper limit is not a rigorous mathematical one for those cases where uncoupled modes do not exist. However, for relatively small amounts of damping, of the order of less than 10 per cent critical for the first mode, it is not unreasonable to use this criterion as an approximation.

Values have been reported [26] of maximum shears in structures with 4, 8, or 16 stories for no damping, subjected to several different earthquake excitations. The results indicate that the calculated maximum shear is slightly less than the sum of the maximum modal values for the 4-story structure, and about equal to the square root of the sums of the squares of the modal maximums for the 16-story structure. It is about half way between the sum of the modal maximums and the square root of the sums of the squares of the modal maximums for the 8-story structure.

The concept that the probable maximum response is about equal to the square root of the sums of the squares of the modal maximums was presented by Goodman, Rosenblueth, and Newmark [29] and further discussed by Rosenblueth [4]. It has been shown that this concept arises from the consideration of equal probability of modal responses in any mode, and is in accord with perfectly random distributions of the expected values for each of the modal components.

Although this chapter considers in detail the procedures for calculating the response of multi-degree-of-freedom systems subjected to earthquake motions, it should not be inferred by the reader that it is generally necessary to make calculations of the complexity described herein as a routine matter in the design of multistory buildings. This material is presented for the general information of the reader so that he has the background necessary to understand why design specifications are set up in the form in which they are used. There are many considerations other than those pertaining to the mathematical analysis of a structure under elastic conditions that must be taken into account in an earthquake-resistant design. There are a great many uncertainties about the input motions and about the structural characteristics that can affect the computations. Moreover, it is not generally necessary nor desirable to design tall structures to remain completely elastic under severe earthquake motion. Considerations of inelastic behavior lead to further discrepancies between the results of routine methods of calculation and the actual response of structures. It is the purpose of the discussion presented in this chapter to show that for multistory buildings, in general, the recommended lateral force requirements of the SEAOC code (Appendix C) are logical and reasonable as minimum standards for public safety. If the discussion herein justifies confidence on the part of the designer in these requirements, it will have achieved its purpose.

Nevertheless, for those interested in the problem of computation of dynamic response, the methods presented herein are described in sufficient detail so that they can be used for general cases of multistory structures.

2.2 Computation of Period of Vibration—Fundamental Mode

Procedures are available for the computation of the periods of vibration of undamped * multi-degree-of-freedom systems [27, 30, 31, 32, 33, 34] and applications of some of these procedures to actual buildings are described in several papers [24, 35]. Consider a system with a number of masses "lumped" at particular points, letting m_n represent the nth mass of the system, and assume that the system is vibrating in the jth mode. If the system is vibrating in a steady-state condition, without damping, the displacement at the nth mass can be written in the form

$$u_{nj} \sin \omega_j t \qquad (2\text{-}1)$$

----

*Damping of less than 20 per cent critical affects the computed periods by less than 2 per cent. Hence nominal damping does not change the period appreciably.

The acceleration experienced by the mass during its oscillatory motion is given by the second derivative with respect to time of the expression [equation (2-1)] and is as follows:

$$-\omega_j^2 u_{nj} \sin \omega_j t \qquad (2\text{-}2)$$

The negative value of this acceleration, multiplied by the mass m_n, is considered a reversed effective force or inertial force, applied at the point n. The inertial forces $\bar{Q}_{nj} \sin \omega_j t$ are considered as being applied to the structure at each mass point, where the coefficient of the sine term in the inertial force expression has the form

$$\bar{Q}_{nj} = m_n \omega_j^2 u_{nj} \qquad (2\text{-}3)$$

Since the inertial forces were considered to take account of the mass effects, the displacements of the structure due to the forces $\bar{Q}_{nj}$ must be precisely equal to the quantities u_{nj}. Consequently, in order to find the square of the circular frequency for the jth mode, ω_j^2, it is necessary merely to find a set of displacements u_{nj} at each mass point n of such a magnitude that forces corresponding to this displacement multiplied by the local mass m_n, and by the square of the circular frequency for the jth mode, ω_j^2, give rise to the displacements u_{nj}. Any procedure that will establish this condition will give both the modal frequencies and the modal deflection shapes. It is clear from the discussion that multiplying the magnitudes of the modal deflections by a constant does not change the situation since all the forces, and consequently all of the deflections consistent with those forces, will be multiplied by the same constant.

However, it is not possible without other knowledge of the situation to write down directly a correct set of displacements for the jth mode. Therefore the calculations must be made by a process which makes it possible to arrive at these deflections as a result of a systematic method of computation. The most useful procedures, at least for the determination of the fundamental mode, are Rayleigh's method or modifications thereof [27, 32, 34, 35], or methods based on a procedure of successive approximations developed originally by Stodola [27, 30]. A description of the successive approximations procedure follows:

1. Assume a set of deflections at each mass point of magnitude u_{na}. Compute for these deflections an inertial force $\bar{Q}_{na}$ given by the expression

$$\bar{Q}_{na} = m_n u_{na} \omega^2 \qquad (2\text{-}4)$$

   where the quantity ω^2 is an unknown circular frequency. It may be carried in the calculations as an unknown.

2. Apply these forces to the system and compute the deflections corresponding to them. Let these deflections be designated by the symbol u_{nb}.

$$u_{nb} = \bar{u}_{nb} \omega^2 \qquad (2\text{-}5)$$

3. The problem is to make u_{nb} and u_{na} as nearly equal as possible. To do this ω may be varied. The value of ω that gives the best fit is a good approximation to the circular frequency for the mode that corresponds to the deflection u_{nb}, which in general will be an approximation to the funda-

mental mode. In general, u_{nb} will be a better approximation to the fundamental mode shape than was u_{na}.

4. Consequently, a repetition of the calculations using u_{nb} as the starting point will lead to a new derived deflection that will be an even better approximation.

In most cases, even with a very poor first assumption for the fundamental mode deflection, the process will converge with negligible errors to ω_1^2 in at most two or three cycles. However, one can obtain a good approximation in only one cycle. The mode shape will not be as accurately determined unless the calculation is repeated several times.

If the quantity shown in equation (2-6) is made a minimum, in effect minimizing the square of the error between the derived deflection and the assumed deflection, the "best" value of ω^2 consistent with the assumed deflection curve can be determined. The quantity it is desired to minimize is

$$\sum_n m_n(u_{nb} - u_{na})^2 = \text{minimum} \tag{2-6}$$

When equation (2-5) is substituted into equation (2-6), one obtains

$$\sum m_n(\omega^2 \bar{u}_{nb} - u_{na})^2 = \text{minimum} \tag{2-7}$$

Now if the derivative of equation (2-7) is taken with respect to ω^2, the result obtained is

$$2\sum m_n(\omega^2 \bar{u}_{nb} - u_{na})\bar{u}_{nb} = 0 \tag{2-8}$$

This is equivalent to the following relationship for the best value of ω^2:

$$\omega^2 = \frac{\sum m_n u_{na}\bar{u}_{nb}}{\sum m_n \bar{u}_{nb}^2} \tag{2-9}$$

The value of ω^2 given by equation (2-9) exceeds, generally only slightly, the true value for the fundamental mode.

Rayleigh's Method

Probably the most-used engineering procedure for computing the period of the fundamental mode is Rayleigh's method. The method without modifications, however, does not generally give accurate values of the mode shape. It is interesting to note that Rayleigh's method for calculation of the fundamental frequency of a building frame can be related to the procedure just described by the simple process of setting u_{na} equal to unity throughout the structure. In the case of a vertical or horizontal beam-like structure, the derived displacements $\bar{u}_{nb}$ will be proportional to the deflections of the structure due to forces equal to the weight of the structure. Since Rayleigh's procedure using a value of u_{na} equal to unity gives a quite accurate determination of the fundamental frequency, it is obvious that the use of equation (2-9) will yield a highly accurate value if any reasonable deflection shape is assumed for the first mode. In either the successive approximations procedure or the Rayleigh method, the effect of foundation rotation, column shortening, or other contributions to deflections can be readily included, although in the following examples these effects are not considered.

Illustrative Example

The simplest illustration of the procedure for computing the period of vibration of a structure is given by the calculations for a single-degree-of-freedom system. Consider, for example, the structure shown in Fig. 1-2, which has a single mass m and a spring constant λ. If the value of the assumed displacement u_a is taken as 1.0, then from equation (2-4) the inertial force has the magnitude

$$\bar{Q}_a = mu_a\omega^2 \tag{2-10}$$

When this force is applied to the structure, because of the fact that the spring constant is λ, the derived deflection u_b has the value

$$u_b = \frac{\bar{Q}_a}{\lambda} = \frac{m}{\lambda}u_a\omega^2 \tag{2-11}$$

It is obvious from equation (2-11) that the value of u_b will be equal to u_a when ω^2 has the following value:

$$\omega^2 = \frac{\lambda}{m} \tag{2-12}$$

From this equation the simple and well-known expression for the frequency of a single-degree-of-freedom system is readily derived as

$$f = \frac{\omega}{2\pi} = \frac{1}{2\pi}\sqrt{\frac{\lambda}{m}} \tag{2-13}$$

and the period T is

$$T = \frac{1}{f} = 2\pi\sqrt{\frac{m}{\lambda}} \tag{2-14}$$

The procedure described will now be applied to the three-degree-of-freedom structure shown in Fig. 2-2. The structure has a first-story spring constant four times that of the top story, and a second-story spring constant three times that

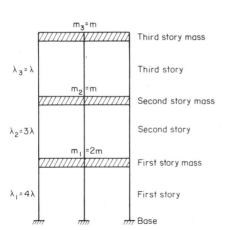

Fig. 2-2. Three-story or three-degree-of-freedom structure.

Masses and spring const's	Assumed displ. u_{na}	Inertial force $\bar{Q}_{na}/\omega^2 = m_n u_{na}$	Shear $V_n/\omega^2 = \Sigma \frac{\bar{Q}_{na}}{\omega^2}$	Increment in story displacement $\delta u_n = \frac{V_n}{\omega^2} = \frac{V_n}{\omega^2 \lambda_n}$	Derived displacement $\bar{u}_{nb} = u_{nb}/\omega^2 = \Sigma \frac{\delta u_n}{\omega^2}$	Ass'd. displ. / Der. displ. $\frac{u_{na}}{\bar{u}_{nb}}$
□m	3	3m			7.5m/λ	0.400λ/m
λ			3m	3m/λ		
□m	3	3m			4.5m/λ	0.667λ/m
3λ			6m	2m/λ		
□2m	2	4m			2.5m/λ	0.800λ/m
4λ			10m	2.5m/λ		
					0	

See Eq. (2-9)

$$\omega_1^2 = \frac{\Sigma m_n u_{na} \bar{u}_{nb}}{\Sigma m_n \bar{u}_{nb}^2} \cong \frac{3m(7.5m/\lambda)+3m(4.5m/\lambda)+4m(2.5m/\lambda)}{m(7.5m/\lambda)^2+m(4.5m/\lambda)^2+2m(2.5m/\lambda)^2} = \frac{46}{89}\frac{\lambda}{m} = 0.517\frac{\lambda}{m}$$

Fig. 2-3. Calculation of fundamental circular frequency.

of the top story. The mass distribution is not quite uniform, the second floor having a mass twice that of the third floor or of the top floor.

It is noted that the values of m and λ can have any magnitudes assigned to them, and they will be kept in general form throughout the calculations. The mass is given in terms of the weight divided by the acceleration of gravity. Consequently, the units used in the calculation have to be taken with consistent values. By reference to equation (2-14), it is apparent that if the mass is stated in terms of a weight in pounds divided by an acceleration of gravity in inches per second squared, and if the spring constant is given in terms of pounds per inch, the period T will be in units of seconds. Another set of consistent units involves displacement in feet, weight in kips, acceleration of gravity in feet per second squared, and spring constant in kips per foot.

It is also apparent that the assumed deflection u_a can have any units whatsoever, and the derived deflection u_b will have the same units. Consequently, it is convenient to take u_a or u_{nj} as dimensionless. This does not affect the results at all and makes it more clear that the modal displacements are quantities that give the shape of the deflection pattern rather than the absolute magnitudes.

The calculations for the fundamental mode for the structure in Fig. 2-2 are tabulated in Fig. 2-3 for an assumed shape of the mode corresponding to deflections at the first, second, and third story, respectively, of magnitudes 2, 3, and 3. The inertial forces $\bar{Q}_{na}$ are computed from equation (2-4). At the first mass above the base, the magnitude of the mass being $2m$, the value of the assumed deflection u_{na} is multiplied by $2m$ whereas the assumed deflections at the second and third levels are multiplied by m only.

The shears V_n in the various stories are obtained by summing the forces from the top down, since there is no force applied at the top. These shears, divided by the spring constants for the various floors, give the tabulated values of the increment in story-displacement δu_n. From these, by starting with the known value of zero deflection at the base, one obtains directly the values of the derived deflection u_{nb}. The final column shows ratios of u_{na} to $\bar{u}_{nb}$. These give the values of ω^2 at the particular mass points for which the derived curve and the assumed curve agree exactly.

It can be noted that if ω^2 has the smallest of these values, namely 0.400 for the top mass, the derived curve will lie everywhere inside the assumed curve or, in other words, between it and the original undeflected position. This indicates that the quantity 0.400 is an absolute lower limit to the value of ω^2 for the first mode. It also can be noted that if the value of ω^2 has the magnitude 0.800, as for the lowest mass in this case, the derived curve will lie everywhere outside the assumed value and therefore this is an upper limit to the value of ω^2 for the first mode. In other words, any value of ω^2 between 0.400 and 0.800 can make the two curves agree in part, although not completely; but values outside these limits cannot make the curves agree at all. Consequently, the true value of ω^2 must lie between the limits described. (These observations are applicable only in the case where the assumed curve and the derived curve of deflections have no nodal points or points of zero deflection.)

If one applies equation (2-9) to the results, one obtains a very good approximation to the magnitude of ω^2 for the first mode, as follows:

$$\omega_1^2 \cong \left(\frac{46}{89}\right)\frac{\lambda}{m} = 0.517\,\frac{\lambda}{m} \tag{2-15}$$

As will be shown later, the exact value for the first mode is $0.500\ \lambda/m$.

The pattern of derived deflections, 2.5, 4.5, and 7.5, relative to a deflection of unity at the first mass above the base, has the values 1.0, 1.8, and 3.0. The true pattern for the first mode has the values 1, 2, 4. The derived pattern is much closer to the first mode than is the assumed set of values corresponding to 1.0, 1.5, 1.5. It is noted that the deflection pattern for the first mode is not, however, nearly as accurate after one cycle as is the best value for the first mode frequency.

An illustration of Rayleigh's method is given in Fig. 2-4. The calculations are made in the same way as in Fig. 2-3, but correspond to the assumption of a set of equal unit displacements. The resulting values are shown, as is the best approximation for the circular frequency as given by equation (2-9). This leads to the approximation

$$\omega_1^2 \cong \left(\frac{19}{3}\,\Big/\,\frac{107}{9}\right)\frac{\lambda}{m} = 0.532\,\frac{\lambda}{m} \tag{2-16}$$

It is seen that the approximation to the first mode circular frequency using Rayleigh's method is indeed accurate, but the modal shape obtained is not very good, having relative values of 3, 5, 8, or 1, 1.67, 2.67.

Masses and spring const's	Assumed displ.	Inertial force	Shear	Increment in story displacement	Derived displacement	Ass'd. displ. / Der.displ.
	u_{na}	$\bar{Q}_{na}/\omega^2 = m_n u_{na}$	$V_n/\omega^2 = \sum \frac{\bar{Q}_{na}}{\omega^2}$	$\delta u_n = \frac{V_n}{\omega^2} = \frac{V_n}{\omega^2 \lambda_n}$	$\bar{u}_{nb} = u_{nb}/\omega^2 = \sum \frac{\delta u_n}{\omega^2}$	$\frac{u_{na}}{\bar{u}_{nb}}$
□m, λ	1	m	m		8m/3λ	0.375λ/m
				m	m/λ	
□m, 3λ	1	m	m		5m/3λ	0.600λ/m
				2m	2m/3λ	
□2m, 4λ	1	2m	2m		m/λ	1.000λ/m
				4m	m/λ	
					0	

See Eq.(2-9)

$$\omega_1^2 = \frac{\sum m_n u_{na} \bar{u}_{nb}}{\sum m_n \bar{u}_{nb}^2} \cong \frac{m(8m/3\lambda)+m(5m/3\lambda)+2m(m/\lambda)}{m(8m/3\lambda)^2+m(5m/3\lambda)^2+2m(m/\lambda)^2} = \frac{57}{107}\frac{\lambda}{m} = 0.532\frac{\lambda}{m}$$

Fig. 2-4. Calculation of fundamental circular frequency by Rayleigh's method.

The reader can verify easily that the modal pattern 1, 2, 4 will lead to precisely the same modal pattern, with a magnitude for the square of the first mode circular frequency of

$$\omega_1^2 = 0.5 \frac{\lambda}{m} \tag{2-17}$$

Incidentally, it is noted that with the assumed set of deflections in Fig. 2-4, the absolute lower and upper limits for the circular frequency have magnitudes of $0.375 \; \lambda/m$ and $1.0 \; \lambda/m$, respectively. These are poorer approximations than are indicated from the results of the calculations in Fig. 2-3 because the assumed deflection curve is not as good.

2.3 Computation of Period of Vibration—Higher Modes

Several methods are available for computing the frequencies of higher modes than the fundamental mode for a multi-degree-of-freedom system. Only two procedures will be described here. The first is an extension of the procedure described for the single-degree-of-freedom system, and involves the process of "sweeping" the lower mode components from the assumed and derived deflection curves, using the same procedures previously described for developing the derived curve from an assumed deflection curve. The method of successive approximations will always converge toward the lowest mode for which any component of deflection exists in the assumed curve. Therefore, all components of the modes lower in frequency than the desired one must be swept out or eliminated from the assumed deflection pattern for this procedure to work effectively.

The sweeping procedure is based on the fact that the modal deflection patterns are "orthogonal" in the sense that the following relationship [27, 28] applies:

$$\sum_n u_{nj} m_n u_{nk} = 0 \tag{2-18}$$

in which u_{nj} and u_{nk} are the deflection patterns for the jth mode and the kth mode, respectively. This relationship applies only when the frequencies of the jth and the kth mode are different, as is always the case for multistory buildings.

With the aid of equation (2-18), it becomes possible to eliminate the components of any mode from an assumed deflection pattern. Consider the assumed deflection pattern u_{na} and think of it as being expanded into a series of modal deflection patterns as in the equation

$$u_{na} = \sum_j \bar{C}_j u_{nj} \tag{2-19}$$

or

$$u_{na} = \bar{C}_1 u_{n1} + \bar{C}_2 u_{n2} + \bar{C}_3 u_{n3} + \cdots \tag{2-20}$$

If both sides of equation (2-20) are multiplied by the quantity $m_n u_{nk}$ and are summed over all mass points n, the following result is obtained:

$$\sum_n u_{na} m_n u_{nk} = \bar{C}_k \sum_n u_{nk} m_n u_{nk} \tag{2-21}$$

in which only the term involving $\bar{C}_k$ appears because all of the terms involving other values of $\bar{C}$ vanish because of equation (2-18). It follows, therefore, that any particular coefficient $\bar{C}_k$ in the expression (2-19) can be written as

$$\bar{C}_k = \frac{\sum u_{na} m_n u_{nk}}{\sum m_n u_{nk}^2} \tag{2-22}$$

Therefore, if the modal deflection pattern is known fairly accurately for any mode k, such as the fundamental mode $k = 1$, the coefficient of that modal deflection pattern which exists in any assumed pattern of deflections u_{na} can be computed. If the coefficient $\bar{C}_1$ multiplied by the deflection pattern in the first mode is subtracted from the assumed deflection pattern, the first modal component is eliminated from the assumed deflection pattern, and the resulting deflection pattern will be free of the first mode and will give a pattern for which the numerical procedure should converge to the second mode.

Theoretically, more than one mode can be eliminated at a time since the coefficient for each modal component of the assumed deflection is computed independently. This means that after the first and second mode have been computed, each of them can be eliminated from an assumed deflection pattern for the third mode and a frequency and modal shape for the third mode determined. In practice, however, because of round-off errors and because of the fact that the modal patterns are not determined accurately by these procedures unless a great many cycles are computed, one never eliminates the unwanted modes completely. In part, this can be compensated for by eliminating the undesired modes both from the assumed deflection pattern and from the derived deflection pattern resulting from the cycle of calculations. Nevertheless, this process becomes almost too tedious for use for more than the first three or four modes in any practical problem.

As an example of the "sweeping" procedure for eliminating the first mode, a complete set of calculations for the second mode frequency is shown in Fig. 2-5. The assumed deflection pattern is taken to correspond with an estimated value for the second mode in the pattern 2, 1, $-$ 3. However, in order to avoid fractions or decimals in the intermediate calculations shown in the figure, and to permit easier checking by the reader, the assumed values are taken as $+$ 22, $+$ 11, $-$ 33.

Because the first mode component is known exactly, it is easy to eliminate this mode completely from the assumed deflection pattern. The calculations for doing so in accordance with equation (2-22) are indicated in the figure. In order to obtain a set of values that does not contain the first mode, the displacements in the first mode multiplied by the calculated first mode coefficient ($\bar{C}_1 = -3$) must be subtracted from the assumed values u_{na}. These values, designated as $\bar{u}_{na}$, differ slightly from the originally assumed values and are shown in the tabulation. From this point on, the calculations are made in exactly the same way as those in Figs. 2-3 and 2-4. The resulting deflections are shown, and the ratios of the derived to the assumed deflections are computed. The same relationship given in equation (2-9) can be used to compute a best value for the second-mode frequency, but in general this would not be necessary. The ratios of the sums of the absolute values of the deflections can be used for a good enough approxima-

Masses and spring const's	Assumed displ. u_{na}	First mode displacement u_{n1}	Assumed displacement "swept" of first mode $\bar{u}_{na} = u_{na} - \bar{C}_1 u_{n1}$	Inertial force $\bar{Q}_{na}/\omega^2 = m_n \bar{u}_{na}$	Shear $\bar{V}_n/\omega^2 = \sum \frac{\bar{Q}_{na}}{\omega^2}$	Increment in story displacement $\frac{\delta u_n}{\omega^2} = \frac{\bar{V}_n}{\omega^2 \lambda_n}$	Derived displacement second mode $\bar{u}_{nb} = u_{nb}/\omega^2 = \sum \frac{\delta u_n}{\omega^2}$	Second mode Ass'd. displ. Der. displ. $\frac{\bar{u}_{na}}{\bar{u}_{nb}}$
☐ m	-33	4	-21	$-21m$			$-10.83\,m/\lambda$	$1.94\,\lambda/m$
λ					$-21m$	$-21m/\lambda$		
☐ m	11	2	17	$17m$			$10.17\,m/\lambda$	$1.67\,\lambda/m$
3λ					$-4m$	$-1.33\,m/\lambda$		
☐ 2m	22	1	25	$50m$			$11.50\,m/\lambda$	$2.17\,\lambda/m$
4λ					$46m$	$11.50\,m/\lambda$		
⟋⟋⟋							0	

See Eq.(2-22)

First mode coefficient, $\bar{C}_1 = \dfrac{\sum m_n u_{na} u_{n1}}{\sum m_n u_{n1}^2} = \dfrac{-33m \cdot 4 + 11m \cdot 2 + 22 \cdot 2m}{m \cdot 4^2 + m \cdot 2^2 + 2m} = -\dfrac{66}{22} = -3$

See Eq.(2-23)

Second mode circular frequency squared, $\omega_2^2 \cong \dfrac{21 + 17 + 25}{10.83 + 10.17 + 11.5} \dfrac{\lambda}{m} = \dfrac{63}{32.5} \dfrac{\lambda}{m} = 1.94 \dfrac{\lambda}{m}$

Fig. 2-5. Calculation of second mode circular frequency by "sweeping" process.

**TABLE 2-1 Modal Deflections and Participation Factors
for Illustrative Structure, Fig. 2-2**

	Mode		
Quantity	1	2	3
ω^2	$0.5\lambda/m$	$2\lambda/m$	$6\lambda/m$
ω	$1.0\sqrt{\lambda/2m}$	$2\sqrt{\lambda/2m}$	$3.464\sqrt{\lambda/2m}$
T	$1.0(2\pi\sqrt{2m/\lambda})$	$0.5(2\pi\sqrt{2m/\lambda})$	$0.289(2\pi\sqrt{2m/\lambda})$
Defl. 3rd floor (roof)	4	-1	1
Defl. 2nd floor	2	1	-5
Defl. 1st floor	1	1	3
$\Sigma m_n u_{nj}$	8	2	2
$\Sigma m_n u_{nj}^2$	22	4	44
γ_j	$8/22^-$	$11/22$	$1/22$

tion. In the particular case shown, the result would be the following for the square of the second-mode frequency:

$$\omega_2^2 \cong \frac{63}{32.50}\frac{\lambda}{m} = 1.94\frac{\lambda}{m} \qquad (2\text{-}23)$$

The true value of the square of the second-mode circular frequency is $2.0\lambda/m$, and the true shape of the second-mode deflection pattern is $+1$, $+1$, -1. This is very nearly the shape of the derived deflection pattern shown in Fig. 2-5.

The complete data on all three modes for the structure shown in Fig. 2-2 are tabulated in Table 2-1. The reader can verify the accuracy of the third-mode values, and can also demonstrate that the modal deflections satisfy equation (2-18) for each pair of modes considered.

Step-by-Step or Holzer Method

The second method described here, attributed originally to Holzer, is discussed in references 27, 30, 31, 32, and 35, and was adapted to buildings by Blume and Hesselmeyer [34]. This involves a procedure described briefly as follows:

Assume a value for the circular frequency for the jth mode. Take the deflection of any mass at a prescribed value. It is usually convenient to take a unit deflection for the first mass above the base. Then compute successively the values of inertial force, shear, and increment in deflection until the top of the structure is reached, in such a way that there is no residual external force on any mass. At the last mass, there will be inevitably a residual periodic force required to maintain the deflection pattern computed in this fashion. If this residual force is actually zero, the correct deflection pattern and frequency are obtained. If it is not zero, the calculation can be repeated for another assumed value of circular frequency, and a better value of trial frequency can be interpolated, if necessary, to make a better estimate for a third calculation.

The procedure is best explained with reference to Fig. 2-6 in which the steps are outlined in detail. A sketch of the mass and stiffness distribution is shown at the left of the figure. The calculations are carried through for an assumed value of the circular frequency squared of $1.0\lambda/m$. The calculation is started by placing a value of $u_n = 1.0$ at the first floor above the ground. The next number that is entered is the calculation of the increment in deflection in the first story. This is obviously 1.0. The shear in the first story is obtained from this increment in deflection multiplied by the first-story stiffness, giving the entry 4λ in the table. The inertial force at the first mass is computed from equation (2-10). Since ω^2 is $1.0\lambda/m$, the result is 2λ. Next, the shear in the second story is computed to be consistent with the load at the second floor and the shear in the first story. Obviously a shear of 2λ is required to be consistent, in accordance with the equation

$$\bar{Q}_n = V_n - V_{n+1} \qquad (2\text{-}24)$$

Having this value of shear of 2λ in the second story, by dividing by the stiffness in the second story of 3λ, an increment in deflection of $2/3$ is obtained. With this increment in deflection, the deflection at the second floor is

$$1 + \frac{2}{3} = \frac{5}{3}$$

The inertial force computed from equation (2-10) is $5\lambda/3$. From equation (2-24) the shear in the top story is computed as $\lambda/3$. This gives an increment in deflection for the top story of $1/3$, and a deflection at the top mass of 2. The inertial force at the top mass is then determined from equation (2-10) as 2λ. The residual force at the top floor is now computed from equation (2-25)

$$R_n = V_n - V_{n+1} - \bar{Q}_n \qquad (2\text{-}25)$$

Since V_{n+1} is zero, because there are no columns above the top floor, one determines a residual force of $-5\lambda/3$. The fact that this is not zero indicates that the assumed value of $\omega^2 = 1.0\lambda/m$ is not a correct modal frequency.

Fig. 2-6. Determination of second mode circular frequency by Holzer's or step-by-step method.

Masses and spring const's	Assumed displ. u_n	Increment in story displacement $\delta u_n = V_n/\lambda_n$	Shear V_n	Inertial force $\bar{Q}_n = V_n - V_{n+1}$	Residual force $R_n = V_n - V_{n+1} - \bar{Q}_n$
		Assumed $\omega^2 = 1.0\lambda/m$			
☐m	2			2λ	$-5\lambda/3$
λ		$1/3$	$\lambda/3$		
☐m	$5/3$			$5\lambda/3$	0
3λ		$2/3$	2λ		
☐2m	1			2λ	0
4λ		1	4λ		
⊥	0				

If now the calculations are made for an assumed value of $\omega^2 = 3\lambda/m$, one will find deflections at the second floor, third floor, and top floor, respectively, of magnitudes 1, $1/3$, $-8/3$. The residual force at the top floor will be $+5\lambda$. Since the residual force has changed in sign, a value intermediate between the two values for which calculations are recorded should be assumed next. If a value of $\omega^2 = 2\lambda/m$ is assumed, a residual force of zero is found, indicating that this is the correct value for a modal frequency and the modal shape determined in this process will be $+1$, $+1$, -1, which checks the values given in Table 2-1 for the second mode. Because there is one reversal of deflection, this is obviously the second mode.

The reader can verify the third mode configuration directly by this process. This procedure is quite general in applicability and is not limited to the lower modes.

2.4 Illustrative Example—Three-Degree-of-Freedom System

Modal Participation Factors

In a multi-degree-of-freedom system that has independent or uncoupled modes of deformation (this condition is generally satisfied for buildings), each mode responds to the base motion or excitation as an independent single-degree-of-freedom system. Since the modal patterns can be multiplied by arbitrary scale factors, a scale factor γ may be defined by which to multiply the modal quantities that are of interest. The factor γ must be such that the response to the base excitation in the particular mode desired is given by the product of the modal excitation factor γ_j, the modal quantity desired α_j, and the deflection response $u(t)$, for a single-degree-of-freedom system subjected to the same ground motion. The quantity α may be the deflection at a particular floor in the mode considered, the relative story deflection in a particular story, the story shear in a particular story, the stress at a particular point in the structure, or any other such quantity it is desired to compute. In order to keep the presentation general, the symbol α will be used to designate any of these various quantities that are of interest.

It is then possible, by proper definition of the modal participation factor γ_j, to write the following expression for the response at the particular point or in the particular manner considered, as a function of time

$$\alpha(t) = \sum_j \gamma_j \alpha_j u(t) \tag{2-26}$$

It has been shown [4, 5, 11, 12] that in order for this relationship to be applicable, the following equation for γ_j must be used:

$$\gamma_j = \frac{\sum\limits_n m_n u_{nj}}{\sum\limits_n m_n u_{nj}^2} \tag{2-27}$$

It is apparent from a comparison of equation (2-27) with equation (2-22) that γ_j is the coefficient for the expansion of a constant unit deflection at all mass points into a modal series of deflections.

The calculations for γ_j, in accordance with equation (2-27), are shown in Table 2-1.

Because of the complexities in computing the response as a function of time, and because the maximum responses in the various modes do not necessarily occur at the same time, one is generally interested only in the maximum possible response. It has been explained in Section 2.1 that an upper bound to this maximum response is obtained by taking the sum of the numerical values of the maximum modal responses. In other words, an upper limit can be written for the particular function under consideration, designated by α, as in equation (2-28)

$$\alpha_m \leq \sum_j \mid \gamma_j \alpha_j S_j \mid \tag{2-28}$$

where the individual modal terms are the product of the participation factor γ_j, the modal quantity desired α_j, and the spectral value of the displacement of the single-degree-of-freedom structure S_j, where the subscript j refers to the value of S for the particular modal frequency or period. Two additional equivalent forms of equation (2-28) are convenient to use in certain cases in order to permit use of the spectral velocity response for the single-degree-of-freedom system S_{vj}, or the spectral acceleration response S_{aj}. These are shown in the following equations:

$$\alpha_m \leq \sum_j \left| \frac{\gamma_j}{\omega_j} \alpha_j S_{vj} \right| \tag{2-29}$$

or

$$\alpha_m \leq \sum_j \left| \frac{\gamma_j}{\omega_j^2} \alpha_j S_{aj} \right| \tag{2-30}$$

The particular one of the three preceding equations that is most convenient to use is generally that one in which the spectrum values are most nearly constant for the range of modal frequencies considered. Consequently, equation (2-28) might be used where the spectral displacement is nearly constant, equation (2-29) where the spectral velocity is nearly constant, and equation (2-30) where the spectral acceleration is nearly constant.

If the modal displacements are chosen appropriately, the values of γ_j can be made unity. In other words, the modal deflections computed in the general case can be modified by multiplying them by the quantity γ_j, and it will be found that these modified modal values will have a modal participation factor of unity. This has been done for the values shown in Table 2-1 and the modified modal values are given in Table 2-2. Tabulated in this table, in addition to the deflections of the three floors, are the accelerations of the three masses, the relative story displacements in each of the three stories, and the shears in each story. These may be considered as values of α for the three modes. With these quantities as given in Table 2-2, the quantities γ_j will be 1.0.

For convenience in checking the numerical values in Table 2-2 and in the further calculations thereafter, the constant factor 22 in the denominator is factored out of the numbers so that only small whole numbers appear in the table. All of the tabulated values are to be divided by 22.

TABLE 2-2   Modified Modal Values (For Unit Values of Modal Participation Factors) for Illustrative Structure, Fig. 2-2

All values to be divided by 22.			
		Mode	
Quantity	1	2	3
$\ddot{u}_3$ = accel. 3rd floor (roof)	$+ 16\lambda/m$	$- 22\lambda/m$	$+ 6\lambda/m$
u_3 = defl. 3rd floor (roof)	$+ 32$	$- 11$	$+ 1$
$u_3 - u_2$ = displ. 3rd story	$+ 16$	$- 22$	$+ 6$
V_3 = shear 3rd story	$+ 16\lambda$	$- 22\lambda$	$+ 6\lambda$
$\ddot{u}_2$ = accel. 2nd floor	$+ 8\lambda/m$	$+ 22\lambda/m$	$- 30\lambda/m$
u_2 = defl. 2nd floor	$+ 16$	$+ 11$	$- 5$
$u_2 - u_1$ = displ. 2nd story	$+ 8$	0	$- 8$
V_2 = shear 2nd story	$+ 24\lambda$	0	$- 24\lambda$
$\ddot{u}_1$ = accel. 1st floor	$+ 4\lambda/m$	$+ 22\lambda/m$	$+ 18\lambda/m$
u_1 = defl. 1st floor	$+ 8$	$+ 11$	$+ 3$
u_1 = displ. 1st story	$+ 8$	$+ 11$	$+ 3$
V_1 = shear at base	$+ 32\lambda$	$+ 44\lambda$	$+ 12\lambda$

It will be noted that the modal deflections are taken as dimensionless, and therefore the dimensions of the responses are determined by the dimensions of the single-degree-of-freedom spectrum response values. This is recommended as a general procedure in order to avoid difficulties in the use of the response spectra, which are appropriately defined in terms of actual motions that have actual dimensions.

Numerical Results

Consider the structure in Fig. 2-2 subjected to a ground motion of a particular type. It is assumed that the spectrum for the ground motion has been determined. For example, consider the response spectra shown in Fig. 1-6 as being representative. Then, three regions of such spectra can be defined:

1. a region in which the values approach a line of constant acceleration response,
2. a region in which the spectral velocity is nearly constant, and
3. a region in which the spectral displacement is nearly constant.

In this illustration only relative values are of interest. Therefore, consider these three regions as being defined by appropriate, consistent, constant values of the three spectral quantities. Furthermore, the period of the first mode may be taken as being some particular value, and it may be considered that the periods of the second and third modes have the appropriate magnitudes, in accordance with the quantities shown in Table 2-1. The relative values of the periods of the three modes are 1.0, 0.5, and 0.289 for this particular structure. For convenience in the computation of the numerical values in Table 2-3, the first mode period has been taken as 1.0 second. However, except for constant multipliers, the results are applicable to any value of the assumed spectral response, and for any value of the fundamental period. In order that the same coefficients can be used for the first mode values in all of the combinations for the particular constant spectral values considered, it is convenient to take the displacement spectrum as 1.0, the velocity spectral value as 2π, and the acceleration spectral value as $4\pi^2/g$, to be consistent with one another at a period of 1.0 second for which the values in the tables are determined. These are only used as relative values in the comparisons, which are generally valid. These values are chosen in this fashion in order that all comparisons will be made for a unit value of spectral displacement for the first mode. Hence the comparisons give correct relative values of response independently of the actual spectrum line used.

In the first column of results in Table 2-3, where the spectral displacement is constant, since the participation factors γ for all modes are unity, a straightforward application of equation (2-28) leads merely to the sum of the absolute modal values for the three modes as taken from Table 2-2. Therefore, in Table 2-3, the maximum possible top-story shear of 44λ in the column $S = 1$ is the sum of the quantities from Table 2-2 of 16λ for the first mode, 22λ for the second mode, and 6λ for the third mode. The negative sign in front of the second mode component is disregarded, of course.

The magnitudes of the maximum possible forces at each floor are given in Table 2-3 and are determined from the accelerations at each floor merely by multiplying the acceleration by the local mass concentration.

In the second column of results, corresponding to uniform values of the spectral velocity, the modal quantities in Table 2-2 are multiplied by the relative magnitudes of the periods (from Table 2-1) for the three modes, namely 1.0, 0.5, and 0.289 for modes 1, 2, and 3, respectively, and the sums of these results are recorded. For the third column of results, the quantities are multiplied by the square of the relative magnitudes of the periods, or the modal values for the first three modes in Table 2-2 are multiplied respectively by the quantities 1, $\frac{1}{4}$, and $\frac{1}{12}$. The sums are obtained in a straightforward fashion and can be readily checked. Given also in Table 2-3 are the quantities corresponding to the first mode only, neglecting the higher mode responses. For comparison, in a single-degree-of-freedom system having a spring constant of 4λ, for all three conditions of excitation, the displacement of the mass would be 22, and the base shear 88λ, or the same as for the lowest mass and the lowest story shown in the first column in the table.

The quantities in Table 2-3 are upper limits or maximum possible magnitudes of the responses for the illustrative spectra considered. The quantities for a uniform value of S can be considered as corresponding to a very long period structure having a long period in each of the three modes, the condition for constant spectral velocity as corresponding to a structure having all three periods in the range in which the response spectrum for velocity has a nearly uniform value or in which the energy input is nearly uniform, and the condition where the acceleration spectrum is constant as corresponding to a very stiff structure having all three of its periods very short. None of these conditions is practical; they are considered to indicate the dynamic behavior under several types of conditions.

TABLE 2-3 Maximum Possible Magnitudes of Response of Illustrative Structure, Fig. 2-2, for Various Excitations

All values to be divided by 22.
1st mode period taken as 1 sec., other values proportional.

Quantity	All modes $S = 1$	All modes $S_v = 2\pi$	All modes $S_a = 4\pi^2/g$	First mode only $S = 1$
		Condition of excitation		
3rd floor acceleration	$44\lambda/m$	$28.7\lambda/m$	$22\lambda/m$	$16\lambda/m$
3rd floor deflection	44	37.8	34.8	32
3rd story displacement	44	28.7	22	16
3rd story shear	44λ	28.7λ	22λ	16λ
3rd floor force	44λ	28.7λ	22λ	16λ
2nd floor acceleration	$60\lambda/m$	$27.7\lambda/m$	$16\lambda/m$	$8\lambda/m$
2nd floor deflection	32	22.9	19.2	16
2nd story displacement	16	10.3	8.7	8
2nd story shear	48λ	30.9λ	26λ	24λ
2nd floor force	60λ	27.7λ	16λ	8λ
1st floor acceleration	$44\lambda/m$	$20.2\lambda/m$	$11\lambda/m$	$4\lambda/m$
1st floor deflection	22	14.4	11	8
1st story displacement	22	14.4	11	8
base shear ·	88λ	57.5λ	44λ	32λ
1st floor force	88λ	40.4λ	22λ	8λ
Maximum possible base shear relative to that in a single-degree-of-freedom system with same fundamental period.	1.00	0.65	0.50	0.36

The effects of the higher modes on the response of the structure are quite apparent from Table 2-3. For example, the base shear is increased from 32λ, obtained by considering the first mode only, to 88λ for the condition in which all three modes have long periods. The higher mode influence is extremely large in this case. The magnitudes of the accelerating forces show an even greater disparity, but these are not of direct significance in design.

The fact that the maximum value of the forces, as shown in any one of the columns, is not consistent with the maximum values of the shears must be taken into account since they do not reach their maximum values at the same time. In other words, if all three floor forces reached their maximums at the same instant, the shears would be, from the top story down, 44λ, 104λ, and 192λ, whereas the actual values of the shears are 44λ, 48λ, and 88λ, for the first column of results. Similar observations apply to the other conditions.

In Table 2-4, the relative values of the maximum story shears are tabulated. Also tabulated are the values of lateral forces at the various floors consistent with these maximum shears. The forces are those which, added successively from the top, give the shears in the various stories. The values are tabulated for a base shear of 100 for all conditions. The top-story shear is in all cases for this structure 50 per cent of the base shear; the second-story shear, depending on the particular condition of excitation considered, varies from 54 to 59 per cent of the base shear, but is 75 per cent of the base shear if the first mode only is considered.

The forces consistent with the shear distributions are shown in the lower part of Table 2-4. The force at the third, or intermediate, floor level is relatively small compared with that at either the top or lowest floor for any of the three conditions where all three modes are excited. For the first mode only, however, the forces are 50 per cent for the top floor and 25 per cent for each of the two lower floors, in terms of the base shear.

For this structure, the lateral forces consistent with the linearly varying acceleration distribution specified in the SEAOC recommendations are shown in the last column. The shears corresponding to these lateral force distributions are also shown for the same base shear of 100. It can be seen that the design values recommended by the SEAOC code are quite reasonable in magnitude compared with the values for the various conditions, and are conservative for

TABLE 2-4 Relative Values of Maximum Shears and Consistent Lateral Forces for Illustrative Structure, Fig. 2-2

	All values computed for a base shear of 100 for all conditions.				
	Condition considered				
Quantity	All modes $S = 1$	All modes $S_v = 2\pi$	All modes $S_a = 4\pi^2/g$	First mode only $S = 1$	SEAOC code
3rd story shear	50	50	50	50	42.9
2nd story shear	55	54	59	75	71.4
Base shear	100	100	100	100	100
3rd floor force	50	50	50	50	42.9
2nd floor force	5	4	9	25	28.5
1st floor force	45	46	41	25	28.6

the second-story shear where the combined modal analyses indicate a relatively low value.

It should be recognized that the structure for which the calculations have been reported is somewhat unusual and irregular in both stiffness and mass distribution. For a more regular structure with a more nearly uniform mass distribution and a more nearly uniformly varying stiffness distribution, the agreement between the SEAOC recommendations and the analysis would be even better.

As further indication of the applicability of the standard design recommendations, it is interesting to compare for the illustrative problem the maximum probable values of the shears and the maximum possible values. The maximum probable values of the shears are computed from the root mean square of the modal values, taking into account the factors to be multiplied by the modal values for the four conditions considered. The values are tabulated in Table 2-5. For the first mode only, of course, the values are precisely those tabulated

TABLE 2-5   Maximum Probable Values of Shears for Illustrative Structure, Fig. 2-2

	All except relative values to be divided by 22. 1st mode period taken as 1 sec., other values proportional.			
	Condition of excitation			
Quantity	All modes $S = 1$	All modes $S_v = 2\pi$	All modes $S_a = 4\pi^2/g$	First mode only $S = 1$
3rd story shear	27.9λ	19.5λ	17.0λ	16λ
2nd story shear	34.0λ	25.1λ	24.1λ	24λ
Base shear	55.9λ	39.1λ	33.9λ	32λ
Relative 3rd story shear, %	50	50	50	50
Relative 2nd story shear, %	61	64	71	75
Relative base shear, %	100	100	100	100
Ratio max. probable base shear to max. possible base shear	0.64	0.68	0.77	—
Ratio max. probable base shear to that in a single-degree-of-freedom system having same fundamental period	0.64	0.44	0.39	0.36

in Table 2-2. The relative values of the maximum probable shears for the three modes show roughly the same general trend as the maximum possible values, although the distribution is slightly smoother and approximates perhaps even better the SEAOC recommendations.

It is of interest to compare the ratio of the maximum probable base shear to the maximum possible base shear for the three spectral conditions considered. This ratio is: 55.9/88 or 64 per cent for the condition where the spectral displacement is constant, 68 per cent where the spectral velocity is constant, and 77 per cent where the spectral acceleration is constant. In other words, the disparity between the shear computed for the first mode alone and that computed for the combination of modes is much less when one takes into account the maximum probable value of the shear rather than the maximum possible value.

A further comparison of interest is that among the various values of maximum possible base shear (or maximum displacement of the first mass above the ground) for the different excitations considered, in terms of the values for a single-degree-of-freedom structure. These values can be studied by examining the third and fourth lines above the bottom in Table 2-3. The value for a single-degree system is the same as for the case where $S = 1$ for all modes; this is a general relation for all systems such as multistory buildings. Hence, for a smooth response spectrum, the actual maximum base shears are always less in a multistory building than in a single-degree-of-freedom system having a period equal to the fundamental period of the multistory building and a spring constant the same as in the lowest story of the building. The relative values of maximum possible base shears for the conditions of excitation considered for illustration are given in the last line of Table 2-3. The corresponding relative values of maximum probable base shear are given in the last line of Table 2-5.

2.5 Behavior of Multi-Degree-of-Freedom Systems in the Inelastic Range

When a structure of many degrees of freedom becomes inelastic, in general yielding occurs first in the story that is relatively the weakest compared with the magnitude of the shearing forces that have to be transmitted. In many cases this yielding will occur near the base of the structure. When an area at the base or within the structure yields, the forces that can be transmitted through the yielded region cannot exceed the value of the yield shear for that story, provided the system is essentially elasto-plastic. Consequently, the shears and the accompanying accelerations and relative deflections for the upper region of the structure are reduced in magnitude compared with the values for an elastic structure subjected to the same base motion.

In other words, since the region above the part of the structure that yields behaves essentially in an elastic manner, the effect of yielding near the base of the structure is to reduce the shear for which the upper parts of the structure must be designed, by limiting the base shear magnitude for which the design must be made. As a consequence of this, if the total base shear for which a structure is designed is some fraction of the maximum computed value for an elastic system, yielding will occur in the lowest story and the shears in the remaining part of the structure will have magnitudes appropriate to the revised value of the base shear. Consequently, if provision is made for the absorption of energy in the lower stories, a structure will in general be adequately strong provided that the shearing forces for which it is designed in the upper stories are consistently related to the base shear design even though the structure may yield near the base. The SEAOC recommendations provide for a consistent set of shears for the design.

When a structure deforms inelastically to a major extent, in effect its higher modes of oscillation are inhibited and its major deformation takes place in the one mode in which the inelastic deformation is most prominent, generally the fundamental mode. However, there are situations where the mode in which principal plastic deformation occurs may be a higher mode than the fundamental mode.

In effect, when the lower portion of the structure becomes inelastic, the period of vibration is effectively increased. In any event, where large amounts of plastic behavior occur, the modal analysis concept is no longer applicable, and the structure behaves in many respects almost as a single-degree-of-freedom system corresponding to the entire mass of the structure supported by the elements that become plastic. The base shear can therefore be computed for the modified structure, considering its fundamental period as defining the modified spectrum for which the design should be made. However, the fundamental period of this modified structure *generally* will not differ materially from the fundamental period of the original elastic frame structure or will be longer in the case of a shear-wall structure. It is partly a consequence of this fact that makes it usually appropriate to use in design recommendations the frequency of the fundamental mode without taking the higher mode frequencies into account directly.

It is desirable to consider, however, a distribution of shearing stresses in the structure which considers the higher mode excitations of the part above the region that becomes plastic. This is done implicitly in the SEAOC recommendations by the provision for a consideration of a variation of lateral force coefficient with height of the structure. In other words, the distributions of local seismic force over the height of the building, corresponding to a uniformly varying acceleration ranging from a zero value at the base to a maximum at the top [36], accounts quite well for the moments and shears in the structure, and takes into account the fact that local accelerations at higher elevations in the structure are greater than those at lower elevations because of the greater magnitudes of motion at the higher elevations.

2.6 Effects of Foundations, Soil Conditions, and Other Factors

The motion transmitted to a structure depends on the way the structure is supported on or in the soil. The coupling between the structure and the soil may permit energy to be absorbed, or may change the motion of the base of the building somewhat from that of the general motion of the surrounding ground. Consequently, there is some loss of energy between the ground and the structure itself, and the structure is generally not subjected to as high a value of acceleration as the surrounding earth. It can be seen from Fig. 1-1 that the maximum accelerations are consistent with relatively high-frequency oscillations, whereas the maximum velocities and maximum displacements are consistent with successively lower frequency motions in general. Since the loss in energy and the lack of coupling between the ground and the structure becomes greater the higher the frequency, the maximum velocities in the structure are more likely to be close to the values of the maximum ground velocity, and the maximum displacements the structure must undergo in space are practically equal to the maximum ground displacement. It is for these reasons that the upper limit of acceleration one computes from the spectrum may reasonably be reduced in designing a structure, but the upper limits of velocity and displacement in the spectrum response curve should not be reduced in the same proportions. This is taken into account in the SEAOC design recommendations implicitly in the way in which the design curve depends on the period of the structure. This will be discussed in the next chapter in greater detail.

CHAPTER **3**

Principles of Earthquake-Resistant Design

3.1 Details of Basis for Rational Design

The concept of earthquake-resistant design described in this manual involves the structure remaining elastic or nearly so under the influence of moderate earthquakes of frequent occurrence, and the structure yielding locally into the inelastic range, but with safety from collapse, even under the conditions of the most severe probable earthquake to which the structure will be subjected unless it is built over a fault. This probability is estimated from consideration of past earthquake motions.

Under earthquakes of intensity that might occur several times during the life of the structure, the structure is to be designed in such a way that it will have no visible indications of damage, and no actual damage that might impair its efficiency or load-carrying capacity. The structure will then be able to resist a number of earthquakes, even if they should occur fairly frequently, without being subjected to undue disturbance or without requiring more than minor repairs from the combined effects of these earthquakes following one another.

The second part of the design criterion involves the concept that the structure should not collapse, with consequent loss of life, or suffer severe structural damage, even under the conditions of the most severe probable earthquake to which it will be subjected during its desired life. The reserve of strength in the inelastic range, provided by the design procedures and recommendations contained herein, is intended to provide for the unusual situations in the infrequent major earthquakes that might occur. To design for such earthquakes by requiring that the structure remain in the elastic range would be grossly un-economical and would represent the payment of too great a cost to provide for the probability of such an occurrence.

If an unusual earthquake, somewhat greater than the most severe probable earthquake that is likely within the expected life of the building, should occur, the structure may undergo even larger deformations and have serious perma-nent displacements and possibly require major repair, but it will not collapse.

It is possible to meet these criteria by considering design provisions based on an earthquake of intensity and characteristics very much like that of the El Centro earthquake of 1940, and by permitting moderate mobilization of the energy-absorbing capacity of the structure in the inelastic range. When this is done, earthquakes of lesser intensity that occur more frequently will be resisted without requiring mobilization of the resistance of the structure beyond the yield range. Moreover, even more severe earthquakes will not cause collapse, provided that the recommendations made herein including the arrangement of reinforcement and proportioning of the sections are followed.

The procedure used to obtain these objectives includes design based on the SEAOC recommendations (Appendix C), which are generally consistent with the forces and displacements computed by more elaborate procedures, and which provide a reasonable basis for earthquake conditions similar to those in the western United States. More precise calculations are generally not needed. However, methods are available and are described in this manual for making special analyses for unusual situations such as very high or very slender struc-tures.

It will be shown later in this chapter that the application of the SEAOC recom-mendations to an El Centro-type earthquake requires that the structure be able to yield locally into the inelastic range without serious consequences. It is the purpose of the design recommendations presented in this manual to indicate how the necessary amount of ductility may be achieved in reinforced concrete structures without impairing the load-carrying capacity of the structure, and how even additional ductility can be achieved to prevent collapse under the most severe probable conditions.

3.2 Dependence of Behavior of Structure on Design Basis

In general, the behavior of a structure depends on its design. For example, if a design provision is used that involves very much larger horizontal design forces than those provided for here, the structure required will be much stiffer and will have a shorter period of vibration than a structure designed in ac-cordance with the provisions recommended. Because the shorter period of vibration results in higher spectral accelerations, the stiffer structure may at-tract more horizontal force than would the structure designed as recommended. Consequently, designing for too large a force will not necessarily make the structure safer if in the process the structure becomes considerably stiffer or less ductile.

On the other hand, designing for a smaller force than that recommended will make the structure more flexible, and in general it will be lighter and generate somewhat less force. The greater flexibility of such a structure, however, may invite more energy input since the spectral velocity could be greater at a longer period. Also, the greater flexibility may cause undesirable characteristics of vibration under earthquake or wind, and the structure may be unsatisfactory for reasons entirely separate from those associated with its structural behavior.

The selection of the design criteria for structures to resist earthquakes is based in large part on the experience of engineers in earthquake regions. Much of the background of this experience is described in reference 36. The accelerated recent studies on earthquake effects on structures have led to some revisions in the design concepts that engineers now use, and the latest and most up to date of these are in the SEAOC recommendations. For this reason, the design procedures described herein are based on these recommendations.

3.3 Comparison of Design Recommendations

The discussion in Chapters 1 and 2 has indicated the nature of the response of single and multistory buildings to earthquake motions. It has been shown that the response of a single-story or a single-degree-of-freedom system can be represented by a response spectrum. Such response spectra for the 1940 El Centro earthquake motion, for elastic systems with 2 and with 10 per cent of critical damping, are shown in Fig. 3-1. Also shown is an idealized elastic response spectrum drawn in accordance with the predictions of Section 1.4.

An idealized elasto-plastic spectrum reduced from the idealized elastic spectrum by a factor of 4 is also shown in Fig. 3-1. It is to be noted that this reduction for elasto-plastic action would occur for ductility factors μ of the order of 4 to 6. However, since multistory buildings would generally have less base shear response than single-mass systems for the same period and lower-story stiffness (see end of Section 2.4), slightly lower μ values would be applicable to this idealized spectrum for the lower stories of such structures.

It is of interest to compare the lines that would be drawn on the chart corresponding to the SEAOC recommendations. The fundamental relationship in the recommendations requires that the building be designed to withstand a minimum total lateral seismic force of magnitude given by

$$V = KCW \tag{3-1}$$

where W is the total weight of the building, and C is a coefficient given by the following relation:

$$C = \frac{0.05}{\sqrt[3]{T}} \tag{3-2}$$

The forces determined by these equations are to be used with modified working stresses corresponding to a one-third increase in the ordinary allowable

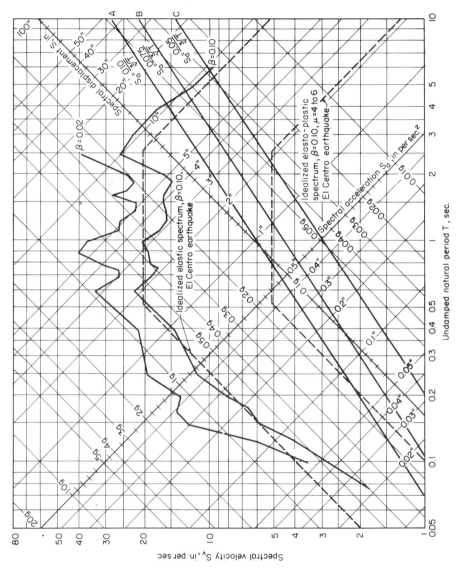

Fig. 3-1. Comparison of spectra, 1940 El Centro earthquake, N-S component.

working stresses. For the reinforcing steel there is a factor of safety of at least 1.5 between the increased working stress and the minimum required yield value of the material. For the concrete, the factor of safety is even greater and, furthermore, according to the design procedures herein, the amount of reinforcement and its yield point always controls the capacity of reinforced concrete members. Consequently, to make the comparisons in Fig. 3-1, the magnitude of the lateral force must be considered at the minimum specified yield point for the reinforcement. By increasing the coefficient in equation (3-2) by 50 per cent, the following value is obtained:

$$C = \frac{0.075}{\sqrt[3]{T}} \qquad (3\text{-}3)$$

This line is plotted as line B in Fig. 3-1. This is consistent with a value of $K = 1$, which corresponds, in accordance with Table 23-C of the SEAOC recommendations, to all building framing systems except those with a box system or with partial or complete frames. For buildings with a complete moment-resisting space frame, the value of K is 0.67, which gives the same result as equation (3-2), and which is plotted as line C in Fig. 3-1. For buildings with a box system, the value of K is 1.33, which gives the following results:

$$C = \frac{0.10}{\sqrt[3]{T}} \qquad (3\text{-}4)$$

This is plotted as line A in Fig. 3-1.

Over the range of practical building periods these lines agree in general, although not in detail, with the idealized elasto-plastic spectrum shown in Fig. 3-1.

3.4 Estimate of Period of Vibration

In using the design recommendations, it is necessary to compute or make an estimate of the fundamental period of vibration of the structure. Methods of doing so for a structure that has been designed have been described in Section 2.2. However, before the structure is designed it is necessary to make an estimate of what the period is likely to be in order to proceed with the design. Methods are suggested for this purpose in Chapter 4. In general, the period of vibration can be computed from the height H of the building and its dimension D in a direction parallel to the direction of motion, by the formula (Appendix C) [36]:

$$T = \frac{0.05H}{\sqrt{D}} \qquad (3\text{-}5)$$

However, for buildings in which the lateral resisting system consists of a moment-resisting space frame that resists 100 per cent of the required lateral forces, and which is not enclosed by or adjoined by more rigid elements, the value of the period T can be taken as 0.10 times the number of stories above the exterior grade.

Where a preliminary design has been made, or where the structure has been designed and a review estimate is desired of the period of vibration, the methods described in Section 2.2 for the fundamental mode, and in Section 2.3 for higher modes of vibration, may be used.

3.5 Summary of General Concepts

The following summary is made of the basic points discussed in the preceding chapters and sections of this chapter.

1. Earthquakes produce random motions of the ground of a violent and continuing nature for various lengths of time. Buildings founded on the ground are forced to respond to these motions and are therefore set into vibration. The earthquake produces only ground motions, and therefore exerts forces on the building only at its base. The shears induced in the building at higher elevations are those developed as a result of the dynamic response of the structure.

2. There is only limited information as to the expected motions, both in terms of magnitude and characteristics, for any particular location. However, from study of previous earthquake records the general magnitude and nature of the motions to be expected have been determined, and the nature and relative magnitude of the response spectra have been indicated.

3. Theoretical analyses of the elastic response of structures subjected to the basic ground motions can be made. However, such analyses appear in general to overestimate the stresses produced or the design strengths required [20, 25]. The reasons for this are not completely known. Inelastic energy absorption, as well as energy absorption due to damping, no doubt account for a considerable portion of the overestimate. There are probably other reasons as well, including "feedback" or modifications of the input motion caused by the mass and stiffness of the building. Only exploratory studies have been made of these effects to date. It is important to recognize, however, that actual earthquake effects are generally less than those computed on an elastic basis for the excitations of the ground that have been measured.

4. Although it is possible to arrive at an equivalent set of forces, by analysis, for which a building can be designed, these must be interpreted properly. It is possible to compute such forces for the elastic range of action of the building, subject to the limitations mentioned in the preceding paragraph. However, if the building does become inelastic, it absorbs more energy and the elastic force requirements may be reduced in accordance with the displacement or energy preservation methods outlined here. Possible secondary effects must be considered.

5. Precise analyses for earthquake response involve techniques that are unnecessarily complicated in view of the many unknown factors in ground motion. Nevertheless, an explanation of the analytical techniques gives a better understanding of the problem. It is of interest and importance that the general nature of the design procedures recommended and now more or less commonly used are based on rational concepts and agree reasonably well with the analytical approaches in general form.

6. Because the major part of the earthquake-resistant capacity of a building may be mobilized in the inelastic range beyond yielding, it is important to have ductility in the building in order to absorb energy inelastically without failure. In the light of the studies reported herein, it appears that tall structures should have a minimum ductility factor of about 4 to 6 in order to resist the probable major earthquakes of the West Coast of the United States. Additional ductility beyond this range is desirable for occasional more severe earthquakes.

7. For multistory structures depending entirely on a moment-resisting frame to carry seismic shears, with no other elements such as partitions, walls, and stairways to provide supplementary resistance, dynamic analyses indicate that for a given base shear a greater shearing resistance in the upper part of the building is desirable as compared with the shearing forces computed from the inverted triangular acceleration.

CHAPTER 4

Design Considerations and Code Requirements

4.1 General Considerations

Earthquake-resistant design involves engineering judgment and experience as well as an application of scientific principles. Because it is a relatively new field of endeavor with many different approaches and developments, it has become oversimplified in practice although complex in theory. Earthquake-resistant design involves economic considerations and probabilities. It is entirely possible to design most structures to resist the greatest earthquake experienced thus far, and possibly even greater, with no damage. However, in view of the small probabilities of occurrence of major earthquakes at any specific location and the additional cost that may be involved, such investment usually would not be warranted.

The term "earthquake-proof" should not be used because earthquakes more violent than those experienced thus far can occur, and unusually severe earthquakes can and probably will cause some damage to many structures designed according to "accepted practice." However, the results to date have been generally good when buildings designed by use of seismic codes have been subjected to earthquakes. Because there has been only a small sampling of potential seismic exposure, reliance in the future must be placed on theory as well as practice.

The basic objective of seismic codes is to protect the public in and about buildings from loss of life and serious injury from major earthquakes, which, judging from past history, can occur in any given area. Attainment of the objective involves the prevention of collapse and of dangerous major damage. By providing this protection against severe earthquakes, the modern design codes may, and usually do, also provide resistance against property damage in the more frequent, less severe earthquakes.

Early earthquake design codes provided for resistance to assumed static lateral forces. Actually, many other dynamic loadings such as wind or the impact of moving loads on bridges are considered as static forces. In seismic design, great reliance was placed on the concept of an assumed constant lateral acceleration, which permitted the computation of lateral force as simply the weight of the element considered times the ratio of the selected lateral acceleration to the acceleration of gravity. This ratio, called the seismic coefficient (usually designated as C), varied for the entire building from as little as 0.02 in some codes to as much as 0.20, with values as high as 1.00 for the most vulnerable parts of buildings such as parapet walls. The wide spread in values is due to the neglect of many important parameters in the greatly oversimplified design assumptions, as well as to the recognized vulnerability of various types of structures and parts of structures. Nevertheless, the coefficient C has been retained even in the most modern codes because it is simple in design application, it is so well established, and it can be modified by other coefficients to approximate more closely the actual dynamic phenomena.

The design of extremely high or slender buildings, special structures, or those involving unusual risks should not only conform to the applicable seismic design code but should be based on special structural-dynamic studies irrespective of the materials used.

The following general statements [20] compare traditional and modern curtain-wall office buildings with reference to structural-dynamic phenomena and seismic code applicability:

> Moderate to severe earthquakes produce deflections and lateral reactions the amount of which depends to a considerable degree upon the structural-dynamic characteristics of each specific structure. In general, the dynamic shears developed by major earthquakes are greater than those required by the earthquake provisions of seismic design codes, particularly for rigid buildings and buildings with low damping values.

> The strength and rigidity of traditional type buildings with non-calculated filler walls, partitions and stairs are many times those of the frames which were intended to provide the entire structural resistance. This generally accounts for the relatively good seismic and windstorm history of multistory framed buildings of the traditional type. However, the frames cannot function effectively in lateral resistance under severe shocks until the surrounding rigid materials have failed, perhaps with considerable economic loss.

> The modern type building, without any appreciable lateral resistance

except in the frame proper, will be subject to possibly large story distortions even in moderate earthquakes in spite of meeting present-day seismic codes. Engineers and architects should revise the customary procedures of injecting rigid but brittle elements into otherwise flexible structures without provision for story distortion, since the "non-structural" damage may constitute not only a severe financial loss but also a physical danger to persons in and about such buildings. All brittle elements should either be permitted to move freely within the structure or should be expected to fail, in which case they should be so designed and detailed as to protect building occupants and people on the streets. It should be noted that walls or partition elements floating free of the frame or which fall out under minor distortions do not contribute beneficial damping values nor energy absorption.

Rigid bracing members or shear walls in a modern glass-walled multistory building stiffen the structure against mild earthquakes and wind but also invite greater seismic shears. Unless designed for more shear than code values generally prescribe, such rigid elements should be considered expendable and other provisions made for severe emergencies. Where a ductile moment-resisting frame cannot be provided to resist all the design lateral forces, the design can be accomplished by (a) providing rigid elements to carry the shear for moderate shocks of quite frequent occurrence, and also to supply the necessary rigidity to prevent excessive drift due to normal wind force; and (b) providing a ductile frame to control flexibility, absorb energy, and prevent building collapse in a severe but possible earthquake (of say 50-year frequency) in which the rigid elements may fail.

The fundamental period of vibration is a logical index to use in determining relative base shear for design purposes. The height and width of the building, considered either individually or together, may not be adequate indicators of the period of modern flexible structures without walls. The periods may be specifically calculated or improved approximate methods used to estimate the values.

Competent supervision and inspection of construction are essential to obtain the results desired from code requirements and design procedures.

This chapter covers some of the key factors and the evolutionary changes in seismic building codes and design requirements, and gives detailed recommendations of a specific code for general design purposes.

4.2 Working Stresses and Loading Combinations

Design codes for earthquake-resistant structures have consistently used allowable design stresses one-third greater than normal design stresses. In no case, however, are the normal design requirements for dead and live load reduced because of lateral forces in combination.

Wind-force design is also allowed a one-third increase in allowable unit stresses, as for earthquake forces, and in the same combinations. Wind and earthquake are never assumed to occur simultaneously. Also, wind or earthquake is normally assumed to occur parallel to each major horizontal axis of a building but only on one of these axes at a time. The vertical component of the earthquake motion has been generally ignored. Whichever situation separately governs the design at any level, section, joint, or member—whether from wind or earthquake effects in a particular direction—is the final design criterion.

It is recognized that earthquakes move in all directions simultaneously (as does wind around structures) and that certain more critical stress combinations might be developed across the diagonals of square or rectangular sections. However, because of simplicity, tradition, and the many other uncertainties, such considerations are generally ignored except in cases of some special structures such as water tanks.

On at least two occasions, higher unit stresses (more than $1\frac{1}{3}$ times normal) have been proposed for California earthquake codes, along with greater seismic coefficients. Japanese codes do use greater allowable unit stresses [37] and there is a logical reason for them. It can be shown that the reserve capacity of structural members to resist severe earthquake loading will depend upon the additional stress required to cause yielding and failure. Thus a bracing member proportioned only for earthquake stress (no dead or live load participation) will tend to have less reserve strength and energy capacity than a member the size of which is determined by dead and live load requirements as well as earthquake. The result is an inconsistency in the strength provided for different members in the same structure, when a working stress or even a modified working stress design procedure is used. Nevertheless, because of custom, this procedure is followed herein. A design procedure based on ultimate strength or energy capacity would avoid these inconsistencies [38].

Another question is whether live load should be included with dead load in computing earthquake forces. It is customary to compute the earthquake forces using dead load only, or with the dead load and a reduced average live load except for warehouses, which have higher average live loading. The earthquake forces are determined by the actual effective mass in a structure. In most buildings the design live load is not realized over the whole area; in fact, the actual average live load can be very low or even negligible. Moreover, all of the live load mass is not effective in earthquake loading since loose, unattached objects like chairs, desks, files, etc., can rock or slide on polished floors. In spite of the low average live loading, there may be heavy live loads at certain points on a floor, such as a concentrated assembly of file cabinets over a girder span. It would seem logical and realistic, therefore, to use the lateral force from the small average live load in general, and when designing members to combine the stresses caused by such lateral forces with those from the live load specified for the floor. This latter live load, of course, should be reduced in accordance with the normal tributary area or tributary floor reductions provided by building codes. The one-third increase in allowable unit stresses applies only to the combination with the lateral forces.

4.3 Lateral Force Coefficient for Total Shear

Early seismic codes simply specified that the lateral seismic force on each story or part of a building or structure, to be used in computing the total shear at the base, was a certain coefficient C times the weight of that story or part. The coefficient was the same for every story of a particular building and varied only with the site. For example, if C were 0.08 (commonly referred to as 8 per cent of gravity), and a building had several stories, 8 per cent of the weight (including a proportion of the live load) at each story was applied as a lateral force at each floor level. Thus for most buildings, the lateral forces considered in computations of shears increased only slightly from the top floor levels downward because many of the massive elements such as filler walls, floor slabs, stairs, partitions, etc., do not vary in weight from story to story.

The actual story weights of a slender, traditional-type 15-story building [35], based on the assumption that the weights are concentrated at the floor levels, are shown in Fig. 4-1. If a hypothetical coefficient of 0.08 had been used in the design of that building, the shears would have been as shown in Fig. 4-1. It is to be noted for this case that the use of the average building weight would not have materially altered the shear curve if allowance had been made for the relatively heavy penthouse. The sum of all the forces from the top down represents the shear at the base, or the "base shear," a term that is referred to frequently throughout this manual. The shears computed according to the SEAOC recommendations are also shown in Fig. 4-1 for comparison.

Early codes generally, but not always, provided that the coefficient C, even though constant for the building as a whole, would have different values depending upon (a) the soil conditions upon which the structure was founded and (b) the seismic rating of the geographical zone in which the structure was to be located.

Soft soil such as a deep alluvial deposit is subject to greater earthquake motion than hard material such as rock. This is especially true where the soils are poorly consolidated or saturated. Buildings situated on such material have been severely damaged or completely destroyed during earthquakes. On the other hand, there have been some instances where buildings situated on firm material suffered more damage than other buildings on soft soil. A possible explanation is that there are many more parameters than the three considered in the early codes—namely, the soil conditions, the coefficient C, and the permissible degree of damage. A few of the other factors:

1. Many of the damaged buildings situated on soft soil were of a different and more vulnerable type than those on better soil; for example, large, open,

unreinforced warehouses and commercial buildings as compared with multipartitioned office buildings and residences.

2. Many of the buildings on soft soil had severe strain from previous differential settlement of the ground; the earthquake was merely the trigger cause of failure that took all the blame.

3. It is possible with well-constructed buildings that under certain seismological and structural-dynamic conditions (because of slight differences in period of vibration or period of the excitation) nearly identical buildings would fare better on soft ground than on hard ground. In other words, generalizations can be misleading.

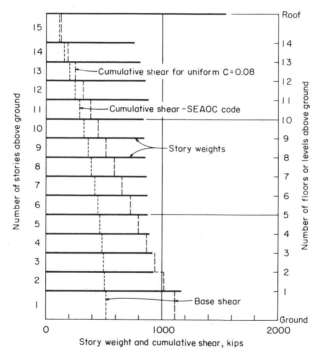

Fig. 4-1. Story weights and hypothetical cumulative shears for a traditional-type office building.

Recent codes do not vary C with the soil conditions, partly because of the conflicting evidence and the complexities involved, but basically because an increase in the lateral force coefficient does not necessarily provide for the situations posed by soft soil conditions; there are too many other factors involved. It must also be recognized that a building site is subject to earthquakes not only of various intensities but from various points of origin. The various combinations of magnitude and epicentral distance add another parameter to the already involved problem. One thing is certain: good foundations and the relative motions of the parts of a building are important considerations in the earthquake-resistant design of buildings on soft soil; the structures must be particularly well tied together in all three dimensions.

The considerations involved in the establishment of seismic risk or seismic zoning for code purposes or design is beyond the scope of this manual except for the following brief discussion. As for many other problems in seismological engineering, there are no clearcut criteria that can be adopted. Earthquakes cannot yet be predicted in time, location, and intensity. However, past (especially recent past) seismic history is naturally used as a basis for forecasting or evaluating the risk. Whether a decrease in the number and magnitude of earthquakes indicates a decrease in risk or a possible accumulation of energy for future seismic activity is another important question without a precise answer. Related to this question is the length of time of earthquake intensity histories necessary to establish either increased or decreased risk. A hundred years may be a long time to man but geologically it is an insignificant period. Earthquakes occur comparatively frequently in California but many other Western states have also had major earthquakes in recent decades, notably Montana, Washington, and Nevada. A major portion of the whole United States has experienced earthquakes in the last century or two, including some major shocks. More serious consideration should be given to the desirability of designing important buildings to be earthquake-resistant, even in areas generally thought to be non-seismic.

Certain seismic design codes do not differentiate seismic risks by area. These include codes for such major cities as Los Angeles and San Francisco, the California State Administrative Code administered through the Division of Architecture of the Department of Public Works for all public school construction, and also the minimum ($C = 0.02$ and 0.03) requirements of the California State Health and Safety Code. The *Recommended Lateral Force Requirements* of the Structural Engineers Association of California, 1959, does not attempt to establish or use existing zones since it is intended for the maximum risk areas of California. The document does recognize that the design shear requirements may be reduced by a zone factor of less than 1.0 where local governmental areas adopt the code and declare themselves in a reduced risk area upon the recommendation of qualified engineers and seismologists.

It must not be inferred that the cost of earthquake resistance is a direct function of zone rating or of coefficient C. The actual additional cost of seismic over wind-resistant construction may vary from essentially nothing to 1 or 2 per cent, and certainly never over 5 per cent, of the typical building cost, depending upon a great many factors. All buildings should be designed for wind storms, and many for winds of hurricane velocity. Earthquake-resistant design, properly done, often provides also for wind requirements at little if any additional cost.

Just as cost does not increase directly with the coefficient C, neither does true structural-dynamic resistance for extreme emergencies. This fact has been recognized in some degree in the SEAOC code by requiring different design shears for types of framing systems with different estimated ductility values.

4.4 Variation of Seismic Force with Height

The use of a coefficient C as described in Section 4.3, providing for a constant proportion of the weight of each part of the building in computing shear, is fairly logical as a design basis for low, rigid structures. However, its application to tall buildings, such as illustrated in Fig. 4-1, is not only illogical from the dynamic standpoint, but would produce an inconsistent strength for the upper stories as compared with the lower stories. If the upper stories are properly designed, the result would be much heavier and more costly construction in the lower stories than in buildings that have withstood severe earthquakes satisfactorily. The basic premise that *force equals total mass times average acceleration* can be applied directly and as a sole criterion to the earthquake problem is untenable for the multistoried building, although it may be entirely adequate for low, rigid structures. No building is infinitely rigid, and in a tall building the maximum accelerations increase greatly over its height. The top of a high building is subjected to greater movements than the lower portions; it can be said that the top of a slender building is subject to a "whip" action. Obviously, in the fundamental mode of vibration the acceleration must increase with height. In addition, as shown in Chapter 2, the higher modes of vibration contribute even greater shear values in the upper stories than those that develop from the fundamental mode alone.

Because of these considerations, the Los Angeles building code and the Uniform Building Code of the International Conference of Building Officials were revised in 1949 to provide for a new coefficient C that, instead of being constant over the entire height, would vary for each story level in accordance with the following formula for the most severe risk zone:

$$C = \frac{0.60}{\bar{N} + 4.5}$$

where $\bar{N}$ was the number of stories above the story under consideration. The coefficient C was applied in the formula

$$F = CW$$

where W equaled the total dead load tributary to the point under consideration, except for warehouses and tanks, in which case W equaled the total dead load plus the total vertical design live load tributary to the point under consideration. Machinery or other fixed concentrated loads were considered as part of the dead load. This formula, therefore, gave the total shear at any elevation.

For the upper story of all buildings, C became 0.133, and for the lowest story of various buildings it became as follows:

$\bar{N}$ = number of stories above bottom story	C for base
0	0.133
5	0.063
10	0.041
15*	0.031
20*	0.024
25*	0.020

In 1947, San Francisco adopted its first earthquake code, which established the value of C, in nearly the same terms, as

$$C = \frac{2}{24 + \bar{N}}$$

However, $\bar{N}$ had a different significance from that in the Uniform Code. $\bar{N}$ was defined as "the number of stories counting from the top of the building to the plane under consideration. The top story of the building shall be designated as number one." This (now superseded) San Francisco code also developed a story shear rather than applied force at each level by applying C to "total dead and live column design load at and above the plane under consideration. . . ."

Additional and significant steps in the evolutionary attempt to make static design specifications approximate more closely the dynamic conditions in earthquake design came when the Joint Committee of the San Francisco Section of the American Society of Civil Engineers and the Structural Engineers Association of Northern California released its report *Lateral Forces of Earthquake and Wind*[36]. For the first time, the period of vibration of the building was introduced in a suggested code as a means of determining the base shear coefficient C:

"In the building as a whole the coefficient C shall be

$$C = \frac{0.015}{T}$$

in which T is the fundamental period of vibration of the building in seconds in the direction considered. The required value of C shall not be less than 0.02 nor more than 0.06."[36]

This value of C was used to obtain, not a force or shear at each level, but simply the total seismic force or shear at the base by use of the relation

$$V = CW$$

where W is the total weight of the building above the base plus a portion of the design live load. A means was provided for distributing lateral forces over the height of the building to account for the shear at any elevation, including the base.

---

*These values were academic for Los Angeles because of the then-existing height restriction of 150 ft.

The lateral force F_z at any level z was specified in proportion to the base shear V by the equation

$$F_z = V\frac{w_z h_z}{\sum wh} \tag{4-1}$$

in which w_z is the weight at level z, and h_z is the height of level z above the base, and $\sum wh$ is the sum of all weights w multiplied by their respective heights h above the base. The summation is to be taken for the entire building. Thus, if all the story weights were the same, the lateral forces accounting for the base shear V would be distributed in the form of an inverted triangle with nothing at the base and twice the average force at the top level. In other words, the accelerations considered have this triangular distribution for *any* story weight distribution.

These Joint Committee specifications, although basically simple, were determined only after detailed consideration of many factors. Allowance was made for the fact that in the fundamental mode of vibration, the basic consideration for the code, there is for most tall buildings some flexural distortion as well as shear distortion. The effect of the second and third modes in increasing shear at the upper levels was also considered. Finally, the inverted triangle type of distribution was selected as satisfying best all factors involved in a simple manner suitable for code purposes with a degree of accuracy consistent with that of the overall problem.

With the inverted triangle distribution of the lateral forces, it is of course not correct to compare the coefficient C of the Joint Committee code to that of previous codes except for the base. The new concept is simply that (a) the total force or base shear is a function of the building's response to an earthquake, which response in turn is a function of the fundamental period, and (b) the lateral forces accounting for this base shear are distributed over the height with some regard to the envelope of maximum relative story deflections. This code technique produces reasonable results for general design purposes.

The City and County of San Francisco revised its seismic code in 1956. The revision essentially adopted the Joint Committee code except that the formula for C was changed to approximate more closely the San Francisco coefficients previously in effect. The formula adopted was

$$C = \frac{0.02}{T}$$

"where T is the fundamental period of vibration of the building in seconds in the direction considered. The required value of C shall not be less than 0.035 or more than 0.075."

The next major step in the evolution of earthquake codes in California was the creation of a special statewide committee of the Structural Engineers Association of California to develop a code that would embody the best provisions from existing and proposed codes in the light of all research developments and essential design requirements. This work has been completed (Appendix C), and has been adopted by the International Conference of Building Officials in the Uniform Building Code, by the City of Los Angeles, and by Los Angeles County.

The base shear concept and the triangular distribution of accelerations used in determining lateral forces for computing shears are essentially retained as in the Joint Committee report [36]. There are some changes in lateral force distribution: (1) "one and two-story buildings shall have uniform distribution" of accelerations; and (2) "where the height to depth ratio of a lateral force resisting system is equal to or greater than five to one, 10 per cent of the total force *V* shall be considered as concentrated at the top story. The remaining 90 per cent shall be distributed as provided for in the formula." The formula [see equation (4-1)] is exactly the same as in the Joint Committee report.

The first change quoted is basically for simplicity in dealing with low, rigid buildings. The second change is intended to increase the shear and deflection of the upper portions of slender structures by using a simple but fictitious loading in order to approximate more closely the actual conditions when flexural deflection predominates over shear deflection.

Subsequent studies indicate that where the building is flexible in character with the primary resistance in the frame, it is desirable to use the design loading principle of item (2) with perhaps even greater lateral force concentrations applied at the top level for height-to-width ratios as low as 3 to 1 or 2 to 1.

In the SEAOC code, the use of the fundamental period *T* is also retained but the base shear coefficient is obtained from the formula

$$C = \frac{0.05}{\sqrt[3]{T}}$$

In addition, a new coefficient, K, was introduced to increase or decrease the base shear V in accordance with the estimated ductility and reserve energy capacity of the structure, taking into account also the record of seismic performance of the different types of framing systems. The base shear V is determined from the equation

$$V = KCW$$

where W is the total weight of the building, and K is assigned various values from 0.67 to 1.33 for buildings having different framing systems (see Appendix C). It was a major step forward in code writing to provide in some degree for the real substance of the problem—energy absorption—and for the first time to recognize that equivalent acceleration or base shear coefficient alone is not necessarily a direct index of earthquake-resistance and public safety.

The SEAOC code represents the practical utilization of considerable research data obtained over the years. It is probably as close to reality in its relative results, if not in its approach or quantitative values, as can be accomplished in the present state of knowledge with the retention of the concept of an equivalent static design coefficient C and elastic design procedures [6, 157]. Therefore, the methods presented in this manual are based on the SEAOC code. However, attention is directed to the statement of the SEAOC committee:

"Like any progressive building code, this is an interim code. The committee realizes there is still much work to be done as the results of research and further study become available. . . . These lateral force requirements are intended to provide minimum standards as design criteria toward making buildings and other structures earthquake-resistive. . . ."

It may be assumed from the above that the SEAOC code is neither intended to be nor expected to be the final answer to all aspects of the problem of earthquake-resistant design.

4.5 Period of Vibration

The determination of the natural fundamental mode of vibration of a building or other structure assumes more importance now that the value T has become a code basis for determining lateral design forces.

The Joint Committee report [36] used a formula for period T, in seconds, as follows:

$$T = \frac{0.05H}{\sqrt{D}}$$

in which H is the height of the building in feet above its base or above "the level at which the structure is positively connected to the ground" and D "is the width in feet in the direction under consideration." This formula has survived numerous attacks for inaccuracy and, in fact, is retained in the SEAOC code, with the exception that

$$T = 0.10N$$

"in all buildings in which the lateral resisting system consists of a moment-resisting space frame which resists 100 per cent of the required lateral forces and which frame is not enclosed by or adjoined by more rigid elements which would tend to prevent the frame from resisting lateral forces." N is the total number of stories above exterior grade.

The reasons for retaining a formula that was not even intended to be rigorous or accurate in the first place are: (1) it is simple; (2) it is generally conservative; and (3) it is probably as adequate for its purpose as other short cuts in earthquake design procedures. The codes also permit a more rigorous or accurate determination of T with "properly substantiated technical data."

Although the computation of period is relatively simple for those modern buildings that are essentially frame and floors with curtain walls, it is quite complex for other building types. Methods of computation are described in Sections 2.2 and 2.3 for both the fundamental and higher modes of vibration. The period, particularly the fundamental period, can be computed for any structure if the individual masses (or weights divided by the acceleration of gravity) and the flexibility or influence coefficients for deflection can be determined for the structure. The walls, stairways, and other elements affect the periods and should be considered.

For a "shear-beam" type of structure, in which the deflection of any story is caused only by the shear in that story, the resistance per unit of story deflection or drift is, of course, the measure of story stiffness. However, other factors enter the problem, at least academically. Not only must the so-called shearing deflection between floors be obtained (which includes true shear distortion plus the displacement due to flexure of fixed-end or partly fixed-end columns and the rotation of column-girder joints), but also any appreciable deflection due to cantilever action of the building as a whole must be determined, wherein the floors tilt because the columns undergo axial shortening or lengthening. The yielding due to ground rotation and rocking below the foundations should also be considered. Fortunately, the latter influence is usually not large. Precise calculations of period are not essential if a reasonably good approximation to the fundamental mode period can be made. The contributions of each of the above-mentioned factors for an actual 15-story building, for the fundamental and the three higher modes in each direction, have been presented [35] and simplified procedures for calculating any mode of vibration of buildings in the elastic stage are available (Sections 2.2, 2.3, 3.4, and references 34 and 35). The "lumped mass" assumption is sufficiently accurate for all tall buildings, but as the number of stories becomes less than three or four, or if most of the resistance is provided by shear walls (even for buildings as high as 10 stories), consideration has to be given to the flexural behavior of the entire building as well as to the action as a shear-beam, if one desires really precise results. The use of the SEAOC code does not require such precision, although in special cases it may be desirable to refine the period computations.

Dynamic systems have as many natural modes of vibration as they have degrees of freedom. As has been mentioned, it is convenient and reasonably accurate to consider building floors as lumped masses, one at each floor, with the masses connected by weightless springs representing the resistance to lateral deflection of the columns, walls, bracing, stairways, partitions, etc., of the story between each pair of floors [33, 34, 35]. For each of the two horizontal directions of regularly framed buildings there are as many natural modes of vibration as there are stories. For irregular buildings, the horizontal modes are "coupled," that is, they are not independent, but for design this may be neglected. There are also torsional and vertical modes of vibration, but these are not pertinent to the present discussion.

The ratio of the periods of the modes depends upon the relative amounts of shear, flexural, and ground movement distortion in the particular building. The periods and mode shapes for the first three modes of the same traditional building as in Fig. 4-1 are shown in Fig. 4-2. It is generally accepted that in the elastic range only the lowest three or four modes contribute significantly to the shears. These first three modes in Fig. 4-2 may be compared in shape with the

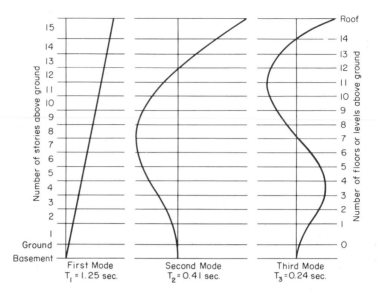

Fig. 4-2. First three mode shapes and periods for the traditional-type building having story weights and shears shown in Fig. 4-1[35].

three modes determined for the illustrative example in Sections 2.2 and 2.3, and summarized in Table 2-1. The marked general similarity is of interest, and is typical of results generally obtained for structures of any height or number of stories.

It will also be noted that the periods for the first three modes have the following ratios to that of the fundamental period:

Three-story illustrative example, Table 2-1	1.0	0.500	0.289
Fifteen-story structure, Fig. 4-2	1.0	0.328	0.192
Uniform cantilever shear beam	1.0	0.333	0.200
Uniform cantilever flexural beam	1.0	0.160	0.057

For the general uniform shear beam, the ratio of the period of the jth mode to that of the fundamental mode is simply $1/(2j-1)$. For most practical purposes, the lower mode periods may be taken as in the ratios 1, 1/3, 1/5, 1/7 if rapid estimates are desired.

4.6 Required Building Separation and Earthquake Deflection

One of the first problems to be settled in the planning for any building is its location in relation to the property lines and adjacent structures. It is generally recognized that buildings sway during earthquakes, but it is not always realized that adjoining buildings can sway out of phase—first away from each other and then toward each other, each in its own natural period of vibration. The result is that buildings can hammer against one another unless adequately separated.

Hammering not only may be the cause of considerable local damage at the point of contact, but it also may result in more serious damage to buildings as a whole and endanger people in the streets. It is desirable, therefore, that buildings be so located and designed as to avoid hammering. Buildings that must be separated into units because of temperature movements or for other reasons should have separations so detailed as to avoid the possibility of hammering.

Building code provisions for separation of adjoining buildings or components have never been too satisfactory, largely because of the various other problems involved. In the congested business portion of most cities, land is extremely valuable. There is usually strong objection when a proposed building code requires a large separation because of the decrease in the usable area and the financial return from the property. The principal argument against separation is that major earthquakes occur seldom, while the full utilization of the land is a continuing and pressing economic factor. Nevertheless, good engineering practice should provide for proper separation and separation details to avoid the possibility of damage from earthquakes.

The SEAOC code has the following statement regarding building separations: "All portions of structures shall be designed and constructed to act as an integral unit in resisting horizontal forces unless separated structurally by a distance sufficient to avoid contact under deflection from seismic action or wind forces."

The question of what width of separation is sufficient must be considered primarily a matter of engineering judgment. Arbitrary rules could cause severe hardship in some cases and be inadequate in others. At any level, the relative deflections of adjoining buildings can be additive, so far as computation of required separation is concerned. Hence the deflection of buildings due to earthquakes becomes a consideration in estimating separation distances.

Wind drift is often used as a basis for determining required building separation, although the true requirement should be the sum of the dynamic deflections under earthquake motion of both buildings considered, plus any space for a safety factor that is considered necessary. Determination of the true dynamic deflection is a complex problem but one which can be solved for the elastic range, and reasonably well estimated for the plastic range, by use of methods of analysis such as described and illustrated in Chapters 1 and 2 and Appendix B.

It is generally adequate to make a less rigorous analysis, for example, by computing the static deflection of each building under the action of the assumed static lateral forces required by the earthquake code. The sum of these computed static deflections is then increased by an appropriate factor; a factor of 2 is suggested, but 1.5 may be used if some possibility of hammering under the design earthquake is acceptable.

A less rigorous appearing rule, but one which may in fact be both more accurate and more rational, is to compute the required separation as the sum of the deflections computed for each building separately on the basis of an increment in deflection for each story equal to the yield-point deflection of that story, arbitrarily increasing the yield deflections of the two lowest stories by multiplying them by a factor of 2.

The horizontal deflection, called drift, of a building under assumed static wind forces can be an important consideration for extremely tall, slender buildings since the occupants may be physically affected, annoyed, or worried by excessive vibratory movement. Although building codes do not ordinarily give limits for wind drift, modern codes, including the SEAOC code, usually require that the designer consider drift in accordance with accepted practice. From the economic, legal, and practical standpoints the engineer must therefore consider and limit wind drift. For many modern buildings, the frame design and weight may be controlled by wind drift rather than wind stress or earthquake stress. However, reinforced concrete buildings, whether essentially a frame or with both a frame and shear walls, have considerable stiffness so that wind drift rarely controls the design, although it may require checking.

From the point of view of comfort of the occupants, there is no need to place a limit on earthquake drift or deflection. Earthquakes occur rarely and frighten almost everyone regardless of drift; since the true dynamic deflections may be quite different from the static force deflections, it would seem that no earthquake drift limitations should be imposed for reasons of human comfort alone.

4.7 Overturning

Despite the many tall, slender structures that have been subjected to violent earthquakes, practically none have been recorded as having simply toppled over as a unit. Some tall structures such as chimneys have broken off at a point above the base, generally in the middle one-third portion. Conversely, there have been shorter, more rigid structures that have tilted at the base. Their base anchorages have probably been designed for full cantilever moments for a force corresponding to an acceleration of $0.10g$ to $0.20g$ down to essentially no anchorage or resistance except that due to the weight of the structure and friction.

The seismic codes have generally required the calculation of and the provision for overturning moment on the basis that the building is a fixed-end cantilever beam loaded with the static lateral earthquake forces accounting for the shears, and acting simultaneously in the same direction. Although this concept is not entirely correct, it is simple in application and for most low- or medium-height buildings it produces results that are fairly reasonable. The application of this concept to tall or slender structures is generally overconservative, because maximum total moments on a section through the building and maximum shears on such sections do not occur for the same combinations of modal components. A more realistic determination of the maximum overturning moment can be made by the methods of dynamic analysis, but such computations are generally unnecessary.

Probably the first earthquake code to do something about the static over-turning moment anomaly was the San Francisco Joint Committee code [36], which contained the following recommendation: "Provision for overturning moment shall be made for the specified earthquake forces in the top ten stories of buildings or the top 120 ft. of other structures, and the moments shall be assumed to remain constant from these levels into the foundations."

It must be noted that this provision applied only to earthquake design. The provision for wind overturning moment, which is considered separately, was not and should not be changed from the full application of wind force to the entire cantilever.

The SEAOC code introduced a new coefficient, J, which modifies the over-turning moment computed from the lateral design forces. The coefficient J has a minimum value of 0.33 and a maximum of 1.00 and is determined as follows:

$$J = \frac{0.5}{\sqrt[3]{T^2}}$$

The SEAOC code states further that the axial loads from earthquake force on vertical elements and footings in every building or structure may be modified in accordance with the following provisions:

1. The overturning moment (M) at the base of the building or structure shall be determined in accordance with the following formula:

$$M = J\sum F_z h_z$$

2. The overturning moment (M_z) at any level designated as z shall be determined in accordance with the following formula:

$$M_z = \frac{H - h_z}{H}M$$

In the above $F_z =$ the lateral force applied to a level designated as z,

$h_z =$ height in feet above the base to the level designated as z,

$H =$ height of the main portion of the building in feet above the base.

If T is assumed to be 0.10 second per story, as the SEAOC code permits for modern curtain-wall buildings, the maximum value of $J = 1.0$ would be obtained for a period of 0.35 second, corresponding to a 3-story building. The minimum value of 0.33 would be that for a period of 1.83 seconds, or for an 18-story building. When J has a value of 1.0, the moments are determined as in the conventional static manner for the lateral forces used in computing shears.

The determination of M_z for any level is another attempt to provide a simple code requirement for a complex dynamic problem. The actual variation of moment over the height of a building depends upon many factors such as the relative importance of the modes of vibration at various levels, which are in turn affected by the relative importance of shear and flexure, and other factors in the building as a whole. The formula given provides simply for a straightline variation of moment from M at the base to zero at the top, even though this is not consistent with the static moments computed from the specified lateral force distribution. However, the specification is a reasonable criterion for slender structures, as may be seen in Figs. 5, 6, and 7 of reference 13.

4.8 Flexibility and Stiffness or Rigidity

If elements of a structure are interconnected, and the structural system is subjected to an external force, the system moves as a unit whether the elements all remain elastic or not. Assuming for simplicity that the force is applied directly to a common rigid interconnecting element, all parts connected to this element are moved by the same amount. In the elastic range they must therefore share the resistance to the external force in proportion to their stiffnesses, or "rigidities" where the stiffness of each element is defined as the ratio of force carried by the element to the deflection of the element. In other words, the more rigid elements tend to resist more of the total force. It does not follow that these more rigid elements are necessarily stronger; they are merely stiffer. It is vitally important in structural design generally, and in earthquake-resistant design in particular, to distinguish between stiffness (or the reciprocal of flexibility) and strength. This holds true under inelastic as well as elastic conditions, if the concept of stiffness is generalized essentially as the secant modulus of deformation.

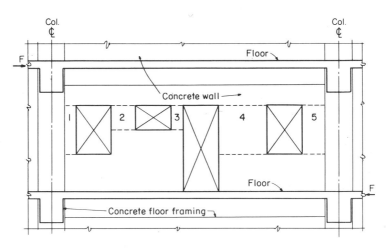

Fig. 4-3. Piers of various stiffnesses and strengths in a reinforced concrete wall act in parallel to resist lateral forces.

A very common system occurs in a building where the floors are rigid plates or diaphragms and the walls transfer earthquake inertia forces to the ground.

Some walls contain windows, doors, and other openings and some do not. The solid wall elements between openings, called piers, have variable sizes and ratios of height to width as indicated in Fig. 4-3. Thus the piers have various stiffnesses and strengths.

Two different piers such as, for example, No. 2 and No. 4 in Fig. 4-3 might have the same stiffness, but one could have a considerably different strength from the other. If an earthquake loaded the weakest pier to the point where it would fail completely, the remaining piers would then share any continuing force in proportion to the remaining relative stiffnesses. The total stiffness of a group of elements having the same deflection (or being in parallel), as in Fig. 4-3, is the sum of the stiffnesses of the individual elements.

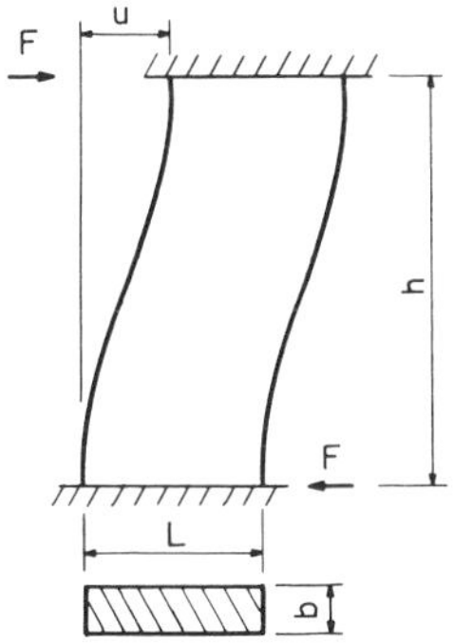

Fig. 4-4. Pier deflected by a lateral force.

If the pier elements in Fig. 4-3 may be considered fixed top and bottom, each will deflect as shown in Fig. 4-4. Because the element is a short, deep beam, the contributions of both flexure and shear to the deflection must be considered as indicated by the following equation:

$$u = u_f + u_v = \frac{Fh^3}{12E_cI} + \frac{1.2Fh}{GA} \tag{4-2}$$

The total deflection due to a unit force F is called the flexibility, and the reciprocal of the flexibility is the stiffness, λ.

In combining stiffnesses of wall assemblies to each other or to framed bents, account must be taken of the end conditions of the elements. For example, equation (4-2) would not be applicable if the wall or floor framing above and below the pier element were inadequate to develop the fully fixed condition shown. The equation can be modified, however, to take account of the actual end conditions.

When two or more deformable elements are in series, i.e., when they carry the same load but have different deflections as shown in Fig. 4-5, the flexibility of the combination is the sum of the flexibilities of the individual elements. The combined stiffness is then the reciprocal of the sum of the flexibilities. For exam-

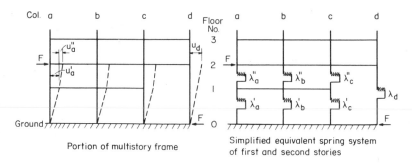

Portion of multistory frame

Simplified equivalent spring system
of first and second stories

Fig. 4-5. Columns in lower stories of a multistory frame often act in series and in parallel, as shown, to resist lateral forces.

ple, column a acts in series from level 0 to 1 and 1 to 2. Columns b and c act similarly. The combined flexibility of column a from level 0 to 2 is therefore:

$$\frac{1}{\lambda_a} = \frac{1}{\lambda'_a} + \frac{1}{\lambda''_a}$$

where

$$\lambda'_a = \frac{1}{\bar{u}'_a} \quad \text{and} \quad \lambda''_a = \frac{1}{\bar{u}''_a}$$

in which $\bar{u}'_a$ and $\bar{u}''_a$ are the deflections due to a unit shearing force acting on column a. The combined stiffnesses of each column are

$$\lambda_a = \frac{\lambda'_a \lambda''_a}{\lambda'_a + \lambda''_a} \quad \lambda_b = \frac{\lambda'_b \lambda''_b}{\lambda'_b + \lambda''_b} \quad \lambda_c = \frac{\lambda'_c \lambda''_c}{\lambda'_c + \lambda''_c} \quad \lambda_d = \frac{1}{\bar{u}_d}$$

where $\bar{u}_d$ is the deflection due to a unit shearing force acting on column d.

Considering larger units of the structure, all vertical resisting elements in a story may be compared on the basis of stiffness and, therefore, of participation in the story shear in each direction providing the upper floor (or the roof) has sufficient rigidity and strength to perform as a rigid diaphragm in distributing the story shear to these vertical resisting elements. These elements can be columns, bents, walls, inclined bracing, or any combination of such elements. They will share in resisting horizontal shear in accordance with their relative stiffnesses up to their elastic limits. When one or more elasto-plastic elements yield, the shear in the yielded elements may be considered to remain constant at the yield value, and the remainder of the shear is carried by the elastic elements in accordance with their relative stiffnesses.

For example, columns a, b, and c in Fig. 4-5 act in parallel with column d when the stiffness of the two-story portion of the building is considered, since $u'_a + u''_a = u_d$. The total stiffness of story 0 to 2 is

$$\lambda_{(0)-(2)} = \lambda_a + \lambda_b + \lambda_c + \lambda_d$$

A hypothetical situation of complete framework, exterior walls placed integrally with the frame, and an interior core wall of concrete masonry is shown in Fig. 4-6. For this discussion, it is assumed that the resisting elements are either symmetrical or that their "center of rigidity" coincides with the center of mass so that torsion (see Section 4.9) is not under consideration. The exterior walls obviously are much more rigid than the framework that encloses them. For all practical purposes, the stiffness of this exterior element is controlled by the solid walls. The exterior framing, without walls, would have much less rigidity. The interior bents with reinforced masonry filler walls present a special situation. The interaction of the masonry and the framing depends upon many factors, including the manner in which the masonry is fitted or connected to the framework. Should there be a gap on one or more of the four sides, only the framework would resist lateral force until its deflection brought the wall into action. The usual situation is a composite action unless and until the wall should fail, after which the bent tends to perform as a framework without a wall or with partial wall restraint. The interaction of walls and framing requires consideration.

A conservative design procedure, but often a desirable one for tall or slender buildings, is to design the framing without regard to the resistance of filler walls. The walls will actually offer some or all of the initial resistance, in proportion to their stiffnesses in the overall structure, whether or not so calculated. They must be reinforced and tied to the framework so as not to create a hazard to occupants.

A procedure is sometimes followed whereby the walls are made essentially adequate for the nominal, more frequent earthquakes but are expected to absorb some energy and then fail under a rare and severe earthquake, after which the more ductile moment-resisting framework resists the remaining portion of

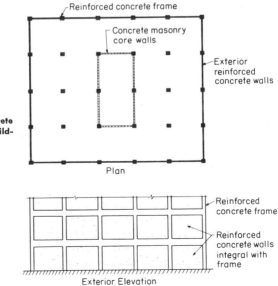

Reinforced concrete frame

Concrete masonry core walls

Exterior reinforced concrete walls

Fig. 4-6. Exterior reinforced concrete walls placed integrally with the building frame.

Plan

Reinforced concrete frame

Reinforced concrete walls integral with frame

Exterior Elevation

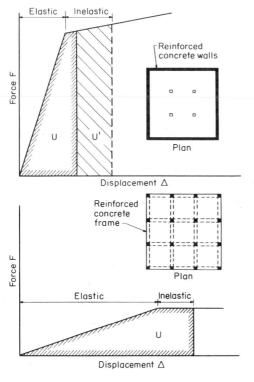

Fig. 4-7. Idealized force-displacement curves for reinforced concrete shear walls and a reinforced concrete frame.

the earthquake [20]. Since the more flexible framework has a longer period of vibration, it has smaller shears from the earth motion and its ductility offers efficient energy absorption. This system involves the consideration of the relative stiffnesses of two (or more) subsystems under various degrees of damage or failure. The "reserve energy" technique described in Appendix B gives more details for this procedure.

Typical force-displacement curves for concrete shear walls and for a concrete frame are shown in Fig. 4-7. The differences in stiffness and in behavior beyond yielding are important points to be considered. The latter point will be discussed in Section 4.10.

The slope of the F-Δ graph is the stiffness λ. It must be realized that deterioration, or loss of resistance and perhaps of stiffness also, progresses at a declining rate with additional cycles of extreme loading. On the other hand, dynamic or rapid loading tests generally show greater values in flexural yielding than for the slow (static) tests usually reported. Since these two factors tend to compensate each other, and in view of other uncertainties, the use of static force-displacement curves without modification is generally adequate for energy design purposes.

Buildings with exterior walls largely of glass or nonstructural panels of

concrete or metal are popular in comtemporary architecture. These are sometimes referred to as curtain-wall buildings. All of the lateral resistance must
come from the framework and interior walls. Often an interior portion of a
building consisting of elevator openings, stairways, duct shafts, and perhaps
storage or mechanical rooms, is surrounded by walls referred to as core walls.
The structural designer realizes that for buildings that are not tall or slender,
such core walls have greater stiffness than the framework. The temptation is to
design the framework for the vertical loads and the walls for the lateral forces.
This procedure may be legally (or from the point of view of some codes)
acceptable if symmetry indicates no torsional tendency, but there is an interaction between the elements even with no torsion. Besides, torsion may develop
despite the apparent symmetry. A design in which core walls are the only
significant lateral resistance elements may lead to a building too weak in polar
moment of inertia to resist accidentally induced torsion. Any structure of considerable height or slenderness requires lateral strength and rigidity where it
will do the most good, generally at or near the plan perimeter. It is difficult to
specify for what number of stories or slenderness a complete frame should be
provided (whether or not there are rigid and convenient walls), because of the
many factors involved. The SEAOC code requires a complete space frame, capable
of resisting at least 25 per cent of the seismic load, for buildings over 13 stories
or 160 ft. in height. These limits, arising from the combined experience of a
large group of structural engineers, should be generally followed as a minimum
requirement.

In some tall or slender buildings having a complete moment-resisting framework, there may be fairly narrow wall elements, usually alongside elevators
or stairwells, as illustrated in Fig. 4-8. The framework, if it acted alone, would
tend to deflect as shown (b) where the floors remain essentially level even
though the joints rotate. The frame may also have an appreciable amount of
overturning moment, producing deflection by column shortening and lengthening. Whether or not this is the case, the very high and narrow shear wall would
have, if by itself, primarily a flexural deflection as shown (c). For a wall 20 ft.
wide and 240 ft. high, the shearing deflection of the wall would be insignificant
compared with its cantilever flexural deflection. The natural unhindered
deflection curve of the wall unit is incompatible with that of the framework to
which it may be connected. Provision must be made for this.

Possible solutions are many and varied. Sometimes the walls are not considered in the resistance at all. Sometimes the connections between the wall and
the frame are planned to permit relative motions, or the designer may provide
for the complete interaction by modifying the shear stiffness for each story by
taking into account both the frame and the wall, using the general procedure
described in Section 4.10, which can take into account the relative restraints
offered by the floors of the structure. It is suggested that, in general, tall, slender
walls be carefully considered and preferably located between columns that can
function as the flanges of a vertical girder.

This discussion of relative rigidity has assumed rigid common interconnecting elements, which in the case of whole stories are the floor systems above and below, acting as diaphragms. A diaphragm must be able, by both rigidity and strength, to distribute the horizontal forces from above, especially when the vertical resisting elements for lateral forces are discontinuous or their relative stiffnesses change from one story to another. It must also transmit those forces originating within its zone of influence to the resisting elements below.Although no diaphragm is absolutely rigid, concrete floor systems are almost invariably sufficiently rigid and do their job without any excessive deflection of the vertical elements below.

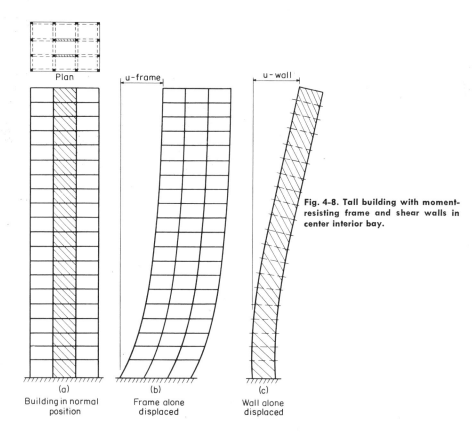

Plan   u-frame   u-wall

Fig. 4-8. Tall building with moment-resisting frame and shear walls in center interior bay.

(a)
Building in normal
position

(b)
Frame alone
displaced

(c)
Wall alone
displaced

For either horizontal or vertical walls or diaphragms, the requirements of the SEAOC code are: "Total shear in any horizontal plane shall be distributed to the various resisting elements in proportion to their rigidities considering the rigidity of the horizontal bracing system or diaphragm as well as the rigidities of the vertical resisting elements."

A diaphragm of concrete is designed essentially as a deep girder [66, 154, 155, 156] with both transverse shear and longitudinal shear properly considered and with adequate provision for flange action in tension as well as compression. Spandrel beams or specially reinforced exterior wall bands function as the flanges for floor diaphragms. Floor openings are treated as openings in the web of a girder, and beams and girders function as stiffeners against web buckling. The SEAOC code requires: "Floors and roofs acting as diaphragms shall be designed for a minimum value of C_p of 10 per cent applied to loads tributary from that story unless a greater value of C_p is required by the basic seismic formula $V = KCW$."

4.9 Torsion

Torsion is normally assumed to occur when the centroid of rigidity of the various vertical resisting elements in a story fails to coincide with the center of gravity. The distance between the two, called the eccentricity e, times the amount of lateral force is a torsional moment that must be resisted in addition to and simultaneously with the normal design lateral forces. Torsion is simply a twisting about the vertical axis. A building has natural torsional modes in addition to its translational modes.

It is desirable to eliminate torsion as much as possible by achieving a design with little or no eccentricity. However, some torsion may develop accidentally and provisions should be made for it. The SEAOC code requires the following: "Provisions shall be made for the increase in shear resulting from the horizontal torsion due to an eccentricity between the center of mass and the center of rigidity. Negative torsional shears shall be neglected. In addition, where the vertical resisting elements depend on diaphragm action for shear distribution at any level, the shear resisting elements shall be capable of resisting a torsional moment assumed to be equivalent to the story shear acting with an eccentricity of not less than five per cent of the maximum building dimension at that level."

The latter provision, for an accidental eccentricity, actually requires some provision for torsion even though there be no computed eccentricity. A provision for accidental torsion was first developed for Mexico City after its 1957 earthquake, and was first recommended for use in the United States in the SEAOC code. This is an important consideration which involves a matter of engineering judgment based upon four factors: (1) there has been evidence of torsional damage in earthquakes; (2) no design calculations involving weights, live loads, and rigidities can be so precise as to negate the possibility of torsional moment; (3) the earthquake motion is dynamic and three-dimensional, not static and two-dimensional as the codes and static calculations imply, and torsion may develop from mere lack of symmetry of the earth motions; and (4) any true symmetry that may exist in mild shocks can well be eliminated by the unsymmetrical progression into the inelastic range for major shocks.

It is strongly recommended that torsional phenomena be given serious attention in design. It is also recommended that tall buildings have symmetrical moment-resisting frames regardless of any walls, and that every building have as much lateral resistance as feasible in its outermost periphery of structural support. Modern curtain-wall buildings need particular attention to compensate for the lack of periphery resistance inherent in predecessor structures, the good behavior of which played a significant part in the evolution of earthquake codes [20].

Because calculation of the torsional shears in a building may be unfamiliar to some engineers, a brief summary of a procedure for computation is given here. Consider, for example, a very simple unsymmetrical building plan such as in Fig. 4-9 where the floors are assumed to be completely rigid. In the particular story shown, the floor above rotates (about an as yet unspecified axis) relative to the floor below. If the building is not symmetrical, for any arbitrary axes, rotation as well as translation of the elements must be considered in arriving at the location of the center of rotation.

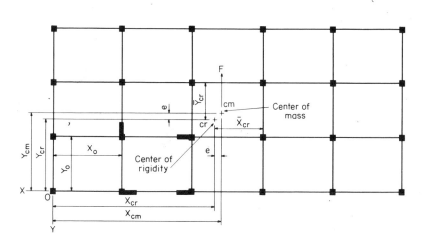

Fig. 4-9. Plan of building subject to torsion due to unsymmetrical column stiffnesses.

Assume an origin at point *0*, which may be chosen arbitrarily and need not be at a corner of the building. The coordinates X_{cr} and Y_{cr} of the center of rigidity or center of rotation can then be calculated as follows:

$$X_{cr} = \frac{\sum X_o \lambda_y}{\sum \lambda_y} \qquad Y_{cr} = \frac{\sum Y_o \lambda_x}{\sum \lambda_x}$$

where X_o, Y_o are the coordinates and λ_x, λ_y are the stiffnesses of the column and wall elements in the respective directions.

The total rotational stiffness I_p about the center of rigidity *cr* is

$$I_p = \sum (\lambda_y \bar{X}_{cr}^2 + \lambda_x \bar{Y}_{cr}^2)$$

where $\bar{X}_{cr}$, $\bar{Y}_{cr}$ are the distances to the respective elements from the new origin at point cr. The quantity I_p has the dimensions of and is similar to a polar moment of inertia. It would be equal to the polar moment of inertia if $\lambda_y = \lambda_x$.

It may be helpful in the calculations to use the following equation relating the total rotational stiffness about point cr to the stiffness about point 0:

$$I_p = \sum (\lambda_y X_o^2 + \lambda_x Y_o^2) - X_{cr}^2 \sum \lambda_y - Y_{cr}^2 \sum \lambda_x$$

If the torsional moment $\bar{M}_{cr} = Fe$ is known, the torsional shears V_x' and V_y' at each column can be calculated from the relations

$$V_y' = \frac{\bar{M}_{cr}\bar{X}_{cr}}{I_p}\lambda_y \qquad V_x' = \frac{\bar{M}_{cr}\bar{Y}_{cr}}{I_p}\lambda_x$$

The shears due to torsion on any column line, V_x or V_y, can be computed from the equations

$$V_y = \frac{\bar{M}_{cr}\bar{X}_{cr}}{I_p}\lambda_{yy} \qquad V_x = \frac{\bar{M}_{cr}\bar{Y}_{cr}}{I_p}\lambda_{xx}$$

where λ_{yy}, λ_{xx} are the total stiffness of the column line being considered. Of course, these torsional shears are to be added to the shears due to lateral loading or motion. However, when the torsional shears act in the opposite direction to the direct shears, the greater shear should be used for design without reduction.

In these computations the result is rigorous if the floors are infinitely rigid, and the stiffnesses are therefore readily determinable, story by story. When the floors deform substantially (even though they may remain undistorted in plan), so as to permit end rotations of the columns, only an approximate solution to the problem can be obtained. This can best be done by modifying the shear stiffnesses of the column (and wall) elements in accordance with the procedures described at the end of Section 4.10.

4.10 Framing, Ductility, and Energy Absorption

A moment-resisting frame having adequate ductility is a means of providing a total reserve energy capacity in a multistory structure that will be adequate for the severe but rare earthquakes. Although adequate energy-absorption value can be provided in a rigid building without a frame, and often entirely in the elastic range, this may become impractical for buildings of more than 10 or 12 stories.

The word "frame" may denote different things to different persons. In the sense in which it is used herein, it refers to a structural system of individual members connected only at joints as distinguished from a "box" system with flat or plate-type elements such as walls, floors, roof, and partitions as the lateral-resisting system. The SEAOC code provides the following definitions:

"SPACE FRAME is a three-dimensional structural system composed of interconnected members, other than shear or bearing walls, laterally supported so as to function as a complete self-contained unit with or without the aid of horizontal diaphragms or floor-bracing systems.

"SPACE FRAME—VERTICAL LOAD-CARRYING: a space frame designed to carry all vertical loads.

"SPACE FRAME—MOMENT-RESISTING: a vertical load-carrying space frame in which the members and joints are capable of resisting design lateral forces by bending moments. This system may or may not be enclosed by or adjoined by more rigid elements which would tend to prevent the space frame from resisting lateral forces.

"BOX SYSTEM is a structural system without a complete vertical load-carrying space frame. In this system the required lateral forces are resisted by shear walls as hereinafter defined.

"SHEAR WALL is a wall designed to resist lateral forces parallel to the wall. Braced frames subjected primarily to axial stresses shall be considered as shear walls for the purpose of this definition."

It is to be noted in the above definitions that there are two primary types of space frames considered: (1) vertical load-carrying and (2) moment-resisting. According to the definition of a shear wall, a third type of frame, namely a braced frame, is considered to have the same inherent rigidity and qualities as a shear wall. Elsewhere in the code are further requirements and conditions for framing, for example:

"*Structural Frame.* Buildings more than 13 stories or one hundred and sixty feet (160') in height shall have a complete moment resisting space frame capable of resisting not less than 25 per cent of the required seismic load for the structure as a whole. The frame shall be made of a ductile material or a ductile combination of materials. The necessary ductility shall be considered to be provided by a steel frame with moment resistant connections or by other systems proven by tests and studies to provide equivalent energy absorption."

In Chapter 6 of this manual, procedures and details are given to ensure that reinforced concrete frames designed in accordance with the recommendations will have the requisite ductility and energy absorption.

Table 23-C of the SEAOC code (Appendix C) provides a modifying factor K for use in the formula for base shear

$$V = KCW$$

to modify the required base shear in accordance with the inherent ductility of the various types of framing systems. Although the specified factors K are admittedly not precise values, they are nevertheless the result of the combined judgment of a great many experienced structural engineers.

It will be noted that the value of K varies from a low of 0.67 for a moment-resisting space frame capable of resisting all of the required lateral forces, to double this value, or 1.33, in box-type buildings that have no frame conforming to the code definition. It should be further noted that a multistory building with a complete space frame, unhampered by more rigid elements such as shear walls, will normally have a longer fundamental period of vibration than other more rigid structures. With this longer period the coefficient C will become somewhat less in accordance with the code formula for C, which depends on the inverse cube root of the period. In other words, for a multistory building the smallest required design forces are obtained with a complete moment-resisting frame of rather long period of vibration. Occasionally in such frames, drift (with long periods of vibration) may become an important factor and control the design rather than the lateral forces. Although drift is rarely a controlling design problem in reinforced concrete buildings, it should always be checked.

In general, it can be argued that in an earthquake a structure has to do as much work as the net energy input to the structure from the ground. Work can be represented by the area under a force-displacement curve. Fig. 4-7 illustrates two hypothetical situations, one for a very rigid story of a building and another for a more flexible and more ductile story. If it be assumed that the total energy requirement is the same for both cases, the necessary equal areas or stored energies U are shown in the figure. It is to be noted that in order to develop the energy for the more flexible structure, considerably more displacement must occur. It is also noted that the response at this displacement is not completely linear in either case, although the residual displacement would be relatively small. Another assumption could be that the rigid element may require more energy value as well as strength for the same earthquake since its rigidity could place its period in a high spectral acceleration range. The area shown as U' in Fig. 4-7 together with the area U shows a case where the required energy is considered to be twice as much as for the U area alone. The resulting displacements to obtain twice the energy value are shown in the figure. There are differences, however, between earthquake force and energy demands. A long-period structure may be subjected to less shear but the energy demand is generally equal to or greater than that for a short-period structure of the same mass. Appendix B provides a detailed discussion of this subject.

A complete moment-resisting concrete frame reinforced so as to have ductility under all possible reversals of loading and moment has great energy-absorbing value, offers less overall resistance to movement, and is thus stressed less severely than a more rigid structure. In addition to these valuable properties, it has the third great value of being redundant—it provides several possible stress paths rather than just one. Thus, when hinges tend to develop, stress is transferred elsewhere to members having a remaining great residual capacity for resistance and energy absorption. The whole structure tends to offer resistance in severe emergencies and the value is not limited merely to that of the weak link of an element in the elastic range. The record has shown, and research and analysis have confirmed, the value of indeterminate, ductile, moment-resisting construction for multistory buildings in earthquake regions.

In computing the stiffness of the stories of a building, consideration must be given to the rotations of the columns at their intersections with the floors.

Consider the elements of a portion of a building frame shown in Fig. 4-10(a) where the columns and girders have moments of inertia represented by I_c and I_g and the modulus of elasticity for these members is E_c and E_g, respectively. The height of the column is denoted by H_s and the span of the girder by L. A reasonably accurate estimate of the stiffness of a column, from which the stiff-

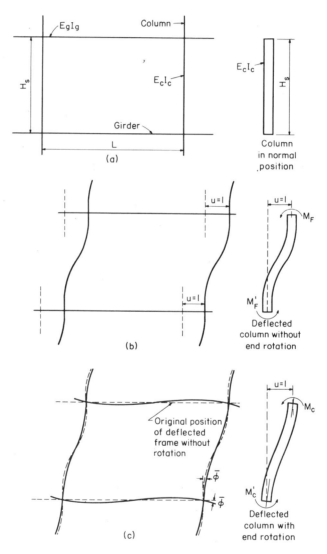

Fig. 4-10. (a) Elements of a building frame in normal position; (b) frame with unit deflections in each story; (c) deflected frame after joint rotations.

ness of a story can be readily computed by summing up the shear stiffnesses of all of the columns in the story, can be made by the following procedure.

Consider a section of the building of several stories in which it is desired to determine the stiffness. The entire building may be considered, if it is desired to do so. Take a unit story deflection for all of the columns in any one story, as shown schematically in Fig. 4-10(b). Assume that this deflection takes place without rotation of the column-girder connections. For this configuration, fixed-end moments M_F at each end of each column can be computed. The beam stiffness can be determined from the sum of the numerical values of the fixed-end moments in the columns divided by the story height.

Because of the fact that the girders have no fixed-end moments, and the fixed-end moments of the columns above and below a girder joint tend to rotate that joint in the same direction, the moments in the columns will be relieved somewhat by rotations of the joints. The general tendency is for all of the joints to rotate in the same direction; a schematic diagram of the rotation and of the deflections of the structure after the rotation takes place is indicated in Fig. 4-10(c). This rotation is assumed to take place without further lateral deflection. The moments resulting from these rotations are computed most simply by merely distributing moments by the method of moment distribution throughout the frame, considering all the joints as fixed in position laterally during this process. This may be done as accurately as desired. However, one can make a very quick approximation to the results, quite accurately, by noting the rotations will be generally equal throughout the structure, and therefore one can use modified stiffnesses for both the columns and the girders corresponding to equal rotations at the two ends of these members. In other words, if the moments are distributed at each joint in proportion to the stiffnesses, taking into account the fact that the far ends rotate in the same way, it is necessary only to distribute the moments at each joint and no carry-over moments are required. The column moments M_c at the ends of the columns will in general be less than the fixed-end moments M_F in the columns. A diagram of the configurations of the columns showing the moments at the end is shown in Fig. 4-10, where (a) shows the undeflected column, (b) shows the column deflected with fixed-end moments and without end rotations, and (c) shows the deflected column with end rotations after the moment distribution has taken place.

The final shear in each column is given by the sum of the final end moments divided by the story height.

As a quick guide to the magnitude of the modified stiffness of the story, caused by the flexibility of the girder, one can derive an equation applicable to a single column for the relative stiffness λ compared with the stiffness for infinitely stiff girders λ_{inf} based on the assumption that all rotations are exactly the same. The resulting expression is

$$\frac{\lambda}{\lambda_{\text{inf}}} \cong 1 - \left(\frac{K_c}{\sum K_j} + \frac{K_c'}{\sum K_j'} \right) \qquad (4\text{-}3)$$

in which

K_c is the stiffness at the top of a column

K'_c is the stiffness at the bottom of a column

$\sum K_j$ is the summation of all of the stiffnesses at the joint at the top of a column

$\sum K'_j$ is the summation of all of the stiffnesses at the joint at the base of a column

In deriving this equation, it is assumed that the fixed-end moments above and below each joint are equal and the fixed-end moments at the top and bottom of the column in a story are the same. The equation can be simplified in the case where all of the column stiffnesses in the structure are equal and all of the girder stiffnesses are equal. If the girder stiffnesses are designated by K_g, the following result is obtained:

$$\frac{\lambda}{\lambda_{\inf}} \simeq \frac{K_g}{K_g + K_c} \tag{4-4}$$

It can be seen from this relationship that when the girder stiffness is very much larger than the column stiffness, the effective shear stiffness of the story is the same as that for infinitely stiff girders. However, when the girder stiffness is small compared with the column stiffness, the shear stiffness of the story is considerably reduced from the value corresponding to infinitely stiff floors. This reduction must be taken into account in defining the flexibility of the structure.

As an aid to the reader the following well-known relations for stiffness of a column or girder are given:

When one end of a column or girder is rotated, the other end being fixed, the stiffness of the column or girder is

$$K_c = \frac{4E_c I_c}{H_s} \tag{4-5}$$

$$K_g = \frac{4E_g I_g}{L} \tag{4-6}$$

The change in moment at the fixed end, due to the rotation, is half the change in moment at the rotated end.

When equal rotations occur at the two ends, the modified stiffnesses become

$$K_c = \frac{6E_c I_c}{H_s}$$

$$K_g = \frac{6E_g I_g}{L}$$

These values, however, are proportional to those in equations (4-5) and (4-6), or are proportional to the moment of inertia divided by the span, and any of these values may be used in equation (4-3).

The fixed-end moment in a column due to a deflection u without end rotation is

$$M_F = \frac{6E_cI_c}{H_s^2}u \qquad (4\text{-}7)$$

Consequently, the fixed-end stiffness or the stiffness for infinite floor stiffness is

$$\lambda_{\text{inf}} = \frac{12E_cI_c}{H_s^3} \qquad (4\text{-}8)$$

In general, the preceding simplified procedure will be applicable throughout the greater portion of a typical tall multistory building except in the lower and, under certain conditions, in the upper stories. In these regions the stiffness of the individual stories is sensitive to the ratios of the stiffnesses of the girders to those of the columns and, particularly in the lower stories, to the restraint offered at the base. In some cases, as when the girders are relatively flexible compared to the columns, the point of inflection may not occur within the story and therefore the assumption of equal rotation at both ends of the column upon which the previous formulas have been predicated is no longer valid. Consequently, for the lower and upper stories a more exact solution should be made, especially when there exists an irregular arrangement of beams and columns or when the girder stiffness is appreciably less than that of the columns.

For buildings in which the columns are approximately uniformly spaced and story heights are about equal, Figs. 4-11 to 4-16 can be employed advantageously to determine readily the moment at the top and bottom of the columns, and from these, by the slope deflection relationship, the shear stiffness of the columns. Curves are shown for the first three stories only in Figs. 4-11 to 4-14 because the points of inflection in columns above the third floor are at or close to midheight except near the top of the building under certain conditions that will be discussed later.

In the preparation of the curves, an idealized 20-story building consisting of three equal bays and constant story-heights above the first floor was selected. With the exception of the structure in Fig. 4-16, it was assumed that the moment of inertia of the top column is one-twentieth that of the first-story column and that a uniform change in the moment of inertia occurs every second floor. The moment of inertia of the girder was assumed to increase in constant increments every two floors from top to bottom, with the top girder having half the value of the bottom. The values for plotting the curves were computed by the Maney-Goldberg modified slope deflection method[39]. This procedure features the rapid determination of final values by first making rational approximations and then by iteration converging to exact values by the slope deflection method.

The ratio of the moment at the top of a column to the moment at the bottom is plotted as the ordinate. The ratio of moments for the first three stories is obtained by entering the applicable figure with the ratio of the exterior first-story column stiffness to the first-floor girder stiffness as the abscissa and reading the value on the ordinate at the appropriate curve. For example, in Fig. 4-11,

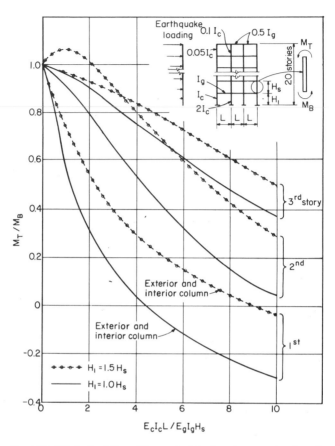

Fig. 4-11. Effect of relative stiffness of girder to column on location of point of inflection in exterior and interior columns fixed at the base and having stiffnesses of I_c and $2I_{cr}$ respectively. The solid line curves are for all stories of equal height and the broken line curves are for a first story 1.5 times the height of the stories above.

for $E_cI_cL/E_gI_gH_s$ equal to 4.0 and $H_1 = H_s$, $M_T/M_B = 0.03$ for the first story. Since this ratio is positive, the point of inflection is within the first story. Where the value is negative, the point of inflection falls outside the column. A value of 1.0 indicates that the point of inflection is at midheight.

Although all the curves presented show a building three bays wide, they are applicable without any great loss of accuracy to any number of bays having the same ratio of column-to-girder stiffness. Where the moment of inertia of the interior column is twice that of the exterior columns, as assumed in the preparation of Fig. 4-11, it has been found that the M_T/M_B ratios for one- and two-bay buildings coincide exactly with those for the three-bay building. From this it appears that the curves given in Fig. 4-11 are independent of the number of bays.

To provide additional guidance on the location of inflection points in the lower stories, curves for the first story equal to 1.5 times the heights of the stories above have been included in Fig. 4-11. It is apparent from a comparison of the curves for $H_1 = H_s$ and $H_1 = 1.5H_s$ that the ratio of M_T/M_B is sensitive to difference in story heights of adjacent floors. While this sensitivity is partly due to the effect of the column height on the stiffness of the columns, the primary cause for the differences between the solid and dash curves is due to the increase in moment that occurs because of the increased column height. Therefore, those sections of multistory buildings in which marked differences in story heights occur should receive special attention.

In contrast to the effect of a difference in story heights, marked departure from the variation in the relative stiffness assumed in the idealized structure of equal story heights in Fig. 4-11 showed little influence on the value of M_T/M_B. For example, increasing the stiffness of the columns on the second and other floors by 50 per cent over that of the first-story columns, while maintain-

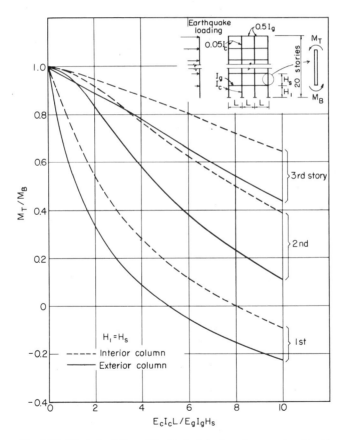

Fig. 4-12. Effect of relative stiffness of girder to column on location of point of inflection in exterior and interior columns fixed at the base and having equal stiffness.

81

ing the story height uniform, gave almost identical M_T/M_B ratios for the first-story columns to those indicated by the solid curve using the I_c of the first-story column to compute the abscissa. As would be expected, the M_T/M_B ratios for the second and third stories were found to be almost equal to the solid curve value using as abscissa the average of the $E_c I_c L/E_g I_g H_s$ ratios of the first and second stories.

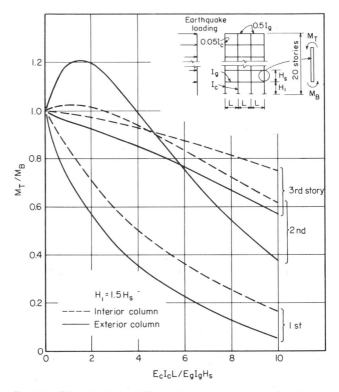

Fig. 4-13. Effect of relative stiffness of girder to column on location of point of inflection in exterior and interior columns fixed at the base and having equal stiffness and the first story 1.5 times the height of the stories above.

It should be noted that when $H_1 = 1.5H_s$, the M_T/M_B ratio for the second story can be more than 1 for small ratios of $E_c I_c L/E_g I_g H_s$. This unique behavior is due to the influence of the larger moments occurring at the first story and means that the point of inflection in the second story is slightly below the mid-point of the column.

For the case in which the same moment of inertia was assumed for all the columns in a story, as in Fig. 4-12, the M_T/M_B values for a two-bay building differed slightly from a three-bay building. However, even for $E_c I_c L/E_g I_g H_s$

equal to 10, the difference between the two was only 10 per cent, with this difference decreasing to about 2 per cent for $E_c I_c L / E_g I_g H_s = 1.0$. Therefore, Fig. 4-12 can be used without significant error for any number of bays.

A comparison of the curves in Fig. 4-11 and Fig. 4-12 indicates that the M_T / M_B ratio for the exterior column is not greatly affected by changes in the moment of inertia of the interior column. In contrast to this, the M_T / M_B value for the interior column is affected substantially. For the building shown in Fig. 4-11, the M_T / M_B ratio of the interior column is identical to that of the exterior column. This is primarily due to the fact that $K_c / \sum K_j$ at each joint in each floor is the same. For the building shown in Fig. 4-12, the $K_c / \sum K_j$ of the interior column is less than that of the exterior column. Because of this, the rotation occurring at the joint of the interior column will be less than that at the exterior column. Consequently, as shown in Fig. 4-12, the M_T / M_B ratio of the interior column differs appreciably from that of the exterior column and is nearer to that of a fixed column.

The curves in Figs. 4-11 to 4-16 can also be used to determine the moments in each column. Where the point of inflection is the same for all columns, the

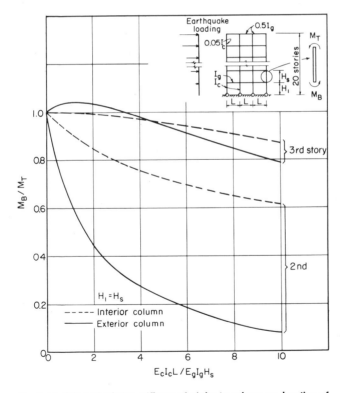

Fig. 4-14. Effect of relative stiffness of girder to column on location of point of inflection in exterior and interior columns hinged at the base and having equal stiffness.

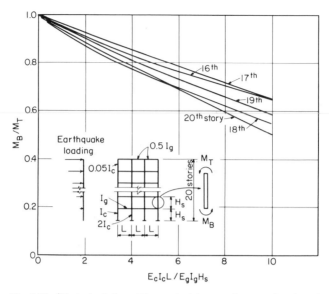

Fig. 4-15. Effect of relative stiffness of girder to column on location of point of inflection in the upper story columns of a building in which the members have the same stiffness and base condition as in Fig. 4-11. All stories are of equal height.

amount of shear carried by each column is proportional to the moment of inertia. If V is the proportion of shear taken by a column, then

$$M_B = \frac{VH_s}{1 + \dfrac{M_T}{M_B}} \tag{4-9}$$

Where the point of inflection varies from column to column, the proportion of shear carried by each column in the first story, assuming the base fixed, can be computed from

$$V_n = V_m \frac{I_n \left[1 - 0.5 \left(\dfrac{M_T}{M_B}\right)_m \right] \left[1 + \left(\dfrac{M_T}{M_B}\right)_n \right]}{I_m \left[1 - 0.5 \left(\dfrac{M_T}{M_B}\right)_n \right] \left[1 + \left(\dfrac{M_T}{M_B}\right)_m \right]} \tag{4-10}$$

in which n and m designate any two columns. This relation is valid only for the first story when the base is fixed. By determining the proportion of shear carried by each column in terms of one column and equating the sum of the proportions to the total shear acting at the first story, the shear resisted by the individual columns can be obtained. The moment can then be obtained from equation (4-9).

In some cases, it will not be feasible to achieve full fixity of the columns at the base and partial rotation will occur. To determine the magnitude of the rotation, due account must be taken of the soil modulus or of the restraint offered by the foundation structure or adjoining members. When there are inadequate foundation data or for preliminary investigation, it is possible to interpolate between the fixed and hinged condition based on judgment. As a possible aid, Fig. 4-14 is provided. It shows the ratio of moments for the second- and third-story columns when the first-story columns are hinged at the base. It should be noted that the ordinate for this figure is the reciprocal of that used in Figs. 4-11, 4-12, and 4-13.

The curves shown in Fig. 4-14 have the same range of applicability as the other curves. Only slight differences were found between the two- and three-bay structures. Above the third story and even in the third story, the point of inflection is about at midheight. The values of M_B/M_T slightly greater than unity, which occur for low ratios of $E_c I_c L/E_g I_g H_s$ for the third story, are due to the fact that as the effect of the hinge becomes less, the bending moment at the bottom is almost equal to or slightly more than the moment at the top of the column.

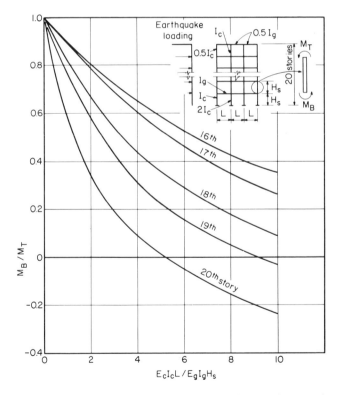

Fig. 4-16. Effect of relative stiffness of girder to column on location of point of inflection in the upper story columns of a building in which the top story column stiffness is 10 times that of the top story column in Fig. 4-15.

In structures with the base of the first-story column fixed, it is possible to determine the shear stiffness of the column from the M_T/M_B ratio by proceeding upward from the base. When the columns are hinged it is necessary to proceed downward from a known joint rotation. For such computation one can assume that the joint rotation at the top and bottom of the fourth story are equal. This assumption permits the evaluation of the rotation by slope deflection equations. With the rotation at the top of a column known, it is possible to determine the rotation of the bottom from the M_B/M_T ratios.

To a minor extent, the location of the point of inflection in the columns in the top stories of tall multistory buildings is influenced by the relative stiffnesses of columns and girders in a manner similar to the lower stories. For a building of the usual dimensions, such as that shown in Fig. 4-11, there is a slight tendency for the point of inflection to be below the midheight. Values of M_B/M_T for the upper stories of the idealized building in Fig. 4-11 are shown in Fig. 4-15. Because member sizes were assumed to be changed only at every other story, there is not a uniform change in the M_B/M_T ratios from floor to floor. The ratios are consistent for every pair of stories. It should be noted that even for the extreme case of $E_cI_cL/E_gI_gH_s$ equal to 10, the M_B/M_T ratio is only 0.5 in the top story.

When the stiffness of the column relative to the girder is large in the upper stories, the moment at the bottom of the column may be considerably less than at the top. To give some insight on the behavior of a structure that is extremely stiff in the upper stories, the ratios of M_B/M_T are shown in Fig. 4-16 for an idealized building in which the relative stiffnesses of the columns to girders are uniform throughout the building. For cases between the conditions shown in Figs. 4-15 and 4-16, interpolation of values will give reasonable answers.

For consistency the curves in Fig. 4-15 have been presented in terms of the moment of inertia of the first-story column and girder. A more suitable representation would have been to present the data in terms of the moment of inertia of the columns and girders of the top story. In order to relate the values of M_B/M_T in Figs. 4-15 and 4-16 to the ratios of the stiffnesses in the upper stories, the abscissa of Fig. 4-15 must be divided by 10 while Fig. 4-16 remains as it is. If this is done, it will be found that the M_B/M_T values for the curves in Fig. 4-15 are in the general range of the M_B/M_T values in Fig. 4-16 for the same value of the altered abscissa. This indicates again that the M_B/M_T ratio is not sensitive to variations from floor to floor in the relative stiffness of columns to girders. It should be noted that the ordinate for these two figures is the reciprocal of that used in Figs. 4-11, 4-12, and 4-13.

4.11 Limit Design of Frames

When designing a frame for given lateral forces, it may often be desirable to use the concepts of limit design, involving "plastic-hinge" moment capac-

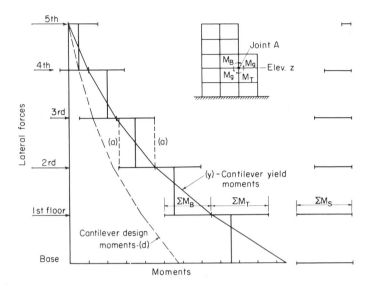

Fig. 4-17. Cantilever moments due to lateral forces and possible column yield moments by the concepts of limit design.

ities of the members meeting at a joint, in order to select the preliminary proportions of the columns and girders. The procedure described here may also be helpful to indicate the different ways in which the required lateral resistance may be provided in the frame.

Consider the simple frame shown in outline at the upper right in Fig. 4-17 for purposes of illustration. The design lateral forces are shown at the left of the figure and the cantilever design moments (not to be confused with overturning moments) corresponding to these forces are indicated by curve (d). The design moments, multiplied by the appropriate overload factor, normally of the order of 1.5 to 2.0, give the cantilever yield moments as shown by curve (y). The problem is to select the proper yield capacities of the members in the frame to develop a resistance corresponding to the yield moments.

The following notation is used in the procedure described here: At any joint such as A at the elevation designated by z in the figure, let

M_g = sum of yield moment capacities at the ends at joint A of the two girders connected to joint A.

M_B = yield moment at the lower end of the column at joint A in the story above elevation z.

M_T = yield moment at the upper end of the column at joint A in the story below elevation z. (For the lowest elevation, $z = 0$; M_T and M_g may be taken as infinitely large.)

M_s = smaller of the two quantities, M_g or $M_B + M_T$ at joint A.

The symbol Σ preceding any of the four quantities defined above indicates a summation for all the joints at elevation z.

87

At each elevation z the value of $\sum M_T$ is plotted to the right, and $\sum M_B$ to the left, of the yield moment curve (y). A line corresponding to the magnitude of $\sum M_s$ at each level is determined also and is shown to the right of the figure for purposes of comparison.

A stepped vertical line is drawn that satisfies the following criteria:

1. In any story the vertical line must intersect the previously plotted horizontal lines at the top and bottom of the story. For example, the broken lines marked (*a*) are extreme locations of possible vertical lines in the third story. Any line between the two (*a*) lines would conform to this criterion.

2. The step or distance between the vertical lines at any elevation must be less in magnitude than $\sum M_s$ at that elevation.

The resulting diagram gives a ready means of determining the ultimate capacity of the structure, assuming the formation of plastic hinges. The multiple of overloads that can be carried will be equal to the minimum ratio of (a) the sum of the moments at the top and bottom of the columns in any story to (b) the horizontal projection of the segment of the cantilever yield moment curve for that story, provided that criteria 1 and 2 are satisfied.

Furthermore, by superimposing on the cantilever yield moment curve the moment curve as obtained by an elastic analysis multipled by the overload factor, it is possible to determine where the first hinge will form. In this case, the plot of the elastic moment curve must intersect the cantilever moment curve at each story. By adjustment of the capacities, on the basis of this observation it is possible to ensure that the first hinge will form in the girder rather than in the column.

By progressive adjustments made on the basis of taking into account the effect of the hinge formed, it is possible to make the next hinge also form in the girder. Since after the formation of several hinges the dynamic forces acting on the structure remain nearly constant, it is possible, in fact, to have all hinges form in the girders rather than in the columns. The advantage in doing so is that the columns can more readily resist vertical forces if the yield hinges are kept in the girders, while the columns remain elastic in flexure.

4.12 Parts of Buildings

The discussion in this and the preceding chapters has been concerned with buildings as a whole. Parts or elements of a structure respond to earthquake motion, however, and must also be considered. Certain elements such as parapet walls and heavy building ornamentations have had a very poor seismic history, actually much worse than buildings as complete units. Such elements, in falling or in being loosened, are especially dangerous to persons in the streets about the buildings.

There has been no particular question or discussion about the design coefficients for parts of buildings, as there has been for buildings as a whole, for three principal reasons:

1. There can be little doubt about the very poor record of building parts in actual earthquakes—the damage has been obvious to all.
2. Since they are usually simple elements structurally or mathematically, their strength and response have been easily reconciled.
3. The additional cost to design and build such elements, even for very large force coefficients, is small and usually negligible. For example, in designing a reinforced concrete parapet wall for lateral forces it makes little difference in the overall cost of the structure whether the design coefficient is 20 per cent or 50 per cent or even 100 per cent of gravity.

Three basic factors are important in the design of attached elements or parts of buildings:

1. The element itself usually has a short period of vibration, which may "tune in" to the high spectral peak accelerations.
2. The damping is often small and the local structural system may completely lack the desirable quality of being indeterminate.
3. Many elements, such as parapet walls, are subjected not to the ground motion but to a high-level building motion of increased accelerations. It can be said that the building motion has a "whip" effect on the part since the accelerations at the roof level may be much greater than at the ground.

Code design coefficients for parts and appendages of buildings are usually quite high compared with the structure as a whole. The design factors for various elements are given in Table 23-D of the SEAOC code (Appendix C), where factors ranging from 0.10 to 1.00 are specified.

It is not intended that the coefficient specified for the design of these parts of structures be used simultaneously in the design of the whole structure. For example, the 50 per cent *g* requirements on a unit would apply only to the design of that unit, and the reactions from this 50 per cent *g* would be carried to but not through the structure as a whole, which is designed for its own coefficient; in this case the mass of the element would be multiplied by the lower building factor. Actually, there are several vibrating systems under consideration and even though these might be in motion simultaneously, either independently of each other or coupled with each other, it is assumed for the purpose of static code design that only one of these situations occurs at a time.

If the design of building parts were considered for dynamic conditions, it would be quite logical to investigate any building elements that had periods of vibration of, say 0.20 second or longer, as not only reacting to the earthquake spectrum as an individual unit but also of possibly reacting with the structure as a whole in one of the structure's modes of vibration. For example, if a building should have a third mode of vibration of 0.3 second and if a floor diaphragm system should have a natural period of vibration at some value near the 0.3 second, there would be a possibility that distress might occur at the end walls that would have to participate in the reaction from both modes of vibration simultaneously. The design values for parts of buildings specified in the SEAOC code, however, are large enough to take some account of these possibilities.

Code coefficients pertaining to parts or elements of buildings apply in both directions. If a wall, for example, is to be designed for a factor C of 0.20, this force must be considered to be applied in either direction normal to the face of the wall. The same is true for floor diaphragms, roof diaphragms, parapet walls, and all other parts. The reactions from these building elements under their seismic design coefficient must also be provided for at the connections or boundaries.

All elements or parts of a building in some degree affect the overall dynamic properties of the building in vibrational response. They may also affect the damping capacity of the structure and the energy dissipation. All elements and parts must be properly joined and connected, so that no matter in which direction motion occurs, there will be integrity of resistance and inherent ductility. The designer's judgment is very important in these as in all seismic design matters. The thoroughness of the planning and the detailing, and the manner in which the parts of the structure are joined or intentionally separated, can do a great deal toward improving the seismic resistance, regardless of the specific design coefficients used.

4.13 Reserve Energy Technique for Inelastic Design

Research efforts have indicated that damage to buildings in earthquakes cannot be reconciled with normal building code design coefficients and unit stresses unless inelastic action is considered with the capacity of the structure to dissipate energy beyond the elastic range. There are various ways this problem can be approached, including the modification of building code requirements in an attempt to provide in some measure for inelastic behavior and ductility.

The procedures described in Chapter 1 involve spectral responses for elasto-plastic systems and simply reduce the elastic spectral response to an equivalent one that, although still used in elastic design, allows for elasto-plastic action. An elasto-plastic system, however, is a special case of inelastic response and many structures do not show true elasto-plastic characteristics. Buildings consist of frame, walls, stairways, and other elements which participate structurally but which have widely different ductilities, and consequently share in carrying the dynamic forces in a manner that changes with the magnitude of the response. Multiple "plastic" elements of a building do not necessarily reach yield values simultaneously. The "reserve energy" technique [17, 20] was developed to provide a simple method to take account of these considerations in terms of the structural designer's normal procedures and terminology.

The procedure is based upon a comparison of the strain energy plus energy dissipation value of a structure, or a basic element of a structure, to the net kinetic energy input obtained from a specified earthquake spectrum. Acceleration coefficients are maintained as a design criterion as for static design. The basic requirement, in addition to the specified earthquake spectrum, is a force-deflection diagram from no load to complete failure of an element or of the structure, including the participation of all significant building elements and materials. For the degree of accuracy required for this problem it is generally feasible to use static force-deflection data as a basis to plot the force-deflection diagram without alteration for dynamic conditions.

It is not intended that the reserve energy technique be a rigorous solution of the earthquake problem. It naturally contains empirical data and assumptions and some allowances for uncontrollable variations. As for any procedure, the accuracy can be no better than the manner in which the load-deflection curve represents the true structural resistance as constructed.

Because of the special considerations involved in applying the reserve energy technique, a detailed discussion and presentation of the method is given in Appendix B of this manual. The presentation follows along the lines of references 17 and 20, but with some differences in notation to be as nearly as possible consistent with the other procedures described in this manual.

CHAPTER **5**

Strength, Ductility, and Energy Absorption of Reinforced Concrete Members

5.1 Introduction

The object of this chapter is to define the strength and deformation characteristics of reinforced concrete members which are important in the design of
buildings to resist lateral forces. To accomplish this purpose, it is desirable first
to examine the pertinent fundamental properties of the two materials that make
up the reinforced concrete section. Representative stress-strain relationships for
both concrete and steel are discussed in Section 5.2.

The behavior of reinforced concrete sections under bending only, evaluated
in terms of the relationship between bending moment and curvature, is treated
in Section 5.3. The effect of axial load on the moment-curvature relationship is
discussed in Section 5.4 with the aid of an interaction diagram. In Section 5.5,
the behavior of members subjected to combinations of shear, bending, and axial
load is presented in order to develop simple rules for the proportioning of web
reinforcement.

The deformation of beam-column connections is discussed in Section 5.6,
and the shearing deformation of reinforced concrete members is discussed in
Section 5.7 in connection with the response of shear walls to lateral loads.

The influence of rapid loading and reversed loading on the response of
transversely loaded reinforced concrete members is described in Sections 5.8
and 5.9.

It should be emphasized that this chapter is intended to describe the behavior of reinforced concrete loaded well beyond the range of ordinary working stresses and to show why it exhibits a plastic range and how this plastic range is related to the critical parameters. How a desirable amount of plasticity can be achieved in a practical design under various loading conditions is discussed in Chapter 6.

5.2 Stress-Strain Relationships

A knowledge of the stress-strain relationship is essential to the understanding of the dynamic behavior of structures since it provides the link between deformations and external forces. In the linear range it is sufficient to know only the initial slope of the stress-strain curve, i.e., the modulus of elasticity. However, in order to understand and describe the complete response of the structure, the complete stress-strain relationship must be known.

In reinforced concrete structures, the reinforcing bars are almost always subject to direct axial stress in tension or compression. These conditions are simulated in simple coupon tests. However, the concrete in the structure is usually stressed in a manner different from that in a simple axial compression test. Nonetheless, the stress-strain curve determined from a cylinder test provides an excellent picture of the behavior of concrete in compression that has been checked against and complemented by tests on specimens in pure bending [40, 41] and combined axial load and bending [42, 43, 44].

Stress-Strain Relationship for Reinforcing Steel

Stress-strain curves for two types of steel used in reinforced concrete construction are shown in Fig. 5-1. The curves exhibit an initial "elastic" portion, a yield point beyond which strain increases with little or no increase in stress,

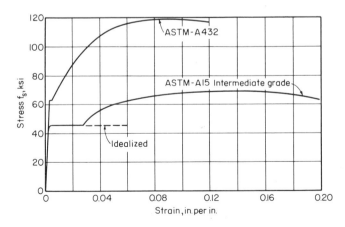

Fig. 5-1. Representative stress-strain relationships for two grades of reinforcing steel.

and a "strain hardening" range in which stress increases again with increase in strain.

It is worthwhile to note particularly the properties of intermediate-grade steel because it is the most common type of reinforcing steel. Ordinarily, an intermediate-grade reinforcing bar develops a stress of about 45,000 psi at yield and a maximum stress of about 70,000 psi. The yield strain ϵ_y is about 0.0015 and the strain at the initiation of strain hardening ϵ_h varies between 0.015 and 0.030. The maximum stress is reached at a strain of approximately 0.15, and fracture at about 0.20. Thus, the plastic portion of the stress-strain curve, the range between ϵ_y and ϵ_h, is about 10 to 20 times the elastic range. The portion of the curve beyond ϵ_h is about 8 times the plastic range, and over 100 times the elastic range. For reinforced concrete beams of ordinary proportions, the significant portion of the stress-strain curve is that up to a strain of about twice ϵ_h. Consequently, the curve may be further simplified by idealizing it as two straight lines, with the increase in stress beyond f_y ignored as shown by the broken line in Fig. 5-1.

Stress-Strain Relationship for Concrete

UNCONFINED CONCRETE. The term "unconfined concrete" refers to a condition in which concrete is stressed in one direction only. This is seldom realized under actual conditions. Some degree of restraint exists in almost every case. However, in this discussion, concrete will be considered as unconfined unless positive measures are taken to confine it. If such measures are taken, both the strength and the ductility of the concrete are increased considerably.

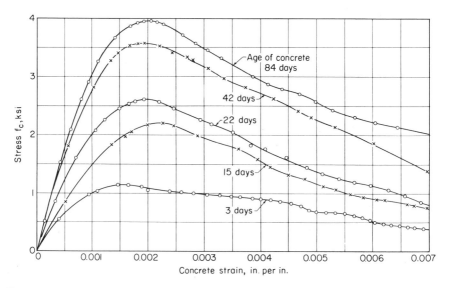

Fig. 5-2. Stress-strain curves from compression tests of concrete cylinders. (Adapted from reference 45, ASCE.)

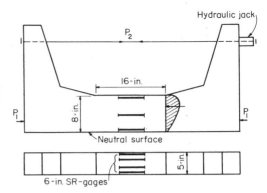

Fig. 5-3. Eccentric load specimen used in tests[46] to determine the stress-strain curve of concrete under combined bending and axial load.

Typical stress-strain curves for unconfined concrete in compression are given in Fig. 5-2. The curves were obtained from tests [45] on 3x6-in. cylinders made from the same batch of concrete and tested in compression at different ages. All the curves have certain common characteristics. Up to a stress of about 50 per cent of the maximum, the curves are practically linear. The slopes of the curves decrease until the maximum stress is reached at a strain of approximately 0.002. There is no sharp break in the stress-strain curve as it passes the point of maximum stress.

It is significant, even though longitudinal cracking may be observed in concentric compression test specimens at strains ranging from 0.0025 to 0.0040, that failure is not necessarily indicated by these cracks. The specimen continues to deform and carry load. Furthermore, recent unpublished data indicate that at strains lower than 0.003 to 0.004, the load may be removed and reapplied and still reach the original maximum load level.

The curves in Fig. 5-2 are comparable in form and characteristics with stress-strain curves obtained by tests [42] on 6x12-in. cylinders having similar strengths at 28 days and on 5x8x16-in. prisms. Likewise, eccentric compression tests [46] on specimens shown in Fig. 5-3, which were unreinforced except in the brackets, resulted in stress-strain curves closely similar to those obtained from concentric compression tests.

It may be incorrectly inferred from Fig. 5-2 that a notable decrease in *capacity* of a section of unconfined concrete occurs beyond a strain of 0.002 or 0.0025. This is true only for compression cylinders subject to pure axial load, which are not comparable to members in reinforced concrete structures. Because of the integral action of reinforced concrete frames, all members are subject to combined bending, axial load, and shear. The girders generally are subject to almost pure bending with the axial load negligible, and the columns are subject to various degrees of bending or eccentricity of the axial load. Even for ratios of eccentricity-to-depth as low as 0.05, the compressive strains in columns will vary from about zero at one surface to a maximum value at the other surface. Consequently, for all practical cases the capacity cannot be related directly to the stress at maximum strain but due account must be taken of

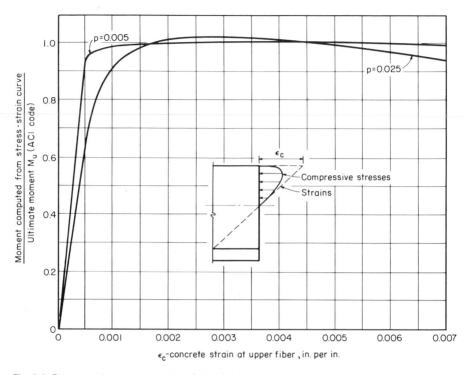

Fig. 5-4. Representative moment-strain relationship based on compression tests of concrete cylinders.

the resistance supplied by the portion of the cross-section not subject to the maximum strain. When this is done, it will be found that the descending portions of the curves shown in Fig. 5-2 have practically no effect on the capacity.

This can be seen readily in Fig. 5-4, in which for two steel percentages the resisting moment of a cross-section, expressed in terms of the ultimate capacity computed according to the ACI code, has been plotted against the strain in the outer fiber. In the computations, the stress-strain curve for cylinders tested at 42 days shown in Fig. 5-2 was used. For various strains, the total area under the stress-strain curve and its centroid were determined. The moment capacity was then computed for the two steel percentages shown. For $p = 0.005$, the decrease in capacity at $\epsilon_c = 0.007$ was less than 1 per cent. For $p = 0.025$, the reduction in capacity is still less than 6 per cent at $\epsilon_c = 0.007$.

CONFINED CONCRETE. The term "confined concrete" refers ideally to a condition in which the concrete is stressed in all directions. In reinforced concrete members, concrete is considered confined if closely spaced spiral reinforcement or hoops are provided to restrain it in directions perpendicular to the applied stress. In earthquake-resistant design the use of confined concrete is often advantageous because of the considerable increase in both strength and ductility over the values for unconfined concrete.

Before considering the case of concrete confined by transverse steel reinforcement, it is helpful to examine the behavior of concrete loaded axially with lateral restraint provided by fluid pressure. Fig. 5-5 shows stress-strain curves measured in tests [47] of 4x8-in. cylinders loaded axially to failure while subjected to various intensities of lateral fluid pressure. The strength of the unconfined cylinders was 3,660 psi. It is seen that both the strength and ductility of the concrete increases as the lateral pressure is increased. For a lateral pressure of 4,090 psi, the concrete attains a maximum stress of 19,000 psi at a strain of 0.05, the latter value being about 25 times what would be expected for unconfined concrete at maximum stress.

On the basis of these tests the following simple expression was derived [47] for the axial compressive strength of concrete cylinders subjected to a lateral pressure:

$$\sigma_a = f'_c + 4.1\sigma_l$$

σ_a = axial strength
f'_c = strength of unconfined specimen
σ_l = lateral confining pressure

It is interesting to note that after the axial and lateral stresses were released, the specimens, which had undergone large strains ranging from 2 to 6 per cent, still were able to carry about half their expected unconfined strength in subsequent loadings.

The practical problem is the behavior of concrete when it is confined laterally

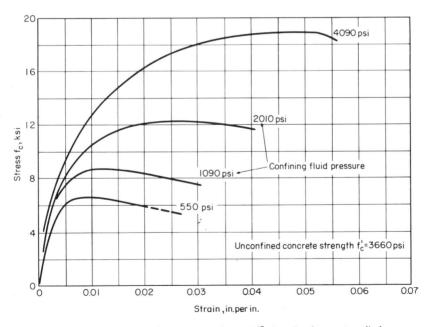

Fig. 5-5. Stress-strain curves from compression tests[47] of confined concrete cylinders.

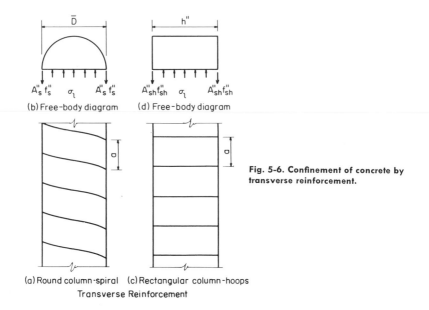

$A_s'' f_s''$ σ_l $A_s'' f_s''$

(b) Free-body diagram

$A_{sh}'' f_{sh}''$ σ_l $A_{sh}'' f_{sh}''$

(d) Free-body diagram

Fig. 5-6. Confinement of concrete by transverse reinforcement.

(a) Round column-spiral   (c) Rectangular column-hoops

Transverse Reinforcement

not by fluid pressure but by transverse reinforcement. The transverse reinforcement for circular columns may be provided in the form of continuous helical reinforcement (spiral reinforcement), or circular hoops placed at close intervals, and for rectangular columns by rectangular hoops. In this case, the transverse reinforcement is not stressed until a load is reached at which unconfined concrete tends to develop appreciable lateral strains. This occurs at about 85 per cent of the unconfined strength. Thus the concrete is assumed to be virtually unconfined up to this level of loading. Beyond this stress, the concrete tends to push against the transverse reinforcement, thereby creating a confining reaction or force. The relation between the transverse steel stress and the confining pressure is indicated in Fig. 5-6. In this figure, (a) shows in elevation the transverse spiral reinforcement for the core of a circular column. If the equilibrium of the free body diagram, shown in (b), is considered with the assumption that the steel occupies a single plane perpendicular to the longitudinal axis of the specimen, the average unit lateral confining pressure is

$$\sigma_l = \frac{2A_s'' f_s''}{a\bar{D}}$$

where

A_s'' = cross-sectional area of transverse reinforcement
f_s'' = stress in transverse reinforcement
$\bar{D}$ = diameter of confined concrete
a = pitch of transverse reinforcement

The expression for the strength of confined concrete derived from tests with fluid pressure is assumed to apply to concrete confined by reinforcement. Thus the strength may be related to the transverse reinforcement stress as follows:

$$\sigma_a = f_c' + \frac{8.2A_s''f_s''}{a\bar{D}}$$

This relationship was found to represent the test results of spirally reinforced circular columns [48] when $0.85f_c'$ is substituted for f_c' giving

$$f_c = 0.85f_c' + \frac{8.2A_s''f_s''}{a\bar{D}} \tag{5-1}$$

Other tests [49] have shown that spiral reinforcement in a circular column is considerably more effective than rectangular hoops in a rectangular column for confinement of the core concrete.

It is desirable to take into account the reduced efficiency of rectangular hoops, which reduction may be as much as 50 per cent. Accordingly, considering the free-body diagram in Fig. 5-6(d), the lateral confining pressure is to be taken as no greater than

$$\sigma_l = 0.5\frac{2A_{sh}''f_{sh}''}{ah''}$$

where

A_{sh}'' = area of cross-section of transverse hoop reinforcement

f_{sh}'' = stress in transverse hoop reinforcement

h'' = length (longer dimension) of rectangular concrete area enclosed by a particular hoop

a = vertical spacing center to center of transverse hoops

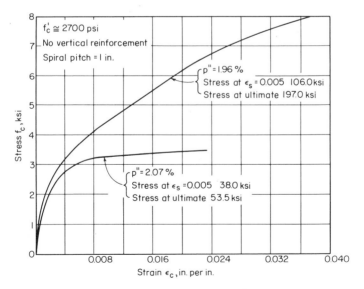

Fig. 5-7. Stress-strain curves from compression tests[48] of spirally confined concrete short columns without longitudinal reinforcement.

The strength of the confined concrete is related to the hoop reinforcement stress f''_{sh} by the equation

$$\sigma_a = f'_c + \frac{4.1 A''_{sh} f''_{sh}}{ah''}$$

and, similar to the core strength of a spiral reinforced circular column, the strength of the core of a rectangular column with closely spaced hoops is

$$f_c = 0.85 f'_c + \frac{4.1 A''_{sh} f''_{sh}}{ah''} \tag{5-2}$$

Two stress-strain curves measured from tests [48] of circular columns are shown in Fig. 5-7. The stress at $\epsilon_s = 0.005$ and the stress at ultimate noted in the figure are stresses in the spirals. The ordinates and the abscissas are, respectively, the computed stresses and measured strains in the concrete in short columns, 10 in. in diameter and 40 in. long, without longitudinal reinforcement.

Three significant points can be defined on the idealized stress-strain curve for the confined concrete core of a circular column. These are shown in Fig. 5-8.

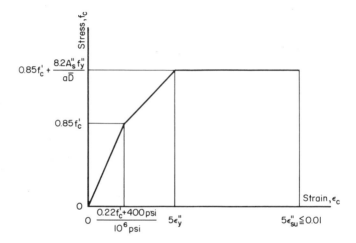

Fig. 5-8. Idealized stress-strain curve for confined concrete in axial compression.

The first point corresponds to the initiation of stresses in the lateral reinforcement. This has the coordinates $f_c = 0.85 f'_c$ and

$$\epsilon_c = \frac{0.22 f'_c + 400 \text{ psi}}{10^6 \text{ psi}} *$$

---

*This expression is based on a study of the measured stress-strain curves for confined and unconfined concrete given in references 44, 48, and 49.

The second point corresponds to yielding of the transverse steel if the steel has a well-defined yield stress. This point has the coordinates

$$f_c = 0.85f'_c + \frac{8.2A''_s f''_y}{a\bar{D}} \tag{5-3}$$

$$\epsilon_c = 5\epsilon''_y \tag{5-4}$$

where
f''_y = yield stress of transverse spiral reinforcement
ϵ''_y = yield strain of transverse spiral reinforcement
The coefficient 5 is based on a total lateral-to-longitudinal strain ratio of 0.2. For cold-worked steels, f''_y can be defined as the stress at a strain of 0.005. The stress coordinate for the terminal point should be the same as in equation (5-3). The strain coordinate for the terminal point should be

$$\epsilon_c = 5\epsilon''_{su} \leqq 0.01 \tag{5-5}$$

where
ϵ''_{su} = strain of transverse spiral reinforcement at maximum stress
The clear spacing of the loops in the pitch of the spiral steel should not exceed 3 in. as required in the ACI building code.

The stress-strain relationship for confined concrete as defined above is well on the conservative side. With an adequate arrangement and amount of transverse reinforcement, it is possible to develop strains as high as 0.06 before the descending portion of the curve starts [47]. However, the usable maximum strain of 0.01 in equation (5-5) is adequate for most applications.

The stress-strain curve obtained from tests under axial compression is applicable to cases where bending is involved. The concrete is still confined even though only part of the cross-section is compressed. In tests [49], strains as high as 0.03 were observed in eccentric loading of transversely reinforced cylindrical specimens. The same tests also indicated that concrete confined by rectangular hoops could develop strains in excess of 0.01.

The idealized stress-strain curve for the confined concrete core of a rectangular column is similar in form to that for a circular column (Fig. 5-8) except that the stress in the concrete corresponding to yielding of the transverse steel is

$$f_c = 0.85f'_c + \frac{4.1A''_{sh}f''_{yh}}{ah''} \tag{5-6}$$

where
f''_{yh} = yield stress of transverse hoop reinforcement

5.3 Reinforced Concrete Sections Subjected to Bending Only

The response of a reinforced concrete cross-section to applied bending moment may be adequately described by the relationship between moment and curvature. This relationship depends upon the material and geometrical properties of the cross-section. The following discussion of the moment-curvature relationship, hereafter referred to as the M-ϕ curve, is limited to cases where the moment is increased continuously to ultimate within a short period of time.

The ultimate flexural capacity of a reinforced concrete member may correspond to:

1. reaching the useful limit of strain* of the compressed concrete *before* yielding of the tension steel,
2. reaching the useful limit of strain of the compressed concrete *after* yielding of the tension steel,
3. reaching the useful limit of strain of the tension steel before the useful limit of strain of the concrete is reached.

Members designed to resist earthquake effects should be designed to be in the range of case 2. Case 1 is definitely undesirable in earthquake-resistant design because it restricts the energy-absorption capacity unless measures are taken to increase the ductility of the member, and case 3 is generally impracticable. A moderately reinforced rectangular beam, one that has a reinforcement ratio of 0.01 to 0.02 and a concrete strength of 3,000 psi or more, will attain its ultimate capacity after development of considerable inelastic strain in the steel and will have the desirable ductility. In the following section, the various stages in the behavior of a moderately reinforced beam will be discussed qualitatively.

Significant Points of the M-ϕ Curve

The M-ϕ curve for a moderately reinforced cross-section exhibits three distinctly different stages as shown by the solid line in Fig. 5-9. The first stage

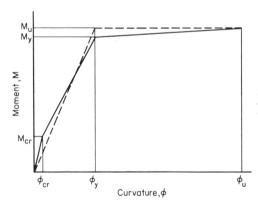

Fig. 5-9. Moment-curvature relationships for a moderately reinforced section subjected to bending only.

corresponds to an uncracked section and the M-ϕ curve is essentially linear. The appearance of the first hairline cracks introduces the second stage, M_{cr}. The third stage begins at yielding of the tension steel and ends when the useful limit of strain is reached in the compressed concrete.

---

*The useful limit of strain of unconfined concrete is approximately 0.4 per cent or 0.004 in. per inch. For reinforcing steel the useful limit of strain is of the order of 3 to 6 per cent or even more corresponding to moderate amounts of strain hardening.

Actually there is a fourth stage beyond ϕ_u in which the moment drops off gradually after the useful limit of concrete strain is exceeded, but this range is not useful in practice and will be ignored.

The coordinates of the significant points at M_y and M_u on the M-ϕ curve can be determined as explained below. In almost all cases the first break in the curve corresponding to M_{cr} has little significance and the curve can be idealized to that shown in Fig. 5-9 by the broken line.

Yielding of the Tension Reinforcement

The yield point of the cross-section is the point at which the slope of the M-ϕ curve decreases considerably. This is easily related to the point where the break in the stress-strain curve occurs.

Distributions of strain and stress at yielding are shown in Fig. 5-10. The strain distribution in compressed concrete is assumed to be linear. It is also assumed that the relation between steel and concrete maximum strains is

$$\epsilon_s/\epsilon_c = \frac{(1 - k)}{k} \tag{5-7}$$

where

ϵ_s = steel strain

ϵ_c = concrete strain at extreme fiber

k = ratio of depth of neutral axis to effective depth

In this derivation it is assumed that concrete carries no tension since the results would not change appreciably even if tension were considered. The strain in the steel is, by definition, the yield strain; therefore the force in the tension steel is $A_s f_y$. The stress distribution in the concrete requires special consideration. The stress-strain curve for concrete is approximately linear up to about $0.7f'_c$. Thus, a linear concrete stress distribution may be assumed as long as the computed extreme fiber stress does not exceed $0.7f'_c$. In that case the depth of the neutral axis can be computed using the straightline formula.

$$k = \sqrt{(pn)^2 + 2pn} - pn \tag{5-8}$$

and

$$M_y = A_s f_y jd \tag{5-9}$$

$$\phi_y = \frac{\epsilon_y}{d(1 - k)} \tag{5-10}$$

provided

$$f_c = \frac{2pf_y}{k} \leqq 0.7f'_c$$

where

$p = A_s/bd$ = tensile reinforcement ratio

$n = E_s/E_c$ = modular ratio

M_y = moment corresponding to yielding of the tensile reinforcement

A_s = total cross-sectional area of tensile reinforcement

$j = 1 - k/3$

If the computed maximum compressive stress is larger than $0.7f'_c$, the depth to the neutral axis should be computed using a stress-strain curve for concrete that is representative of the actual curve. However, if only an estimate of the coordinates of the yield point on the M-ϕ curve is desired, the straightline formula may be used even if the computed stress is as high as the compressive strength f'_c.

Ultimate Conditions—Assumptions

The coordinates of the terminal point of the useful M-ϕ curve are designated as ultimate moment and ultimate curvature. This is a somewhat loose use of the word "ultimate," but it is the accepted use. This point corresponds to the reaching of the useful limit of strain either in the concrete or in the steel; thus, it represents not the "ultimate" but the "useful ultimate."

In addition to the conditions of equilibrium and geometry, several assumptions must be made in order to derive the expressions for ultimate moment and curvature.

1. *The ratio of the steel strain to the concrete strain in the extreme fiber is the same as the ratio of their respective distances from the neutral axis.* This assumption, shown graphically in Fig. 5-11, can be stated as

$$\frac{\epsilon_{su}}{\epsilon_{cu}} = \frac{1 - k_u}{k_u} \tag{5-11}$$

where

ϵ_{su} = steel strain at ultimate

ϵ_{cu} = concrete strain at ultimate

k_u = ratio of depth of neutral axis at ultimate to effective depth

Although this assumption is not strictly valid for every possible condition, the errors involved are generally small enough to be negligible.

2. *The useful limit of unconfined concrete strain in compression, combined with flexure, is 0.004.* The shape of the stress-strain curves for concrete shown in Fig. 5-2 indicates that for axial compression on plain unconfined concrete, a strain of about 0.002 corresponds to the reaching of maximum stress. However, where bending is concerned, there is a stress redistribution and the concrete does strain further with little or no drop in the flexural resistance as shown in Fig. 5-4. This is because of the fact that although the maximum concrete stress in the extreme fiber is reduced, the total force in the concrete remains essentially the same (see Fig. 5-11). Test results on sections subjected to flexure [40, 41, 42, 46] indicate that 0.004 is a realistic and safe value of the useful strain limit for unconfined concrete in bending.

3. *The average stress in the concrete compression zone at ultimate f_{cu} is related to the 6x12-in. 28-day cylinder strength f'_c, as follows:*

$$f_{cu} = 0.7f'_c$$

The average ultimate concrete stress in bending, usually referred to as the effective concrete strength, has been measured [40, 41, 42, 43] to range from about 0.9 to 0.7, the larger value being for low-strength and the smaller value for high-strength concretes. It is convenient to assume $f_{cu} = 0.7f'_c$, which represents a reasonable lower bound to the measured values. Beyond a concrete strength of 5,000 psi, the effective concrete strength may be obtained from the following expression:

$$f_{cu} = 1,500 \text{ psi} + 0.4f'_c$$

4. *The resultant of the compressive force in the concrete acts at a distance of $0.4k_ud$ from the extreme fiber in compression, where k_u is the depth of the neutral axis.* The extreme range of this ratio is between one-half and one-third, corresponding to rectangular and triangular distributions of stress, respectively. Because the stress distribution is nearly parabolic, a value of 0.42 has been adopted by various investigators. Since variations in it affect the ultimate moment negligibly, a value of 0.4 has been adopted here.

5. *Concrete does not carry tension.*

6. *The stress-strain relationship for the steel is known.* For steels having a well-defined yield point, only the coordinates of the yield point need be known since strain-hardening is generally ignored for such steels.

Ultimate Conditions—Derivations

The assumed conditions of strain and stress at ultimate are shown in Fig. 5-11. These conditions are sufficient and necessary to express the ultimate moment and the ultimate curvature in terms of the geometrical and material properties of the cross-section. For the sake of algebraic simplicity, the derivations that follow refer to a rectangular cross-section, or more strictly, to a section that has a constant width at least from the extreme fiber in compression to the neutral axis. The required expressions can be derived for flanged sections, or for sections that have varying widths over the compressed depth, in the same fashion.

The curvature is defined on the basis of the strain distribution

$$\phi_u = \frac{\epsilon_{cu}}{k_u d} \tag{5-12}$$

The ultimate moment may be expressed in terms of the cross-sectional properties by considering moments about the line of action of the resultant compressive force

$$M_u = A_s f_{su} d(1 - 0.4k_u) \tag{5-13}$$

Thus, if the steel stress at ultimate f_{su} and the depth of the neutral axis can be evaluated, the ultimate curvature and the ultimate moment can be determined.

A solution is developed below for f_{su}. The condition of equilibrium is written in reference to Fig. 5-11.

$$f_{cu} b k_u d = A_s f_{su}$$

The condition stated above is combined with equation (5-11) and the definition $p = A_s/bd$ to give

$$\epsilon_{su} = \epsilon_{cu}\left(\frac{f_{cu}}{pf_{su}} - 1\right) \tag{5-14}$$

Since p, ϵ_{cu}, and f_{cu} are known properties of the section, equation (5-14) involves two unknowns, ϵ_{su} and f_{su}. It can be solved with the help of the stress-strain curve for the steel, which provides another relationship between ϵ_{su} and f_{su} to be satisfied simultaneously with equation (5-14).

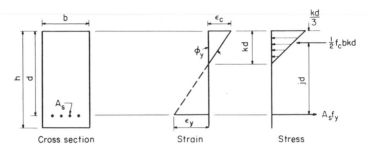

Fig. 5-10. Distribution of strain and stress at yield capacity.

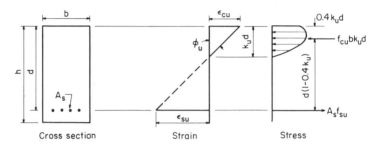

Fig. 5-11. Distribution of strain and stress at ultimate capacity.

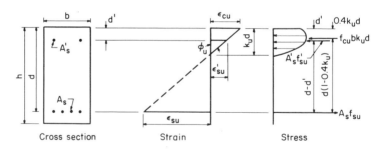

Fig. 5-12. Distribution of strain and stress at ultimate capacity for a section with compression reinforcement.

In sections reinforced with steels having an elasto-plastic or nearly elasto-plastic stress-strain curve, the steel stress at failure may be obtained directly if the proportions of the section are in the ranges defined below. With reference to Fig. 5-11, the ratio k_u can be written in terms of the steel strain and the useful limit of concrete strain as

$$k_u = \frac{\epsilon_{cu}}{\epsilon_{su} + \epsilon_{cu}} \tag{5-15}$$

For a steel having a stress-strain curve with a yield point, the steel stress is essentially constant from the yield strain ϵ_y to the strain at which strain hardening starts, ϵ_h. Therefore, as long as the steel strain at failure of the section remains between these two limits, the steel stress is f_y. With the use of equation (5-14), this condition can be stated as

$$f_{su} = f_y$$

provided that

$$\frac{\epsilon_{cu}}{\epsilon_y + \epsilon_{cu}} > k_u > \frac{\epsilon_{cu}}{\epsilon_h + \epsilon_{cu}}$$

If the steel stress is the yield stress, k_u can be evaluated from the following expression:

$$k_u = \frac{pf_y}{f_{cu}}$$

The ratio pf_y/f_{cu} is a critical property of the section. Since it will be used frequently in describing behavior, it will be called q_u. It should be emphasized here that

$$k_u = q_u{}^*$$

only if

$$f_{su} = f_y$$

Thus, the steel stress in a given section reinforced with an elasto-plastic steel can be evaluated as follows:

If

$$q_u > \frac{\epsilon_{cu}}{\epsilon_y + \epsilon_{cu}}$$

the steel stress at ultimate is in the elastic range, and it can be obtained from a simultaneous solution of equation (5-14) with the expression

$$f_s = E_s \epsilon_s$$

Sections having such proportions are designated as over-reinforced sections and should not be used, especially not in earthquake-resistant design.

If

$$\frac{\epsilon_{cu}}{\epsilon_y + \epsilon_{cu}} > q_u > \frac{\epsilon_{cu}}{\epsilon_h + \epsilon_{cu}}$$

---

*The ratio q_u used here is related to the ratio q used in the ACI building code (318-56) as follows:

$$q_u = q\frac{f'_c}{f_{cu}} = 1.43q \text{ (for } f'_c < 5{,}000 \text{ psi)}$$

The ratio q_u has been selected to describe the properties of the cross-section in this manual because it can be used directly in expressions for the strength and ductility of a moderately reinforced section.

the steel stress at ultimate is in the plastic range, that is

$$f_{su} = f_y$$

Sections having these proportions are designated as under-reinforced sections in which the reinforcement will control the ultimate capacity of the member.

If
$$\frac{\epsilon_{cu}}{\epsilon_h + \epsilon_{cu}} > q_u$$

the steel stress at ultimate is in the strain-hardening range and can be obtained from a simultaneous solution of equation (5-14) with the conditions stipulated by this particular region of the stress-strain curve. Sections having these proportions are designated as greatly under-reinforced sections and are not desirable because the reinforcement may fracture before the useful limit of strain of the concrete is reached.

Effect of Compression Reinforcement

Compression reinforcement has a significant effect on the characteristics of the M-ϕ curve for a reinforced concrete section. Consequently it should receive special consideration. In principle, the analytical interpretation of the action of compression reinforcement is the same as that for sections without compression reinforcement described in the preceding sections. In addition to the previous assumptions, the assumptions are made that the strain in the compression steel is the same as that in the surrounding concrete, and that the compression steel does not buckle within the useful range of the M-ϕ curve.

Effect of Compression Reinforcement on the Useful Limits of Moment and Curvature

The assumed conditions of strain and stress at ultimate are shown in Fig. 5-12. The curvature is defined on the basis of the strain distribution in the compressed concrete and yields the same result as equation (5-12).

The ultimate moment may be related to the cross-sectional properties by taking moments about the line of action of the resultant tensile force, $A_s f_{su}$:

$$M_u = A_s' f_{su}'(d - d') + k_u f_{cu} b d^2 (1 - 0.4 k_u) \tag{5-16}$$

This may be written in a simpler fashion by making use of the following relationships:

$$A_s f_{su} = A_s' f_{su}' + k_u f_{cu} b d$$
$$A_s f_{su} - A_s' f_{su}' = k_u f_{cu} b d$$

Therefore

$$M_u = A_s' f_{su}'(d - d') + (A_s f_{su} - A_s' f_{su}')(1 - 0.4 k_u)d \tag{5-17}$$

Thus, the coordinates of the ultimate point on the useful M-ϕ curve can be determined if k_u, f_{su}, and f_{su}' are evaluated. For most practical cases it can be assumed that

$$f_{su} = f_{su}' = f_y$$

in which case, from a consideration of the equilibrium of the forces shown in Fig. 5-12

$$k_u = \frac{(p - p')f_y}{f_{cu}}$$

It should be pointed out that, if the area of the compression reinforcement is equal to or larger than the area of the tension reinforcement, the simplifying assumption about f'_{su} cannot be true. In such cases, if the value of f'_{su} must be determined, the strain distribution in the beam must be taken into account. However, such calculations need not be made for most design purposes. In Chapter 6 the design recommendations take this possibility into account.

Effect of Confining the Concrete

The effect of confinement on the stress-strain characteristics of concrete was described earlier. Since the M-ϕ curve is directly related to the stress-strain characteristics of the concrete and the steel, the effect of confinement of the concrete produced by lateral reinforcement in the form of hoops or spirals can be described by constructing the M-ϕ curve in relation to the stress-strain curve for confined concrete.

In practical cases all the concrete in the section is not confined. The concrete cover, called the "shell" in columns, behaves as unconfined concrete. Since the lateral reinforcement exerts no pressure on the concrete prior to development of large longitudinal strains in the concrete, and since, in the case of pure bending, the strain is considerably greater in the extreme fiber of the concrete shell than in the confined concrete, the lateral reinforcement does not influence the behavior or the M-ϕ curve of the section until after the useful limit of the shell is reached. At this point, the lateral reinforcement comes into action and makes it possible for the section to sustain much greater deformation, even if not a greater moment.

This phenomenon can be described with reference to Fig. 5-13, which shows the stress and strain distributions at two critical stages of behavior of sections with both tension and compression reinforcement and lateral reinforcement in the form of rectangular hoops. The strain and stress distributions shown in Fig. 5-13(a) are the same as those in Fig. 5-12. They represent the conditions at the useful limit of the section without lateral reinforcement for confinement of the concrete. The strain and stress distributions shown in Fig. 5-13(b) represent the conditions at the useful limit of that part of the section bounded by the lateral reinforcement.

A very significant difference between the conditions shown in Figs. 5-13(a) and (b) is that the useful limit of strain is much greater in the latter. While ϵ_{cu} is about 0.004 for unconfined concrete, it can be as high as 0.01 for confined concrete. Actually, the value of 0.01 represents a very conservative limit; the actual limit can be as high as 0.03 or even more [47, 49].

The location of the neutral axis depends on the stress-strain characteristics

109

of the confined concrete and the width of the confined section. At ultimate, the shell concrete is assumed to be ineffective. The effective strength of the concrete in the beam can be evaluated from the stress-strain curve constructed on the basis of the principles described earlier, which leads to the result

$$f''_{cu} = \frac{\text{Area under stress-strain curve}}{\text{Useful limit of strain (confined concrete)}}$$

Thus, f''_{cu} can be expressed as a function of the cylinder strength f'_c. After the evaluation of f''_{cu} an expression for the depth to the neutral axis can be written by considering the equilibrium of the forces indicated in Fig. 5-13(b)

$$k''_u = \frac{b\left(pf_{su} - p'f'_{su}\right)}{b''f''_{cu}}$$

In the case of moderately reinforced sections, it can be assumed that

$$f_{su} = f'_{su} = f_y$$

at the useful limit of the section having no lateral reinforcement [Fig. 5-13(a)],

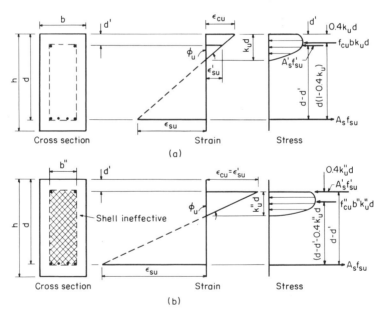

Fig. 5-13. Distribution of strain and stress in a section having a confined concrete core.
(a) At useful limit of strain for unconfined concrete section.
(b) At useful limit of strain for confined concrete core.

and at the useful limit of the section [reduced in effective width and depth as indicated by the cross-hatched area in Fig. 5-13(b)] when it has lateral rein-

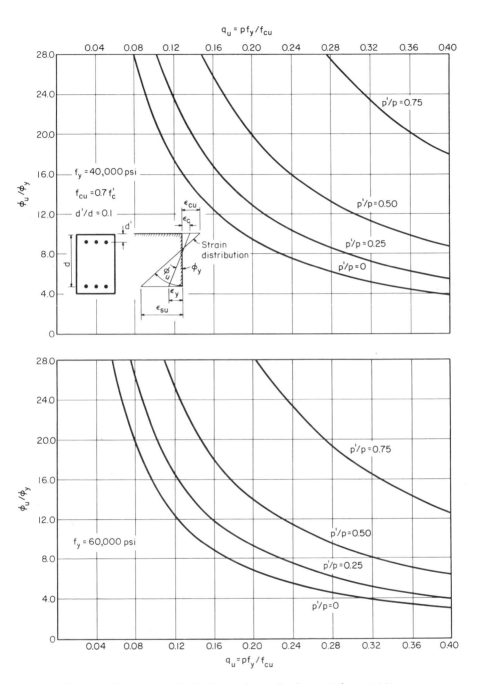

Fig. 5-14. Variation of ϕ_u/ϕ_y for beams of unconfined concrete in respect to q_u.

111

forcement. A study of the conditions of strain and stress in Figs. 5-13(a) and (b) shows that the confined section has a significantly greater ultimate curvature although a smaller computed ultimate moment in relation to that of the unconfined section because of the reduced effective depth. Actually, the ultimate moments for the two sections may be comparable because of the increase in steel stress resulting from strain hardening in the confined section.

Ductility of Reinforced Concrete Sections Subjected to Bending Moment

In engineering literature related to dynamic and also to limit design, the ductility of a material or a member is often defined as the ratio of the deformation at ultimate to that at yield. Consequently, it is desirable to study the relation of the ratio ϕ_u/ϕ_y to the various parameters that affect it.

For a moderately reinforced rectangular section without compression reinforcement, the ratio ϕ_u/ϕ_y can be derived from equations (5-10) and (5-12) as follows:

$$\frac{\phi_u}{\phi_y} = \frac{\epsilon_{cu}}{\epsilon_y}\left(\frac{1-k}{k_u}\right)$$

where

$$k = \sqrt{(pn)^2 + 2pn} - pn$$

$$k_u = \frac{pf_y}{f_{cu}} = q_u \ (\text{since } f_{su} = f_y)$$

The variation of ϕ_u/ϕ_y, which is a measure of the ductility *of the section*, with q_u is shown in Fig. 5-14 for $f_y = 40{,}000$ and $60{,}000$ psi. A typical "balanced design" by the working stress design requirements of the ACI building code (318-56) would have a value of $q_u = 0.25$ and thus a ratio of ϕ_u/ϕ_y equal to about 7.3 for the section without compressive reinforcement and $f_y = 40{,}000$ psi. For values of f_y between 40,000 and 60,000 psi, a straightline interpolation is sufficiently accurate.

It can be seen from an inspection of the expression for ϕ_u/ϕ_y that an increase in ϵ_{cu} increases ϕ_u/ϕ_y directly. Consequently, confining the concrete increases the ductility appreciably. An increase in the yield strength, with all other variables constant, decreases the ductility because it increases both k_u (this trend can be studied with the use of Fig. 5-13) and ϵ_y.

The addition of compression reinforcement increases the ductility because, while it affects the value of k slightly, it reduces the value of k_u significantly since

$$k_u = \frac{(p - p')f_y}{f_{cu}}$$

with the limitations discussed before in this chapter. The effect of compression reinforcement on the ductility is apparent from the curves in Fig. 5-14.

5.4 Reinforced Concrete Sections Subjected to Combined Bending and Axial Load

Because the axial load influences the M-ϕ curve, it is not possible to construct directly a unique M-ϕ curve for a given cross-section as in the case of sections subjected to bending only. On the other hand, it is possible to obtain all the combinations of axial load P, bending moment M, and curvature ϕ for a given section, from which the M-ϕ curve for a particular case of loading can be determined readily.

Plots showing the interrelationship among P, M, and ϕ for various conditions are called interaction curves for combined bending and axial load. Such curves are shown in Fig. 5-15. They can be determined for a given section on the basis of the ordinary principles of mechanics of materials and assumptions about the stress-strain relationships of the materials in the section.*

The curves in Fig. 5-15 refer to the particular cross-section shown in the upper left-hand corner of the figure. The longitudinal reinforcement ratio is 0.05 distributed equally to two sides of the section, the cylinder strength of the concrete is 3,000 psi, and the yield stress of the longitudinal reinforcement 40,000 psi. It is assumed that the section has sufficient transverse reinforcement to make the axial load capacity of the confined core equal to that of the whole (unconfined) section. Idealized stress-strain curves for the concrete assumed in accordance with the principles discussed in Section 5.2 are shown in the upper part of Fig. 5-15 ($f''_y = 60,000$ psi).

Fig. 5-15 contains two plots. One shows the relationship between P and M, and the other the relationships between P and ϕ. The vertical scale for P is the same in both plots. The axial load is plotted in units of $0.85f'_c bh$, and the curvature in units of $1/h$.

Three curves are shown in each plot. Curves 1 indicate all the combinations of P, M, and ϕ corresponding to reaching the useful limit of strain in the concrete or in the steel for the whole section. Thus, for the P-M plot, the area enclosed by Curve 1 is the "useful area" for all conditions of P and M. The P-axis intercept of Curve 1 is the axial load capacity of the section; the M-axis intercept is the ultimate moment capacity for bending only. The break in Curve 1 for P vs. M corresponds to a condition in which the tension reinforcement reaches the yield strain and the extreme concrete fiber in compression reaches the useful limit of strain simultaneously. This point is designated as the "balance point." Curve 1 in the P-ϕ plot shows the useful limit of curvature for the unconfined section corresponding to the combinations of P and M at ultimate. It is seen that the ultimate curvature is decreased significantly by

---

*Interaction curves based on the elastic theory [50] and on ultimate-strength theory [51] are available for eccentrically loaded rectangular, square, and circular columns. A comprehensive series of tables based on ultimate-strength theory for columns subject to axial load and bending are also available from the Portland Cement Association. These tables obviate the necessity of plotting interaction curves; however, if desired to plot such curves for visualization, it can be done readily from the tabular values.

the presence of the axial load, especially for loads larger than that corresponding to the balance point.

Curves 2 represent the combinations of P, M, and ϕ corresponding to first yielding of the tension reinforcement or the limit of elastic deformation. These curves, in reference to Curves 1, give a very good picture of the behavior of the section subjected to combined axial load and bending. In the P-M plot, Curves 1 and 2 lie very close together, but in the P-ϕ plot they separate (Curve 2 stops at the balance point, since above this point the tension reinforcement does not reach its yield strain). Thus, the amount of inelastic bending deformation can be seen from a comparison of Curves 1 and 2 in the P-ϕ

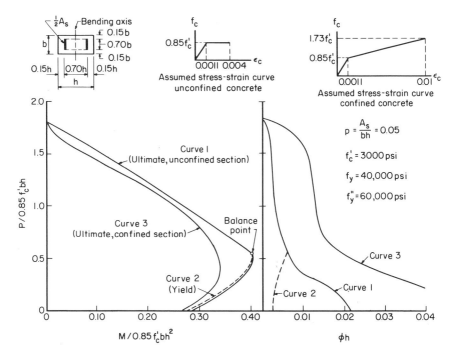

Fig. 5-15. Interaction curves for a rectangular section having a confined concrete core.

plot. The ratio ϕ_u/ϕ_y obtained from these two curves for the unconfined section is shown plotted against the column load P, expressed as a percentage of the axial load capacity in Fig. 5-16. (The axial load corresponding to the balance point is 31 per cent of the axial load capacity.) For an axial load at ultimate of about 15 per cent of the axial load capacity, the ratio ϕ_u/ϕ_y for this unconfined section is 4, but it is less for higher loads.

The "ductility" of the section can be increased considerably by the use of confined concrete. Curves 3 in Fig. 5-15 show the combinations of P, M, and ϕ corresponding to the useful ultimate of the confined core of the section. The ultimate bending moment for any value of P is somewhat reduced (strain hardening ignored) in relation to Curve 1 because of the reduced depth of the section since the shell concrete is considered ineffective in the "spiral range," i.e., when the lateral reinforcement becomes effective in confining the core. On the other hand, the ultimate curvature is increased appreciably. The values of the ratio ϕ_u/ϕ_y for the confined section are also plotted against the axial load in Fig. 5-16. The value of ϕ_y refers to the unconfined section (Curve 2), since yielding occurs before the shell concrete becomes ineffective.

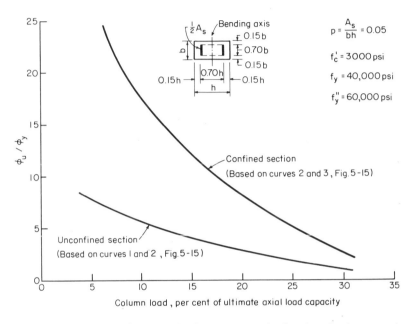

Fig. 5-16. Variation of ϕ_u/ϕ_y for tied columns of unconfined and confined concrete in respect to axial load.

The preceding discussion refers to a particular section. The relationship can, however, be generalized quantitatively for rectangular columns with closely spaced hoops if the longitudinal reinforcement is concentrated principally in two opposite faces. For a specific axial load, the curvature at a section developed at first yielding of the longitudinal reinforcement can be equated to the curvature developed when the confined concrete reaches the probable limit of strain of 0.01 as discussed previously. From this relationship it is possible to obtain an expression for ϕ_u/ϕ_y in terms of the parameters $P/f_c'bd$, the amount of tensile reinforcement, and the ratio of compressive to tensile reinforcement. For ready evaluation of the effect of the individual parameters, the results obtained from a substitution of numerical values are presented graphically in Fig. 5-17 for columns in which the yield point of the longitudinal reinforcement

is 40,000 psi. In this figure

A_s = area of tensile reinforcement

A_{sh}'' = area of cross-section of hoop reinforcement

P = axial load on the column

h'' = length (longer dimension) of rectangular concrete area enclosed by a particular hoop

p' = percentage of compressive reinforcement

p = percentage of tensile reinforcement

$$q'' = \frac{A_{sh}'' f_{yh}''}{ah''f_c'}$$

The value of ϕ_u/ϕ_y for a specific section is obtained by entering the figure

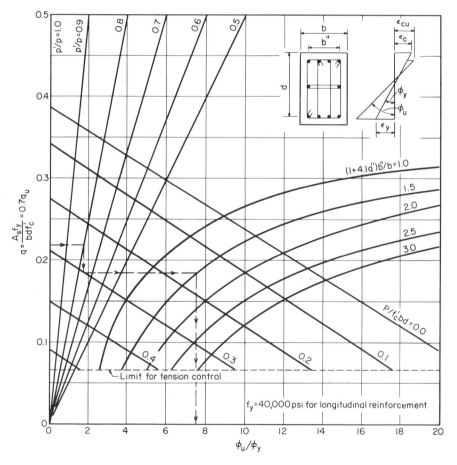

Fig. 5-17. Variation of ϕ_u/ϕ_y for tied columns of confined concrete for various combinations of parameters.

116

with the appropriate value of q and proceeding horizontally to the p'/p value of the section. From this intersection one proceeds vertically to the $P/f'_c bd$ value, and then horizontally to the curves designated as $(1 + 4.1q'')b''/b$. The value of ϕ_u/ϕ_y is read on the abscissa. The procedure is shown in Fig. 5-17 by the broken line marked with arrows.

5.5 Behavior of Reinforced Concrete Members Subjected to Combined Bending, Axial Load, and Shear

When a building frame is deformed, as in an earthquake, shearing forces acting in a direction perpendicular to the axes of the members are developed because of the bending moments at the joints and the inertia forces. These shears may combine with the bending moments to affect both the strength and ductility of the members unless an adequate system of transverse (web) reinforcement is provided. The primary purpose of this section is to show how a member can be reinforced to make sure that its strength and ductility is controlled by flexure alone. It should be emphasized that frame members (both beams and columns) without transverse reinforcement should not be used in earthquake-resistant construction even though shear stresses are less than theoretically required to cause cracking in a member without stirrups, ties, or hoops.

The general phenomena that occur in beams without web reinforcement subjected to combined bending and shear can be described in reference to a particular case of loading: a simple beam with a concentrated load at midspan.

The rectangular member shown in Fig. 5-18(a) is reinforced longitudinally only. After loading is initiated, the first crack occurs at the section of maximum bending moment and in the extreme fiber where the orientation of the stress is parallel to the longitudinal axis unless the span is less than about half the depth. As the load is increased, other points in the beam are stressed to cracking and additional cracks are initiated at the extreme fiber at locations on both sides of the load and at a spacing that depends on the bond, the tensile force in the concrete, and the moment gradient. These cracks usually intersect the longitudinal steel perpendicularly.

Fig. 5-18. Development of inclined cracks in a reinforced concrete beam.

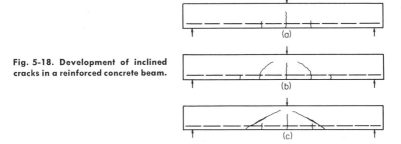

At this stage, two developments may take place:

1. The point immediately above one of the vertical cracks may be over-stressed, and the crack may progress toward the compression side as points above it are overstressed successively [Fig. 5-18(b)]. The crack assumes a shape that becomes more inclined to the longitudinal axis as it progresses toward the compression flange.

2. A crack may be initiated at a point some distance above one of the flexural cracks [Fig. 5-18(c)] progressing rapidly in both directions from the point of origin.

Whatever the details of development, an inclined crack has one profound effect on the mechanism by which a beam without web reinforcement resists load. It severs the path through which the inclined tensile forces, necessary for beam-action, can be carried. The horizontal reinforcement, if it is to act in axial tension only, cannot replace all the tensile force lost by the formation of an inclined crack, as it can in the case of a vertical flexural crack. After the formation of an inclined crack, beam-action is destroyed partially or completely. The beam may be able to sustain the load at inclined cracking or even resist larger loads through partial or complete arch action. It may fail immediately upon the formation of the inclined crack if the resulting "tied arch" is not stable under the applied load, the particular cause of the failure being overstressing of the "arch rib" in compression combined with shear or in tension, or by the inadequacy of the connection between the tierod and the arch rib.

Since the ductility of the flat arch is significantly lower than that of a beam designed to carry the same load, it is mandatory to eliminate the effects of the inclined crack in earthquake-resistant design. Evidently no special measures need be taken if the inclined cracking load for a beam is larger than its flexural capacity. This brings up the problem of being able to predict the inclined cracking load.

A considerable amount of research has been carried out on this subject since the early days of reinforced concrete; during a surge of intense interest within the past decade tests were carried out on more than 500 laboratory beams. The majority of these beams were simply supported beams subjected to concentrated loads. Some beams were tested under uniform loads and some under various conditions of continuity.

Studies of all available test data by the ASCE-ACI Joint Committee on Shear and Diagonal Tension [52] indicated that the nominal shear stress resistance at inclined cracking increased with increases in (a) the concrete strength, (b) the shear-to-moment ratio at the section, and (c) the longitudinal reinforcement ratio. The effect of the longitudinal reinforcement ratio was found to be relatively unimportant. The observed increases in the cracking load with the shear-to-moment ratio was largely in the case of beams having ratios of depth to distance between reaction and load of more than 2, which would put these beams into the deep beam range. In beams slender enough for beam action, the observed trend with the shear-to-moment ratio was not larger than the scatter of the data.

Accordingly, the Joint Committee concluded it is safe and economical to assume a value for the nominal shear at inclined cracking that represents a lower boundary to the test results. This is

$$v_c = \frac{V_c}{b'd} = 1.9 \sqrt{f_c'} \tag{5-18}$$

It should be noted, however, that even though the load indicated by this equation is more than or equal to the load corresponding to the flexural capacity of the member in question, it is still considered necessary to provide transverse reinforcement in building frame members subjected to shearing forces whether they arise from earthquake, wind, gravity, or other loads or forces. In order to ensure the required ductility, the member must be over-designed for shear. This aspect of the problem will be considered quantitatively in Chapter 6.

Effect of Transverse Reinforcement

In members subjected to load reversals, the most practical type of reinforcement is the vertical stirrup since it is equally efficient for shear in either direction and since it can also be used, if desired, as a hoop to confine the concrete and as a tie to restrain the compression steel. Inclined stirrups and bent-up bars are efficient for shear in one direction only. In the following discussion, the function of web reinforcement is described with reference to vertical stirrups only, although the expressions can be extended, if necessary, to apply to inclined stirrups and bent-up bars.

The action of web reinforcement in a member subjected to *combined bending and shear* can be explained through the following idealized interpretation, which involves the principles of equilibrium and the assumptions listed below:

1. The beam can carry the inclined tension cracking load without the aid of web reinforcement.
2. The horizontal projection of the inclined crack at the level of the center of gravity of the longitudinal tension reinforcement is equal to the effective depth of the beam.
3. When the cracking load is exceeded, the web reinforcement is at its yield stress wherever it is crossed by the inclined tension crack.

A portion of a reinforced concrete beam with web reinforcement is shown in Fig. 5-19. This portion represents part of a beam or frame subjected to a constant shear. The bending moment varies along its length but does not change sense.

The shear that can be carried "through" an inclined tension crack, shown in Fig. 5-19(a) according to the above assumptions, can be derived from the free body shown in Fig. 5-19(b), as follows:

$$V_u = V_c + \frac{d}{s} A_v f_y \tag{5-19}$$

119

It should be emphasized that V_c is the lower boundary of the shear that could be carried by a member without transverse reinforcement as shown by tests. In a member with transverse reinforcement, the shear actually carried by the concrete may be substantially greater. V_c was defined in the preceding section as

$$V_c = 1.9 b'd \sqrt{f'_c}$$

for normal-weight concrete. The term $A_v f_y$ represents the force that can be developed in each stirrup and d/s indicates the number of stirrups crossed by the inclined crack.

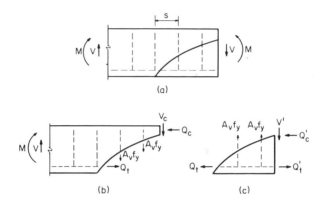

Fig. 5-19. Portion of a beam with web reinforcement subjected to combined bending and shear.

Strength Under Combined Bending, Axial Load, and Shear

The members of a building frame are subjected to axial loads in addition to bending moment and shear. In the case of the vertical members (the columns), the axial loads are generated by a combination of dead and live loads and inertia effects. In the case of horizontal members of the frame (the beams), the axial loads are caused primarily by inertia effects.

The axial load caused by inertia effects can be a tensile or a compressive force. It can sometimes be larger than that caused by the combination of dead load and the live load on the structure at the time of the earthquake.

The shear corresponding to the formation of an inclined tension crack is obviously related to the tensile strength of the concrete. A compressive axial load tends to increase the apparent tensile strength of the concrete, as in a prestressed beam, while a tensile axial load decreases it. Consequently, the shear corresponding to inclined tension cracking should be modified by the presence of the axial load.

A considerable amount of experimental research has been carried out on the effect of compressive axial loads on the shear strength of reinforced concrete beams[53, 54, 55]. The following simple and conservative expression has been derived from the available data for the value of V_c under such conditions:

$$V_c = \left(1 + \frac{P}{16A_{tr}\sqrt{f'_c}}\right)1.9b'd\sqrt{f'_c} \qquad (5\text{-}20)$$

where

A_{tr} = transformed area of uncracked section

This expression is to be used for compressive axial loads only, with P defined as the minimum probable load on the section due to dead load and actual (not design) live load less a portion of those loads due to inertia effects resulting from vertical acceleration of the ground during an earthquake. The minimum P value is used in equation (5-20) in order to obtain the most conservative value of V_c.

The following expression is recommended for evaluating the shear strength of the concrete in a member when subjected to a tensile force P_t

$$V_c = \left(1 - \frac{P_t}{8A_{tr}\sqrt{f'_c}}\right)1.9b'd\sqrt{f'_c} \qquad (5\text{-}21)$$

The values of V_c given by equations (5-20) and (5-21) should be used in equation (5-19) for members subject to axial loads.

5.6 Bending Deformation of Reinforced Concrete Members

Distribution of Curvature at Ultimate

The maximum lateral deformation of a reinforced concrete frame with respect to its base is primarily a function of the magnitude of angle-change that can take place at the connections of the frame. The loading conditions for the portion between the point of contraflexure A and the face of the transverse member B of a frame member at this limiting stage of deformation, are shown in Fig. 5-20(a).

It is assumed that the member in question is moderately reinforced such that the moment-curvature relationship is virtually elasto-plastic. Accordingly, the theoretical distribution of curvature is indicated by the broken line 1 in Fig. 5-20(c), the curvature changing abruptly from ϕ_y to ϕ_u at point B. This condition, whether the change occurs at a point or over a few inches, is not practically admissible. It is quite unreasonable to expect the strains in the concrete to vary so rapidly. A more probable distribution is indicated by curve 2, which remains well above line 1 in the vicinity of the connection but dips below it at points away from the connection. The cross-hatched area under curve 2 represents the spread of the ultimate curvature and is a measure of the useful limit of angle-change for the joint. Curve 2 dips below line 1 as a result of the stiffening effect of the tensile stress in the concrete between flexural cracks. That is, between cracks the section tends to revert to the uncracked section.

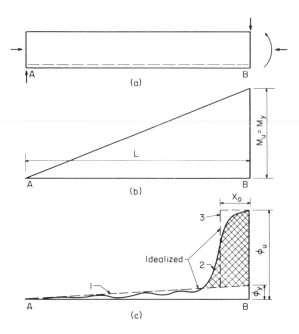

Fig. 5-20. Probable and idealized distribution of curvature in a beam subjected to transverse loading.

It is necessary to be able to estimate the magnitude of the cross-hatched area, or the spread of the ultimate curvature, in order to determine the ductility of a frame member. To accomplish this, the following idealized interpretation of the distribution of curvature is used.

The distribution of curvature shown in Fig. 5-20(c) is divided into two idealized parts. The first part is that between the base line and the broken line 1. This triangular part represents the curvature up to yield and the rectangular part indicated by the broken line 3 represents the increase in curvature beyond yield. The first part can be determined on the basis of the cracked section; the second corresponds to reaching the ultimate capacity and is spread over the distance X_o.

Tests on simulated beam-to-column connections [56, 57] and knee frames [53, 58] indicate that X_o for the members tested was about equal to the effective depth d. It was also shown by tests [56, 59] that X_o equals the length over which constant moment occurs, such as between equal loads at the third-points of a member. The distance X_o is to a minor extent a function of the type of steel used and the strength of the concrete, but to a major extent it is a function of the slope of the moment curve. The flatter the slope, the greater is X_o.

On the basis of these data, X_o can be assumed as being equal to the effective depth of the member, but it is recommended that X_o not exceed one-half the distance to the point of contraflexure.

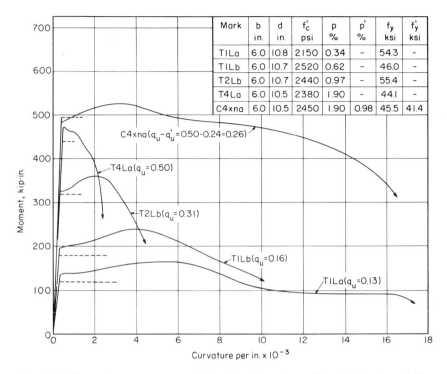

Mark	b in.	d in.	f'_c psi	p %	p' %	f_y ksi	f'_y ksi
T1La	6.0	10.8	2150	0.34	-	54.3	-
T1Lb	6.0	10.7	2520	0.62	-	46.0	-
T2Lb	6.0	10.7	2440	0.97	-	55.4	-
T4La	6.0	10.5	2380	1.90	-	44.1	-
C4xna	6.0	10.5	2450	1.90	0.98	45.5	41.4

Fig. 5-21. Measured moment-curvature relationships for sections subjected to bending only[59].

Measured Moment-Curvature Relationships

SECTIONS SUBJECTED TO BENDING ONLY. A set of measured moment-curvature relationships based on tests [59] of simply supported beams loaded at the third-points are shown in Fig. 5-21. The average curvature, plotted horizontally in the figure, was derived from the measured deflection at midspan with respect to the third-points.

The cross-sectional properties of the beams are listed in the figure. All beams had about the same concrete strength and the same dimensions; however, the amount of the longitudinal reinforcement varied. An example is shown for one beam having compression reinforcement.

The effect of the longitudinal reinforcement can be seen from a comparison of the curves for the four beams without compression reinforcement. As p increases, the strength of the section increases. However, the ductility decreases since the concrete strength is nearly constant. It can be seen from equations (5-12) and (5-13) in Section 5.3 that, for moderately reinforced sections subjected to bending only, strength is directly proportional to the amount of the longitudinal reinforcement while the ductility is inversely proportional to the value of q_u as shown in Fig. 5-14.

The effect of the compression reinforcement can be seen from a comparison of the curves for beams $T4La$ and $C4xna$ in Fig. 5-21. These two beams have similar properties except for the compression reinforcement in beam $C4xna$. The strength difference between these two sections is slight (note the slight difference in yield stresses f_y for the tension steel). However, they differ enormously in terms of ductility because the addition of compression steel reduces the effective value of q_u from 0.50 to 0.26 and because the compression reinforcement stabilized by the ties continues to function after the concrete becomes partially ineffective. The ductility of the beam is even greater than that for a beam having a value of q_u of 0.26 but not having compression reinforcement.

Moment-curvature relationships computed on the basis of the expressions presented in Section 5.3 are shown as broken lines in Fig. 5-21. It is seen that the computed curves are conservative in every case. The primary reasons for this lie in the conservative assumptions for the useful limit of strain ϵ_{cu} and the effective concrete strength f_{cu}.

SECTIONS SUBJECTED TO COMBINED BENDING AND AXIAL LOAD. Measured moment-curvature relationships for sections subjected to combined bending and axial load are shown in Fig. 5-22. These curves are based on tests of eccentrically loaded columns [44]. The lower two curves designated $A10a$ and $A5a$ refer to tied columns; the upper three curves designated $B17a$, $B19b$, and $B20b$ refer to spirally reinforced columns. The cross-sectional properties of the columns are shown in the figure. The concrete in the tied columns is considered to be unconfined since the tie spacing was 10 in. The spiral reinforcement consisted of USSWG No. 3 wire at a pitch of 1.5 in. The average yield-point stress of the longitudinal reinforcement was 43,500 psi and the strength of the spiral wire was 129,000 psi.

Both columns $A10a$ and $A5a$ were loaded with an intial eccentricity of 12.5 in. It is seen that $A10a$ had the larger curvature at ultimate because of the larger amount of compression steel. Without any axial load this section would have developed a much greater ductility, although its flexural strength would have been reduced, compared with its ductility and strength with the axial load applied in the test. Furthermore, if the spacing of the ties had been of the order of 3.0 to 4.0 in. and the ties had been of sufficient area to confine the core concrete, the ductility and hence the energy-absorption capacity would have been substantially greater.

An interesting feature of the curves for columns B is the sudden drop in the moment resistance that corresponds to the failure of the shell concrete. If no confining reinforcement had been present, this point would have been the ultimate. However, the sections continued to resist load and bending moment since the core concrete was confined and the ductility was thereby greatly increased. When the loading on these columns was discontinued, the core concrete was intact and the section gave every indication of being able to resist the maximum moment with further increase in curvature, as indicated by the arrows at the ends of the curves. The tests were stopped because they were primarily aimed at the load-carrying capacity and not ductility.

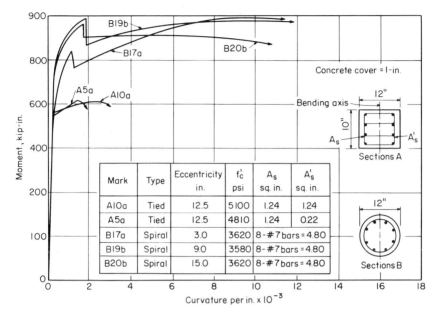

Fig. 5-22. Measured moment-curvature relationships for sections subjected to combined bending and axial load[44].

Measured Load-Deflection Relationships

MEMBERS SUBJECTED TO BENDING ONLY. The measured load-deflection relationship for a simulated beam-column connection is shown in Fig. 5-23. This was obtained from the test of a simply supported beam loaded at midspan through a stub as shown in the drawing of the specimen in Fig. 5-23 and also in Fig. 5-24, which is a photograph of the specimen in the testing machine. Each part of the beam on either side of the stub represented the portion of a frame member between the point of contraflexure and the face of the transverse member as discussed earlier in this section. The test was conducted in the course of an investigation for the Portland Cement Association by the Civil Engineering Department of the University of Illinois. The results of this investigation have not yet been published.

The cross-sectional properties of the beam are shown in Fig. 5-23. The shearing force on the connection, which is equal to half the applied load, is plotted vertically in the figure. The condition of the connection at various stages of loading is shown in Figs. 5-24 through 5-29. Load numbers in the photographs and in Fig. 5-23 indicate the stages of loading at which the photographs were taken and not the magnitude of the load. The deflection of the beam can be

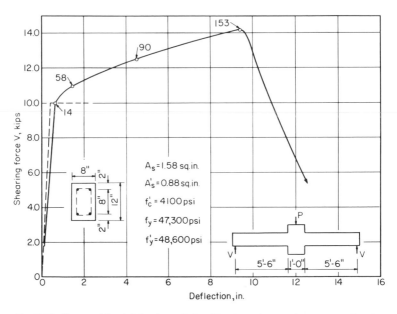

Fig. 5-23. Measured load-deflection relationships for a beam-column connection (see also Figs. 5-24 to 5-29).

Fig. 5-24. Test setup for specimen simulating a beam-column connection.

Fig. 5–25. Beam–column connection at yielding of tension reinforcement.

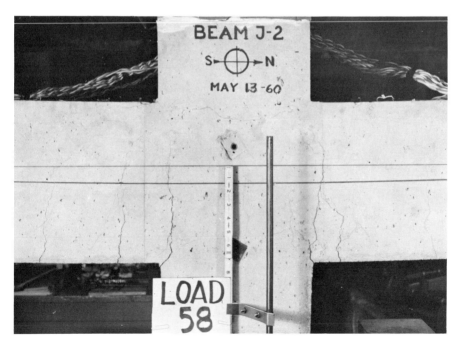

Fig. 5-26. Beam-column connection at first visible crushing.

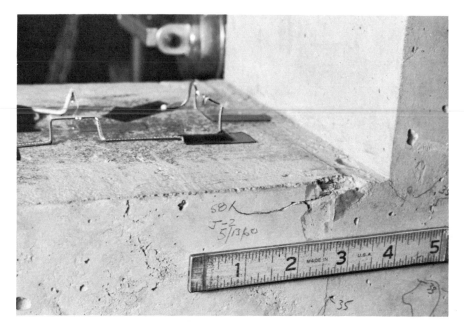

Fig. 5-27. Close-up of first visible crushing.

Fig. 5-28. Beam-column connection at about eight times the yield deflection.

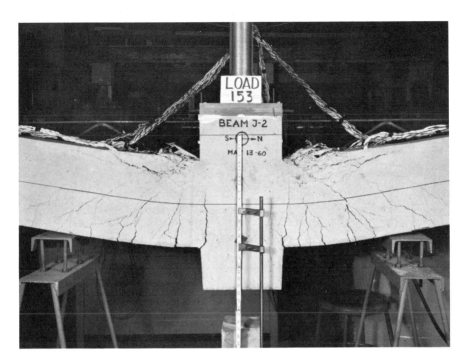

Fig. 5-29. Beam-column connection at about 16 times the yield deflection.

estimated directly from the photographs by comparing the elevation of the horizontal string with the line at midheight of the section.

Fig. 5-25 is a close-up of the connection at yielding (Load 14). Fig. 5-26 shows the beam at first evidence of shell crushing (Load 58) at which the deflection is about three times that at yielding. A close-up of the top surface of the beam (Fig. 5-27) shows that the crushing was local and was limited to the corners of the section. This localized crushing did not impair the strength of the section as evidenced by the increase in load beyond this stage. Fig. 5-28 (Load 90) shows the condition of the connection at a deflection of about 8 times the yield deflection. Although crushing of the concrete was extensive on the upper corners of the section, the connection continued to resist an increasing bending moment up to a deflection of about 16 times the yield deflection (Fig. 5-29). As further deformation was imposed on the connection, the compression reinforcement buckled gradually in the horizontal plane and the resistance started to decrease.

A computed load-deflection relationship based on the methods described in Sections 5.3 and 5.6 is shown as a broken line in Fig. 5-23. The ductility of the section is underestimated greatly because the computations were based on the useful limit of strain for unconfined concrete and ignore the increase made possible by the presence of compression and transverse reinforcement in the member. Research is currently under way to obtain adequate information about this phenomenon so that a quantitative relationship can be established between the useful limit of concrete strain in the member and the amount of compression and transverse reinforcement.

The measured load-deflection relationship of a beam-column connection subjected to reversals of loading is shown in Fig. 5-30. This specimen was tested as a part of the same investigation as that including the previous specimen considered. It is interesting to note that the connection can develop its capacity in one direction after having developed it in the opposite direction. The ultimate shearing force and deflection of the specimen computed according to the methods outlined in this chapter would be 10 kips and about 1.5 in., respectively, in both directions of loading, whereas the measured values are shown to be considerably greater. The problem of reversed loading is discussed further in Section 5.9 of this chapter.

MEMBERS SUBJECTED TO COMBINED BENDING AND AXIAL LOAD. Two measured load-deflection relationships for members without transverse reinforcement subjected to combined bending and axial load are shown in Fig. 5-31. These

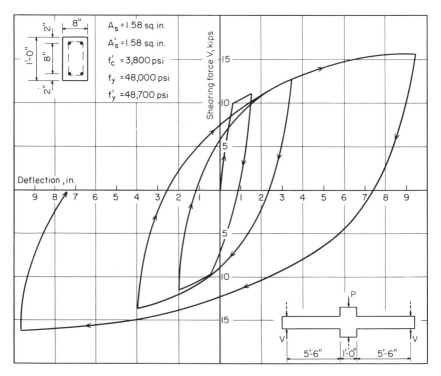

Fig. 5-30. Measured load-deflection relationships for a beam-column connection subjected to reversals of load.

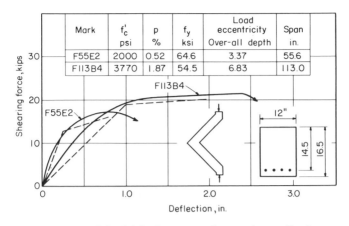

Fig. 5-31. Measured load-deflection curves for members without compression reinforcement or transverse reinforcement subjected to combined axial load and bending[53].

curves are based on tests of knee-frames [53]. The shear on the simulated beam-column connections, which was at the "knee" for these specimens, is plotted vertically. The cross-sectional properties of the knee-frames are shown in the figure.

A comparison of these curves with Fig. .5-14 indicates that the bending ductility of a reinforced concrete member is reduced by a compressive axial load; even for specimens such as these without compression reinforcement or transverse reinforcement, however, the ductility as represented by the ratio of the ultimate deflection to the yield deflection is of the order of 3.5. By the use of such recommended reinforcement, a much greater degree of ductility can be achieved as indicated by Figs. 5-7, 5-16, and 5-17. Computed load-deflection relationships based on the recommendations made in Sections 5.4 and 5.6 are shown as broken lines in the figure.

5.7 Strength and Behavior of Reinforced Concrete Shear Walls

A reinforced concrete shear wall in a multistory reinforced concrete building is essentially a deep, slender cantilever beam. It resists the bending moments and the shearing and axial forces to which it is subjected through essentially the same type of action described for reinforced concrete frame members. Thus, the strength and behavior of a reinforced concrete shear wall can be estimated on the basis of the principles described for reinforced concrete frame members with some modifications to take account of the shape of the shear wall as compared with an ordinary beam.

Two characteristics of the reinforced concrete shear wall demand special emphasis in view of the possible interpretation of the behavior of a shear wall

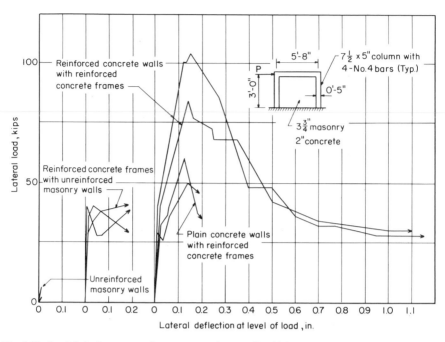

Fig. 5-32. Load-deflection curves for one-story shear walls. (Adapted from references 60 and 61, ASCE.)

in the traditional frame building as an isolated one-story-high panel acting "in parallel" with the enclosing frame. One is that the reinforced concrete shear wall extending monolithically through several stories may be subjected to high bending moments as well as high shearing forces. In fact, flexure rather than shear may govern the strength of the wall. The other characteristic is that the reinforced concrete wall acts together with the surrounding frame as a single structural unit and not as an isolated panel.

The interaction between the frame and the wall is illustrated in Fig. 5-32 by the load-deflection curves measured in tests of one-story shear walls [60, 61]. All the curves in Fig. 5-32 refer to one-story walls having the same overall dimensions and loaded as indicated at the upper left-hand corner of the frame as shown in the figure. The enclosing reinforced concrete frame was composed of members measuring 7.5 by 5 in. in cross-section and reinforced with four No. 4 deformed bars. The wall thickness was 3.75 in. for the masonry walls and 2 in. for the concrete walls. The concrete strength was about 3,000 psi.

The first set of two curves in Fig. 5-32 is for masonry walls without enclosing frames. These unreinforced walls failed in a brittle manner and carried relatively little load. The second set of three curves refers to masonry walls enclosed in reinforced concrete frames. These walls resisted the lateral force P of about 40 kips. The frame would resist a lateral load of about 13 kips acting independently. The sum of the larger measured strength of the masonry wall (6 kips) and the estimated strength of the frame totals 19 kips, a quantity far short of the 40 kips carried by the combined wall and the frame. Evidently, the reinforced concrete frame with the masonry wall cannot be considered as an individual frame and an individual wall acting "in parallel," but must be considered as a single structural unit. It is easy to see that although an unreinforced masonry wall possesses little tensile strength, it can act effectively in compression. Ideally, the action of the masonry wall may be considered as that of a diagonal strut extending from the corner where the load acts to the opposite corner. In this capacity, it possesses considerable strength. As the tensile strength of the wall is exceeded and cracks develop, parallel struts form so that the frame never acts completely as a rigid rectangular frame but behaves as a braced frame with diagonal members.

It follows that if the addition of a masonry wall inside a frame results in a mode of behavior which is closer to that of a beam than that of a frame and wall working in parallel, a reinforced concrete frame with a monolithic plain or reinforced concrete wall tends to act as a single unit. Examples of the behavior of such members are represented by the third group of curves in Fig. 5-32. Of this set, the lower two refer to plain concrete panels and the upper two to reinforced concrete panels ($p = 0.005$ in both the horizontal and vertical directions). Again, both the strength and the behavior of these walls bear no semblance to the strength and behavior of the enclosing frame. These walls with enclosing frames are essentially reinforced concrete beams, two with web reinforcement and two without, subjected to very high shearing forces in relation to the bending moment.

The load-deflection curves shown in Fig. 5-32 may not represent the behavior of shear walls in multistory buildings, because the test specimens were loaded so that the shear-to-moment ratio was very high. An interesting example of the behavior of a three-story frame with and without a masonry filler wall was obtained in the course of the tests [62] to destruction of the Old Dental Hospital in Johannesburg, South Africa. The end-frames of the north and south wings of the building were separated from the structure and were loaded laterally along the ceiling beam of the third story as indicated in Fig. 5-33.

The dimensions of the north and south frames and the arrangement of the reinforcement are shown in Fig. 5-33. It should be mentioned that the frames were not designed to resist lateral loads. Consequently, the top reinforcement in the beams was not extended into the columns. The average concrete strength in the frames, based on 4-in. cores, was 4,550 psi (cube strength). The yield stress of the plain reinforcing bars ranged from 41,300 to 44,800 psi. The south frame was tested to failure after the masonry walls had been removed. The north frame was tested with the 4.5-in. masonry walls in place. The unreinforced masonry was of poor quality. Tests of samples indicated compressive strengths ranging from 390 to 500 psi.

The load-deflection curves for the north and south frames are shown in

Fig. 5-34. The south frame, which did not have the masonry filler walls, carried only about 20 per cent of the load carried by the north frame. Despite the poor "loose-fitting" masonry, the north frame functioned as a single structural unit and carried much greater load than the sum of the capacities of the wall and the frame. Its mode of failure was associated with beam action, a condition for which it had not been designed. It failed in a tension splice in the first-story column (which was designed as a compression splice) in a region of maximum bending moment.

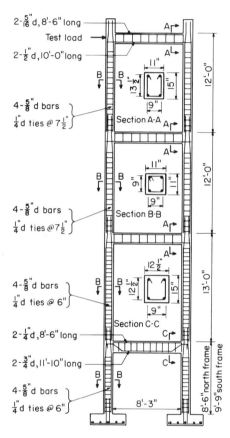

The crack patterns observed in the two end-frames are shown in Fig. 5-35. The crack pattern in the north frame is like that which would be expected in a cantilever beam; the pattern in the south frame indicates rigid frame action. Obviously, if the north frame had been cast integrally with a reinforced concrete wall, it would be unrealistic to consider it as a frame and a wall. Such a member must be considered and therefore reinforced as a single unit; if each element is reinforced for separate action (as a frame and as a wall), the strength may be considerably lessened.

Another example of this integral action is shown in Fig. 5-36, which is a photograph of a model multi-story shear wall tested at the Muto Laboratory of the University of Tokyo. The reinforced concrete model was loaded by a concentrated load as indicated in the photograph and supported at the ends. The crack pattern is typical for reinforced concrete beams loaded over short spans. The whole system should be considered as a single "waffle" beam, rather than a frame with shear walls.

If tall, slender shear walls are treated as webs of waffle beams or I-beams and are reinforced adequately in shear, they will act as cantilever beams fixed at the ground. Their behavior in the ductile range will be controlled by tensile yielding of the vertical reinforcement concentrated in the flanges (or columns) as well as

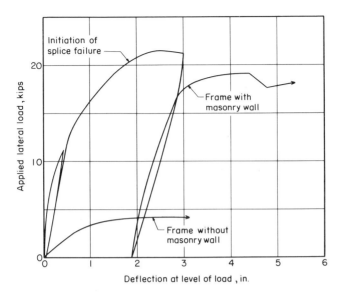

Fig. 5-34. Load-deflection curves for three-story frames with and without masonry filler walls shown in Fig. 5-33. (Adapted from reference 62, CASA.)

Fig. 5-35. Cracks observed during tests of three-story frames. The north frame was tested with masonry filler walls in place. The south frame was tested after removal of walls. (Adapted from reference 62, CASA.)

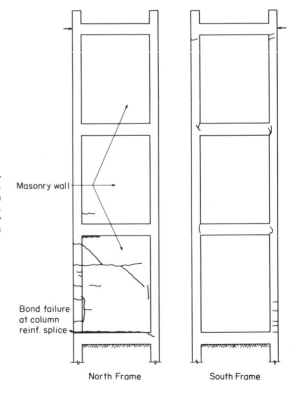

North Frame   South Frame

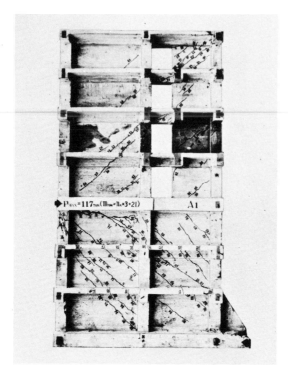

Fig. 5-36. The crack pattern in this multistory shear wall and frame model indicates that the whole system acts as a single "waffle" beam.

—*Photo courtesy Dr. Hiroshi Osawa, Muto Laboratory, University of Tokyo*

of the vertical distributed reinforcement in the wall itself. It is evident from the foregoing discussion that the strength and deformation characteristics of reinforced concrete shear walls are governed by the same criteria as those for frame members discussed earlier in this chapter. Thus, the behavior of a shear wall can be estimated on the basis of principles discussed in Sections 5.3 through 5.6, with the complete wall treated as a single unit. Normally, shear walls do not occur in every bay or column line of a structure. The interaction between the walls and the members of adjoining moment-resisting frames can be resolved in accordance with the discussion presented in Section 4.8 in connection with Fig. 4-8 and by analysis that considers the wall-column element as a vertical frame member of large cross-section.

Stiffness

The stiffness of a shear wall is customarily expressed as the force required to produce a unit lateral deflection per story or per unit of height. The determination of the stiffness of a shear wall is different from that of a reinforced concrete beam of ordinary slenderness only in that the shearing deformation must be considered in addition to the flexural deformation.

Tests on reinforced concrete shear walls [61, 63] with or without openings, and on short deep beams [64], have indicated that the ordinary methods of mechanics of materials can be used to obtain the stiffness of uncracked shear walls. Before computing the stiffness of a shear wall, the designer should consider the magnitude of the possible rotation at the base of the shear wall, the relative restraint against rotation at the top, and the influence of the base rotation and the top restraint on the results of the calculation in which the stiffness of the shear wall is being utilized. For example, when the base is fixed but the upper edge is unrestrained, the lateral deflection relative to its base of a rectangular prismatic shear wall of height H_s subjected to a shearing force V acting along its upper edge is

$$\Delta = \frac{VH_s^3}{3E_cI} + \frac{6VH_s}{5AG}$$

in which the first term on the right is the flexural component and the second the shear component. The shearing modulus for concrete G can be taken as 40 per cent of its modulus in compression ($G = 0.4E_c$). This equation is recommended for use in general unless more definite information is available on the degree of restraint, permitting a change in the first term on the right.

If a moment M is applied at the upper edge of the wall mentioned above, in addition to the force V, its additional deflection relative to the base becomes

$$\Delta = \frac{MH_s^2}{2E_cI}$$

Procedures for computing the stiffness of uncracked shear walls with or without openings and of various shapes are given in references 65 and 66.

5.8 Energy-Absorbing Capacity

A good measure of the energy-absorbing capacity of a reinforced concrete section subjected to earthquake effects is the area under the M-ϕ curve since, especially in the case of frame members, most of the work is done in the course of the lateral deflection of the structure. The relation of the M-ϕ curve to the cross-sectional properties was discussed in Sections 5.2 and 5.3. The object of this section is to point out the important variables affecting the energy-absorbing capacity through the use of simple approximations.

The discussion is carried out in reference to a reinforcing steel having an elasto-plastic stress-strain curve. The effects of rapid loading on the stress-strain characteristics of concrete and steel and therefore on the energy-absorbing capacity of a reinforced concrete section are also discussed.

Sensitivity of the Energy-Absorbing Capacity

If the effect of the tensile strength of the concrete is ignored, the energy-absorbing capacity per unit of length for a reinforced concrete section can be written in reference to the solid lines of Fig. 5-9 as follows:

$$U = \tfrac{1}{2}M_y\phi_y + \tfrac{1}{2}(M_u + M_y)(\phi_u - \phi_y)$$

137

where U, the energy absorbed, is the area under the $M\text{-}\phi$ curve. For moderately reinforced sections, it can be assumed that

$$M_y = M_u$$

since according to equations (5-9) and (5-13)

$$\frac{M_y}{M_u} = \frac{j}{1 - 0.4k_u} = \frac{1 - k/3}{1 - 0.4pf_y/f_{cu}}$$

which is close enough to unity not to warrant complicating the equations by considering M_y and M_u separately. Therefore,

$$U = M_u\left(\phi_u - \frac{\phi_y}{2}\right)$$

The two curvatures, ϕ_u and ϕ_y, were defined as follows in Section 5.3:

$$\phi_u = \frac{\epsilon_{cu}}{q_u d}$$

$$\phi_y = \frac{\epsilon_y}{(1 - k)d}$$

The expression for U can be further simplified by assuming that $1 - k = 1 - q_u$ in the expression for ϕ_y. Although this corresponds to a reduction of as much as 20 per cent in ϕ_y for the range of the reinforcement ratios associated with earthquake-resistant design, the simplification affects the energy-absorbing capacity very little as shown by the areas under the curves in Fig. 5-37. The solid line curve is that constructed according to the expressions given in Section 5.3. The broken line represents the approximate $M\text{-}\phi$ curve. The differences between the two are well within the practical limits of the expressions based on the conservative values assigned elsewhere in this manual to the terms involved which represent a reasonable lower bound to test results.

Thus the expression for the energy-absorbing capacity of a section reinforced in tension only can be written as

$$U = bdf_{cu}\left(\epsilon_{cu} - \frac{\epsilon_y}{2}\right)(1 - 0.4q_u) \tag{5-22}$$

An inspection of this equation brings out quite clearly the variables that have the greatest influence on the energy-absorbing capacity of a unit length of a moderately reinforced section. Obviously, the energy-absorbing capacity is a direct function of the size of the section as represented by the product bd. The useful limit of strain of the concrete is also very important insofar as the energy-absorbing capacity is concerned, since this quantity affects directly the ultimate curvature, $\phi_u = \epsilon_{cu}/q_u d$. Consequently, any improvement in ϵ_{cu}, such as may be gained from confining the concrete with transverse reinforcement, affects the magnitude of U directly.

Since the value of the term $(1 - 0.4q_u)$, where $q_u = pf_y/f_{cu}$, is modified only to a small extent by changes in the value of f_{cu}, the energy-absorbing capacity is almost directly proportional to the effective concrete strength f_{cu}. This is a result of the fact that, although f_{cu} does not affect appreciably the strength of the section, it controls the ultimate curvature, $\phi_u = \epsilon_{cu}/q_u d = \epsilon_{cu} f_{cu}/p f_y d$.

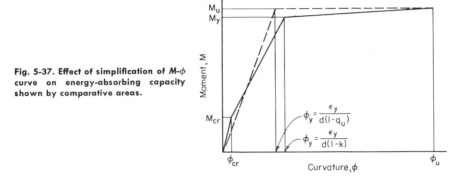

Fig. 5-37. Effect of simplification of M-ϕ curve on energy-absorbing capacity shown by comparative areas.

The expressions presented in this section were derived without reference to compression reinforcement. However, its effect on the energy-absorbing capacity can be seen to be the same as that of the effective concrete strength. For moderately reinforced sections, compression reinforcement has very little influence on strength but has a direct influence on $\phi_u = \epsilon_{cu} f_{cu}/(p - p')f_y d$. In effect, adding compression reinforcement is equivalent to increasing the value of f_{cu}. Fig. 5-14 indicates the increase in ductility with compression steel.

It is interesting to note that the reinforcement ratio p enters equation (5-22) only in the term $(1 - 0.4 p f_y/f_{cu})$. Its effect on the energy-absorbing capacity is quite small compared to that of b, d, f_{cu}, and ϵ_{cu}, if the moment capacity of the member is increased. This can be seen from the graphical comparison shown in Fig. 5-38. The solid and broken line curves represent the M-ϕ relationships for sections with reinforcement ratios p and $2p$, respectively. Increasing the reinforcement ratio from p to $2p$ increases the strength by a little less than 2 but decreases the ultimate curvature by a factor of 2 if all other variables are held constant. Thus, the area under the broken line curve is a little less than the area

Fig. 5-38. Effect of percentage of longitudinal reinforcement on energy-absorption capacity.

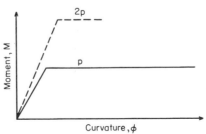

139

under the solid curve in spite of doubling the amount of reinforcement.

The effect of the yield strength of the reinforcement is similar to but somewhat more pronounced than the effect of the reinforcement ratio since, in addition to the inclusion of f_y in the term $(1 - 0.4 p f_y / f_{cu})$, this quantity also affects the value of $(\epsilon_{cu} - \epsilon_y/2)$ in equation (5-22). Accordingly, an increase in the yield strength causes an increase in strength of a member, but it is accompanied by an even greater proportional decrease in ultimate curvature and hence a reduction in the energy-absorption capacity.

The effect of a compressive axial load on the energy-absorbing capacity is mostly a reflection of the fact that the axial load reduces the ultimate curvature, and therefore the energy-absorbing capacity, although it may increase the ultimate moment to some extent.

In a design problem, the bending moment that a section is to carry is often dictated by gravity loads. Consequently, it is more important to study the relationship of the various parameters to the energy-absorbing capacity realizable for a given moment capacity M_u, a multiple of the design moment.

The critical parameters can be established easily from an inspection of Fig. 5-37, as follows. The flexural energy-absorbing capacity per unit length of beam is the area under the idealized broken line curve in Fig. 5-37. The ultimate moment M_u is assumed to be fixed by design considerations. Therefore, the energy-absorbing capacity can be changed only by changing the values of ϕ_y and ϕ_u. Possible changes in ϕ_y, in the practical range of cross-sectional proportions, are negligible in comparison to possible changes in ϕ_u. Thus, for a given ultimate bending moment, the energy-absorbing capacity can be controlled by varying the ultimate curvature, which can be written as

$$\phi_u = \frac{\epsilon_{cu}}{q_u d}$$

or

$$\phi_u = \epsilon_{cu} \frac{b f_{cu}}{A_s f_y}$$

for a rectangular section without compression reinforcement.

The above expressions show that, for a given M_u and ϵ_{cu}, the energy-absorbing capacity can be increased by decreasing the percentage of reinforcement, which results in a decrease in the total force in the longitudinal reinforcement $A_s f_y$ (in which case the effective depth must be increased to maintain M_u) or increasing either b or f_{cu}; or, in short, decreasing $q_u d$. Naturally, compression reinforcement will increase the energy-absorbing capacity for constant M_u while axial compressive loading will decrease it.

The Effect of Rapid Loading on the Energy-Absorbing Capacity

Since earthquake loadings are dynamic in character, it becomes necessary to consider the possible effects of rate of loading on the strength and deformation capacity of reinforced concrete.

There have been several investigations into the behavior of reinforced concrete under loadings simulating a blast load or an explosion [67, 68, 69, 70, 71, 72, 73]. Data from these investigations indicate that reinforced concrete exhibits an increased strength under these conditions. This increase is due primarily to the increased yield strength of the reinforcement. Tests on the reinforcing steel indicate that the degree of this increase depends on the rate at which the load is applied and the rate at which yielding occurs [74, 75]. These increases can reach 40 per cent for intermediate-grade steel under the fastest laboratory loadings, with yielding occurring within 0.005 second of application of the load. The loads induced by earthquake movements, however, are applied much more slowly than shock loadings and the corresponding increase in yield strength is not more than 5 to 10 per cent. It is not advised that this increase be considered directly in design, because not all components of a structure will yield together, and the problem of determining sequences of yielding and corresponding times to yield is unduly complex. Consequently, it is recommended that the static strength of reinforced concrete members be used in design for earthquake loads, an approach that should be conservative.

Some of the investigations referred to above resulted in data on the deformation at collapse of reinforced concrete beams under rapid loading [70, 71, 72]. Two significant conclusions can be drawn from these data. First, beams damaged by rapid loading, and subsequently tested to collapse statically, exhibited no loss in static deformation capacity compared with beams tested to collapse under static loading only. Second, there appeared to be no significant difference between the collapse deflection of beams tested statically to collapse and similar beams tested dynamically.

Since the strength and deformation characteristics of reinforced concrete members are at least as great under earthquake loading conditions as under static loading conditions, it is safe to use static values of energy-absorbing capacity as a basis for earthquake-resistant design.

5.9 Reversed Loading

Buildings subjected to earthquakes undergo several reversals in direction of loading in the course of one earthquake. As long as the deformation and resulting stresses are well below the yield level of the building elements, the loading is similar to a fatigue loading. This is of no particular consequence (other than the fact that the maximum deformations must be provided for as though statically applied) since the number of reversals that may take place even in a great many earthquakes is insignificant compared to the fatigue life of reinforced concrete. However, if a particular movement causes yielding in an element, it may be necessary to consider the effect this yielding would have on the behavior of the element due to deformation applied to that member in the reverse direction. Fortunately, this effect can also generally be ignored. Test data indicate that unless the first damaging load produces deformations in excess of about 80 per cent of the collapse deformation, the capacity in the reverse direction will be only slightly impaired, if at all. Moreover, only a few yield excursions are expected to occur in one earthquake even of long duration.

TABLE 5-1   Properties of Beams Loaded at Midspan*

Beam	f'_c ksi	Reinforcement quantity and size Tens.	Comp.	f_y Tens. ksi	f'_y Comp. ksi	d in.	d-d' in.	Stirrup size and spacing in.	p Tens. (%)	p' Comp. (%)	$\dfrac{p f_y - p' f'_y}{f'_c}$
T-8	2.44	2-6	2-7	45.0	49.3	10.58	8.84	#3 @ 6	1.39	1.89	−0.1251
T-8I		2-7	2-6	49.3	45.0	10.26			1.95	1.43	0.1298
T-10	4.33	2-6	2-3	42.6	46.3	10.58	9.25	#3 @ 6	1.39	0.35	0.0998
T-10I		2-3	2-6	46.3	42.6	10.67			0.34	1.37	−0.0981
T-12	4.37	2-10	2-9	46.0	45.8	10.28	8.44	#3 @ 4	4.12	3.24	0.0944
T-12I		2-9	2-10	45.8	46.0	10.16			3.28	4.17	−0.0954
T-13	4.85	2-9	2-10	56.9	46.0	10.37	8.68	#3 @ 4	3.21	4.08	−0.0107
T-13I		2-10	2-9	46.0	56.9	10.31			4.11	3.23	0.0112
T-14	4.03	2-6	2-6	41.4	40.9	10.58	9.06	#3 @ 6	1.39	1.39	0.0016
T-14I		2-6	2-6	40.9	41.4	10.48			1.40	1.40	−0.0016
T-15	3.70	2-6	2-6	47.0	40.5	10.58	9.08	#3 @ 6	1.39	1.39	0.0248
T-15I		2-6	2-6	40.5	47.0	10.50			1.40	1.40	−0.0249

*Reference 56

The primary source of data in this regard are tests run at the University of Illinois [56]. Six reinforced concrete beams with properties and characteristics as shown in Tables 5-1 and 5-2 and Fig. 5-39 were loaded in the normal direction well into the range of inelastic behavior. The beams were then turned over and loaded to failure in the reverse direction. The results of these tests are illustrated in the figure where the measured load-deflection behavior is plotted to dimensionless scales. In the figure, 100 per cent represents the maximum capacity and its associated deflection determined on the basis of the behavior of other specimens of the same series and not on the basis of the conservative procedures described in this manual. In the normal direction, the nearness of the plot for any one beam to the values of 100 per cent of maximum load capacity and ultimate midspan deflection indicates the degree of damage under the initial loading. The proximity to 100 per cent in the reverse direction is a measure of the effect of that damage on the capacity in the reverse direction. The positions of zero deflection in the reverse direction were all shifted to the origin of the graph for ease of comparison. It should be noted, with regard to Table 5-2, that the deflections listed under "Measured Capacity" are those associated with the measured maximum load capacity. This is of especial interest for Beams T-8, T-12, and T-14, which exhibit considerably more

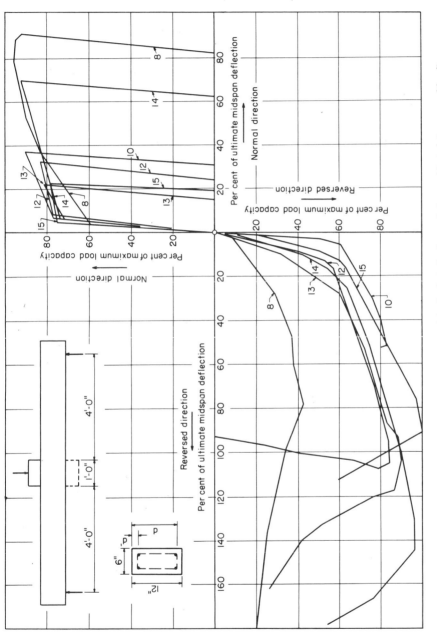

Fig. 5-39. Reinforced concrete beams loaded into range of inelastic behavior and then subjected to reversed loading.

143

TABLE 5-2   Applied Loads and Computed Virgin Capacities of
Beams Loaded at Midspan*

				Normal loading					
	Computed capacity				Applied load				
							P		Deflection ‡
Beam	M_{max} ft.kips	Δ_y in.	P_{max} † kips	Δ_{max} † in.	M ft.kips	kips	% of P_{max}	in.	% of Δ_{max}
T-8	47.6	0.24	23.8	9.0	45.4	22.7	95	7.0	77
T-10	40.2	0.24	20.1	4.9	36.0	18.0	90	1.75	36
T-12	115.0	0.38	57.5	7.8	95.0	47.5	83	2.4	31
T-13	122.6	0.39	61.3	10.7	98.6	49.3	81	2.25	21
T-14	41.2	0.22	20.6	6.0	38.0	19.0	92	4.1	68
T-15	45.4	0.27	22.7	7.0	36.0	18.0	79	1.55	22

				Inverted loading					
	Computed virgin capacity				Measured capacity				
							P		Deflection ‡
Beam	M_{max} ft.kips		P_{max} † kips	Δ_{max} † in.	M ft.kips	kips	% of P_{max}	in.	% of Δ_{max}
T-8I	59.3		29.6	5.0	25.6	12.8	43	3.9	78
T-10I	12.6		6.3	9.8	10.4	5.2	83	5.1	52
T-12I	103.3		51.6	7.2	92.2	46.1	90	7.45	103
T-13I	125.8		62.9	6.0	106.0	53.0	84	5.7	95
T-14I	40.8		20.4	7.7	39.0	19.5	96	11.1	144
T-15I	41.2		20.6	7.9	41.0	20.5	100	7.1	90

*Reference 56
†Represents 100% in accompanying figure.
‡Value associated with P.

deformation capacity in the inverted direction than these values would indicate. It is immediately apparent that the beams exhibit increased flexibility in the reverse direction over that which would be expected if they had been tested undamaged. It is also apparent that it takes a great deal of damage under the initial loading before the strength in the reverse direction is appreciably affected. All of the beams were loaded to the point where they suffered some crushing of the concrete in the normal direction before the reverse loading was applied.

CHAPTER 6

Design of Reinforced Concrete Frames

6.1 General Principles

Consider that at this point in the design of a multistory building a decision has been made concerning the type of building and framing; the forces for which the building is to be designed have been selected; and the moments, thrusts, and shears to be provided for in the design have been determined. In selecting the proportions of the members and the quantity, location, and arrangement of the reinforcement, and in detailing the splices and joints, the designer has a number of options. It is a relatively simple matter to design reinforced concrete members to have adequate strength. It requires either experience or a set of rules for guidance to obtain this strength and, at the same time, the desired ductility. It is the purpose of this chapter to describe in detail how the frame members and walls can be designed to maintain both strength and ductility, so as to achieve the desired objectives in the earthquake-resistant design of reinforced concrete frames.

The types of members considered here are columns, either hooped or tied or spirally reinforced; beams; slabs, including one-way, two-way, and flat slabs and flat plates; and walls, with or without openings and extending for one or more stories high. For convenience in presentation, the design and arrangement of reinforcement for beams and slabs are considered in Section 6.4, and that for columns in Section 6.5. The amount and arrangement of reinforcement in walls is considered separately in Section 6.6.

In general, the design will be made in accordance with standard code requirements. The Building Code Requirements for Reinforced Concrete of the American Concrete Institute [76] is used as a basis in these recommendations. In the detailing of the reinforcement, references 77 and 78 will be found most helpful. In reference 79, recommendations are given for use of welded wire fabric as reinforcement in slabs. References 80 and 81 contain information pertinent to the welding of reinforcing bars.

The limitations outlined in this chapter on amounts and spacing of reinforcement, and on strength and quality of materials, are intended to ensure that a minimum ductility factor corresponding to $\mu = 4$ will be achieved without loss in strength. Additional ductility and energy absorption will be available beyond this value, although possibly accompanied by a moderate amount of spalling or other similar damage to the appearance, but not, in general, to the strength.

Reinforced concrete structures, properly designed in accordance with the recommendations contained in this manual, will have the ductility and strength to resist major earthquakes. The important points in the design to achieve ductility involve the following:

1. Use of transverse or shear reinforcement to make the strength in shear greater than the ultimate strength in flexure.
2. Limitations on the amount of tensile reinforcement, or the use of compression reinforcement, to increase energy-absorbing capacity.
3. Use of confinement by hoops or spirals at critical sections of stress concentration, such as column-girder connections, to increase the ductility of columns under combined axial load and bending.
4. Special attention to details, such as splices in reinforcement and the avoidance of planes of weakness that might be caused by bending or terminating all bars at the same section.

If the designer keeps these principles in mind, he will find it possible, by following the recommendations outlined here, to provide for the expected loading and deformation caused by severe earthquakes with little or no structural damage.

6.2 Working Stress and Ultimate-Strength Design

The lateral loads specified for design by the SEAOC code, and discussed in Chapter 4, are intended for use in design based on a working stress procedure using a one-third increase in the working stresses except for anchorage by bond when lateral loads combined with vertical loads control the design. (See pages 155 and 162 for anchorage requirements.) The use of the ACI design requirements is possible with this procedure and will lead to satisfactory results. The alternative method of design in the ACI code, the so-called ultimate-strength design procedure, may also be used. It should be noted that the load factors applied to the effects of the basic and live loads are applied to the static design load effects. The earthquake lateral loading effects determined in accordance with the SEAOC code or other applicable code should be modified by the load factors shown in Section A604, ACI code (318-56), for wind or earthquake, and the most critical load combination should be used for proportioning members. Under no circumstances, however, should a combination of load factors be used such that the overall factor of safety or load factor with earthquake effects considered, based on the actual capacity of the members as determined by ultimate-strength procedures, would be less than 1.5. This load factor is nominally obtained by the working stress method as indicated by the ratio of the yield stress of intermediate-grade reinforcement to 1.33 times the allowable design stress.

The ultimate-strength procedure for design of building frames is useful and valuable since it results in a more nearly uniform factor of safety than can be achieved by the working stress concept. However, in the use of either procedure, it is important to follow the recommendations contained in this chapter regarding the amount, location, and arrangement of reinforcement in order to achieve the necessary ductility as well as strength.

6.3 Strength of Concrete and Reinforcement

The recommendations in this section are not intended to inhibit the designer's freedom of choice in selecting the combination of materials he believes to be most economical to achieve the purposes he has in mind. However, concrete with a compressive strength in standard cylinders of less than 3,000 psi may not have the requisite strength in bond or shear to take full advantage of the design provisions.

In general, it will be desirable to use concrete strengths of 4,500 to 6,000 psi in columns in order to meet architectural requirements of widely-spaced columns, particularly in the lower stories of very tall buildings. Either in beams or columns, and especially for high-strength concrete, attention must be given to the upper limits of the allowable steel percentage, stated herein in terms of the value of q_u. As indicated by the discussion in Chapter 5 and as shown in Fig. 5-17, the ductility of a section becomes less as the $P/f'_c bd$ ratio increases.

Intermediate-grade steel, having a minimum yield point of 40,000 psi, is generally used in flexural and compression members. However, other grades of steel may be used with appropriate modifications in the allowable percentages of steel and in the working stresses. Structural-grade steel may be used provided that the working or yield stresses are adjusted correspondingly to account for its minimum yield-point stress of 33,000 psi. Nevertheless, no increase in maximum allowable steel percentage should be permitted when structural-grade steel is used.

Hard-grade billet steel, rail steel, or high-strength alloy steels may be used with appropriate values of minimum specified yield-point stress, and with corresponding changes in the permissible working stresses, providing tests show the required ductility as recommended in the following paragraph. However, when such steels are used, the maximum allowable percentage of reinforcement that may be used in flexural members must be in accordance with equation (6-1).

In no case should steel be used that has a ductility in tension corresponding to an elongation in 8 in. of less than that required by ASTM specifications for the respective bar sizes nor less than 7 per cent at maximum load. This limitation does not apply to transverse reinforcement.

The specifications for allowable properties of spiral reinforcement in the ACI code should be followed. The minimum strength for transverse reinforcement should correspond to that for intermediate-grade steel bars.

The use of high-strength reinforcement will generally be found to be governed by the specifications concerning bending properties, since it is necessary in many instances to have hooks or bends to provide for the proper continuity of the steel. The standard ASTM specifications governing bending properties must be met.

Where welding of reinforcement is to be used to provide for continuity, additional requirements on weldability of the steel must be considered. Limitations on carbon content of steel to provide for weldability are appropriate. Where fillet welding is used, carbon contents of less than 0.35 per cent are permissible; carbon contents exceeding this value should not be used without special approved welding procedures because sound welds may not be obtained. For butt welds, the same specification should apply in general, except where such welds are made by a flash welding process or by use of automatic machinery involving pressure between the ends to be connected. In such cases, carbon contents up to 0.45 per cent are permissible. Only low-hydrogen electrodes should be used when welding reinforcing bars. In addition to placing limitations on the carbon content of steel to provide for weldability, proper procedures and inspection are important to ensure good results. It is recommended that Part IX of reference 80 and Part IV of reference 81 be followed as an aid in securing satisfactory welds.

In general, hard-grade or rail steel bars do not meet the requirements of weldability outlined in this section. Such steels may be used where welding is not specified or when appropriate and approved welding procedures are employed.

6.4 Arrangement of Reinforcement for Beams and Slabs

The floor of a building must act in several ways. First, it carries gravity loads to the columns. Standard methods of design are adequate to ensure the capability of the floor slab and the beams not framing into columns to act in this fashion. It should be noted that the more stringent requirements recommended herein apply to those members composing the moment-resisting frame, which should include the beams immediately adjacent to the girders framing into columns. (See Chapter 7, page 173, and Appendix B, page 280.)

Second, the floor acts as a flexural member in resisting the moments at the ends of the columns when the structure is subjected to lateral loading. Under these conditions, high shears are often produced in the members. These shears may act in either direction and are practically constant over the length of the floor members. Furthermore, under this kind of loading, there are large concentrations of flexural stress at the ends of the panel, and provision must be made for them.

Third, the floor must act as a diaphragm [66, 154, 155, 156] to prevent distortion of shape of the structure in the horizontal plane. It must carry the loads from the points where the masses are situated, or where the loads are applied laterally, to the members that resist lateral deformation (either shear walls or columns), and it must do so without large distortions and without loss in strength. The reinforcement provided in the floor must be capable of carrying the moments and shears due to the forces acting in the plane of the floor as well as the forces acting perpendicularly to the plane of the floor. Consequently, the floor around openings must be reinforced in such a way as to maintain the required diaphragm action. The size of openings must be limited unless framed with adequate beams and their location must be carefully considered.

The following recommendations for the amount and arrangement of reinforcement in beams and slabs in floors of reinforced concrete structures are based on the above requirements.

Longitudinal Reinforcement in Beams and Girders

In order to ensure adequate ductility in reinforced concrete beams and girders, the amount of longitudinal reinforcement must be limited in relation to the dimensions of the beam, the quality of the concrete, and the yield stress of the reinforcement. Insofar as earthquake-resistant design is concerned, the critical sections for the longitudinal reinforcement in frames occur at the faces of the beam-column and girder-column connections and at beam-girder connections immediately adjacent to the columns. Hence, the limitations discussed here over and above those imposed by the ACI building code on longitudinal reinforcement refer only to such sections except as otherwise specified.

The amount of longitudinal reinforcement in the beams at continuous connections to columns or to supporting beams should be proportioned to satisfy the following conditions:

$$q_u - q_u' \leqq 0.25 \tag{6-1}$$

but

$$p \leqq 0.025$$

where

$q_u = p f_y / f_{cu}$ *
$q_u' = p' f_y' / f_{cu}$
$p = A_s / bd$
$p' = A_s' / bd$ (A_s' = cross-sectional area of properly tied compression reinforcement within a depth equal to $q_u d$ from the extreme fiber in compression.)

---

*The value of q_u for T-beams is based upon the flange width in accordance with the ACI code.

f_y = yield stress of the tension reinforcement

f'_y = yield stress of the compression reinforcement

f_{cu} = $0.7f'_c$ for $f'_c \leq 5,000$ psi

= $1,500$ psi + $0.4f'_c$ for $f'_c > 5,000$ psi

The minimum limit on the longitudinal reinforcement ratio for rectangular beams for both top and bottom reinforcement should be 0.005. At the columns the positive moment capacity of the girders should not be less than 75 per cent of the negative moment capacity unless an analysis by ultimate-strength procedure is made or an investigation is made of the reserve energy capacity, but in no case should the ratio be less than 40 per cent.

Since earthquake-resistant frames should be designed to withstand reversals of bending moment, even where such reversals are not indicated for the lateral earthquake forces assumed in the analysis, at least minimum reinforcement should be provided in both the top and bottom of all beams throughout their entire length.

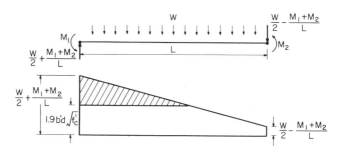

Fig. 6-1. Shear diagram for a beam at ultimate moment at both ends with the gravity load limited to the dead load plus fixed live load.

Web Reinforcement

Sufficient transverse web reinforcement must be provided in the girders of an earthquake-resistant frame to ensure that its capacity will be governed by flexure and not by shear. This can be accomplished by checking the web reinforcement designed for gravity loads to be sure it satisfies the requirements of conditions at ultimate. The "ultimate" corresponds to the development of the shears resulting from the ultimate moments at both ends of the beam, with the dead and live load on the beam.

The shear diagram at ultimate for a beam with a uniform dead load may be idealized as shown in Fig. 6-1. The end moments M_1 and M_2 are obtained from the following equations:

For sections without any longitudinal reinforcement within a depth $q_u d$ ($k_u d$, Fig. 5-11) from the extreme fiber in compression

$$M_u = A_s f_y d(1 - 0.4q_u) \qquad (6\text{-}2)$$

For sections with compression reinforcement within a depth $q_u d$ ($k_u d$, Fig. 5-12) from the extreme fiber in compression

$$M_u = (A_s f_y - A'_s f'_y)d \, [1 - 0.4(q_u - q'_u)] + A'_s f'_y(d - d') \qquad (6\text{-}3)$$

Web reinforcement should be provided according to the following expression:

$$A_v f_y \frac{d}{s} = V_u - 1.9b'd\sqrt{f_c'} \qquad (6\text{-}4)$$

where A_v is the total cross-sectional area of one vertical stirrup and f_y is the yield-point stress of the steel used in the stirrup. Bent-up bars may be considered as web reinforcement only if they are inclined in the proper direction to resist the shears corresponding to the particular conditions assumed in the evaluation of V_u; in which case the effective cross-sectional area A_v will be taken equal to the product of the cross-sectional area of the bent-up bar and the sine of the angle that the bar makes with the longitudinal axis of the beam.

Member sizes should not be reduced to the point where an excessive amount of web reinforcement would be required. Therefore to avoid undesirable congestion of the reinforcement, the shearing stress must not exceed $6\sqrt{f_c'}$.

Web reinforcement should be provided as indicated above for complete reversals of the end moments. If the cross-hatched areas on the shear diagram (Fig. 6-1) indicating the amount of shear assigned to the web reinforcement overlap, this means simply that vertical stirrups provided for one condition will help carry the shear for the other condition and not that the area of vertical web reinforcement should be doubled in this region.

The maximum spacing of the web reinforcement should be equal to one-half the effective depth of the beam. It is recommended that the amount of web reinforcement within a distance equal to four times the effective depth from the end of the beam never be less than that indicated by the following expression:

$$A_v \frac{d}{s} = 0.15A_s \ \text{ or } \ 0.15A'_s \qquad (6\text{-}5)$$

whichever is larger, but in no case should less than No. 3 stirrups be provided at the maximum allowable spacing ($d/2$) throughout the length of the beam.

The open end, if any, of the stirrup must be anchored by a bend or a hook around a longitudinal bar. Stirrups should extend over the entire height of the beam less the required clearances at the top and bottom. Recommended types of stirrups are shown in Fig. 6-2.

If the beam is to be subjected to an axial tensile force without the possibility of any aid from a monolithically cast reinforced slab, the term $V_c = 1.9b'd\sqrt{f_c'}$ in equation (6-4) should be modified as indicated in Section 5.5, equation (5-21).

Stirrup-Ties

Whenever reinforcing bars are called upon to act as compression reinforcement,

151

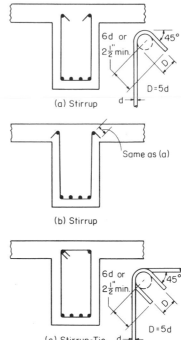

Fig. 6-2. Recommended types of stirrups depending upon location in beams.

(a) Stirrup

(b) Stirrup

(c) Stirrup-Tie

ties should be provided to restrain them from buckling after spalling of the concrete cover.

U-shaped stirrups like those shown in Fig. 6-2(a) and (b) can serve as ties for the bottom reinforcement if they are of the proper size and spacing. These types of stirrups, however, do not constitute a proper tie for the top reinforcement under certain conditions. Where either the top or bottom reinforcing bars may be called upon to act as compression reinforcement as shown by design calculations (bars within the distance $q_u d$ from the compression face), stirrup-ties of the type shown in Fig. 6-2(c) must be used. The maximum spacing should be one-half the effective depth of the beam but not greater than 16 bar diameters or 12 in. The first stirrup-tie must be located within 2 in. and the last one at a distance of at least twice the height of the beam from the column face. The remaining web reinforcement, to a distance of at least $4d$ from the face of the column, should conform to the requirements given in the preceding subsection.

Even when the top reinforcement is required only for gravity loads, it is recommended that at least two stirrup-ties be used at each end of all beams and girders framing into columns.

Arrangement of Longitudinal Reinforcement

Since the distribution of the bending moment along beams or girders framing into columns may be quite different in a severe earthquake from that under

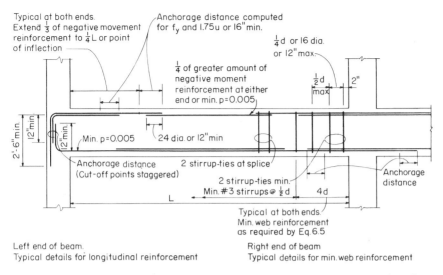

Left end of beam.
Typical details for longitudinal reinforcement

Right end of beam
Typical details for min. web reinforcement

Fig. 6-3. Typical longitudinal and web reinforcement details for girders and beams on column lines.

gravity loads, the cutoff points of the bars require special consideration. It is recommended that only straight bars be used, except that bent bars may be used in beams that do not frame into columns.

The compression reinforcement at the faces of the column should be continuous throughout the girder as indicated in Fig. 6-3. At least one-third of the tension reinforcement provided for negative moment at the support should extend beyond the extreme position of the point of inflection for any combination of loads a distance sufficient for anchorage as provided by code or as recommended in the following subsection on anchorage of longitudinal reinforcement, whichever is the greater. Under all circumstances at least one-third of the tension reinforcement should extend anchorage distance beyond a point $0.25L$ (L = clear span) from the face of the support. One-quarter of the larger amount of the tension reinforcement required at either end of the beam should be continuous throughout the top of the beam. All other negative moment reinforcement may be terminated anchorage distance beyond where needed to resist stress.

A splice in earthquake-resistant construction must continue to function while the members or joints undergo large deformations. The transfer of stress in a lapped splice is accomplished through the concrete surrounding the bars. It is thus essential that there be adequate space in the member to place concrete of good quality around the bars, and there must be assurance that the splicing concrete can continue to function in the range of large deformations. For this reason, lapped splices should not be made in regions of high tension near joints where the concrete may become cracked under large deformations associated with extremely severe earthquakes so that it could no longer transfer stress by bond. If a splice must be made in such a region, the problem should be con-

153

sidered as one of anchorage rather than splicing. That is, the transfer of stress from one bar to another should not be considered; instead the bars required to resist the tension stress should be extended far enough outside the zone of expected large deformations to develop their strength by anchorage.

Although specifications for lapped splices sometimes require a space between the bars, tests have shown that a contact splice will perform just as well. Although some of the stress transfer in a contact splice may be accomplished through lug-to-lug bearing, the stress transfer is primarily through the surrounding concrete, as in a spaced splice, and good concrete around the bars is still essential. The contact splice usually reduces the congestion and makes it somewhat easier to obtain good concrete over and around the bars.

Splices should be staggered whenever possible, but where large amounts of steel are spliced at one location, as in columns, or where splicing of bars in regions of high stresses cannot be avoided, adequate transverse reinforcement in the form of closed stirrups or ties should be provided to minimize the possibility of splitting the concrete and to maintain the integrity of the member and splice if there should be a tendency for such splitting. Even when splices are made in a region of minimum stress, at least two ties should be provided as shown in Fig. 6-3.

A welded splice reduces the need to depend on the concrete for stress transfer but may introduce discontinuities in the chemical and physical properties of the reinforcement in the weld area and impair its ductility. Welding must always be done in such a manner as not to embrittle the bar and this is not always practical under field conditions. Fillet-welded lap splices will usually require adequate transverse reinforcement as mentioned in the preceding paragraph for lapped splices in general. Butt-welded splices, however, may be treated as continuous bars.

Anchorage of Longitudinal Reinforcement

It is assumed that the longitudinal reinforcement will consist of deformed bars meeting the requirements of ASTM Designation A 305. If this is the case, hooks are not usually required. Moreover, tests have shown that hooks on deformed bars of this type function primarily as extensions of length and that little if any additional anchorage is provided as a result of the geometry of the hook itself.

In most cases, satisfactory anchorage can be provided by an extension of the bar. If there is insufficient space for a straight extension, the required anchorage length may be obtained by a hook or simply by bending the bar and extending it in another direction. The radius of bend should not be less than four bar diameters, and preferably should be six diameters. If a large number of bars are bent for anchorage, if very large bars are used, or if the radius of bend is small, consideration should be given to the radial compressive forces developed on the inside of the bend.

Large areas of reinforcement should not be terminated at one section. Bars should not be cut off at points in the span where anchorage would be required in a region of tension under earthquake effects. If cutoffs of this kind cannot be avoided, especially in regions of moderate to high shear, additional transverse reinforcement should be provided because of the discontinuity.

It is necessary in earthquake-resistant construction to maintain continuity through a relatively large range of deformation. Therefore, it is recommended that anchorage length should be that required to develop the yield strength of the reinforcement by bond at 1.75 times the bond stress permitted by code.

TABLE 6-1   Anchorage Lengths for Bottom Bars*

Bar size	Allowable bond stress, u	Concrete strength, psi								
		3,000			3,750			5,000		
		Reinforcement yield strength, ksi								
		40	50	60	40	50	60	40	50	60
		Inches †								
3	$5.50\sqrt{f_c'}$	7	9	11	6	8	10	6	7	8
4		10	12	14	8	11	13	7	9	11
5		12	15	18	11	13	16	9	11	14
6		14	18	21	13	16	19	11	14	17
7		17	21	25	15	19	22	13	16	19
8		19	24	29	17	21	25	15	18	22
9	$4.75\sqrt{f_c'}$	25	31	37	22	28	33	19	24	29
10	$3.75\sqrt{f_c'}$	35	44	53	32	39	47	27	34	41
11	$2.85\sqrt{f_c'}$	52	65	78	46	58	69	40	50	60

*Anchorage lengths $= \dfrac{f_y d}{4 \times 1.75u}$

†Anchorage length for top bars is 1.43 times the tabulated lengths.

Table 6-1 shows anchorage lengths based upon 1.75 times the allowable bond stresses being considered for a pending revision of the ACI code (318-56). Under no circumstances should anchorage length of longitudinal bars in beams or girders be less than 16 in.

Arrangement of Reinforcement in Floor Slabs

Reinforcement designed for gravity loads in the slabs of beam-and-slab-type floors spanning in one or more than one direction is usually adequate to ensure good performance of the slabs both as a flexural member and as a horizontal diaphragm. In view of the anticipated diaphragm action, additional reinforcement should be provided at the sides and corners of openings in slabs as shown in Fig. 6-4. If the amount of reinforcement in either direction interrupted by the opening is greater than that provided by the trimmer bars, then extra bars should be provided to equal the area of the interrupted bars, unless the opening is framed by beams. All such bars should extend beyond the sides of the opening

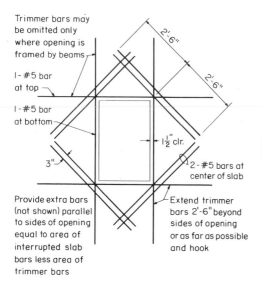

Trimmer bars may be omitted only where opening is framed by beams

1-#5 bar at top

1-#5 bar at bottom

2'-6"

2'-6"

$1\frac{1}{2}$" clr.

3"

2-#5 bars at center of slab

Fig. 6-4. Supplementary reinforcement to be provided at small unframed openings in floor slabs.

Provide extra bars (not shown) parallel to sides of opening equal to area of interrupted slab bars less area of trimmer bars

Extend trimmer bars 2'-6" beyond sides of opening or as far as possible and hook

a sufficient distance to pick up the stress in the discontinuous bars depending upon the size and location of the opening, but not less than 30 bar diameters or 16 in.

Research is currently under way to determine the influence of various parameters on the behavior of flat-plate construction. The transfer of moments and shears between the slab and the columns is being studied. Until results of this research become available, the amount of reinforcement considered as "framing into the column" should be limited to those bars within the width of the column or capital, if there is one, plus a distance equal to twice the thickness of the slab (or drop panel) on each side. Overcrowding of the reinforcement at columns must be avoided and careful consideration must be given to providing adequate ductility.

6.5 Arrangement of Reinforcement for Columns

Column Reinforcement

The proportioning of columns and their reinforcement in earthquake-resistant frames should receive very careful consideration. Full confinement of the concrete in the columns at beam-column connections may be necessary under some circumstances to ensure the required ductility. The following recommendations for transverse reinforcement are based on tests of fully confined concrete and therefore are quite conservative for many cases where partial confinement may be adequate. When test data on partially confined concrete become available, it is anticipated that the requirements given here can be reduced.

It is recommended that the vertical reinforcement ratio in columns be limited to a minimum of 1.0 per cent and a maximum of 6.0 per cent unless a careful study is made based on the information presented in Chapter 5 to determine that each column has the required strength and ductility for the type of loading anticipated.

Special transverse reinforcement is not required if

$$\frac{P}{A_g} \leq 0.12 f'_c$$

where

P = maximum axial compressive load expected to act on the member during an earthquake

A_g = overall area of cross-section

f'_c = compressive strength based on 6x12-in. cylinders

If the condition stated above is not satisfied, the concrete in the column must be confined by transverse reinforcement over a length equal to the overall depth h (h being the longer dimension in the case of rectangular columns) or the diameter of a round column, but not less than 18 in. from the face of the

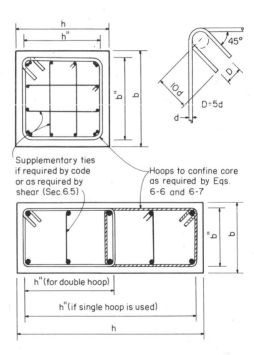

Fig. 6-5. Typical arrangements of transverse reinforcement in square and rectangular columns in which confinement of core is required to increase strength or ductility.

connection. Ideally, the amount of transverse reinforcement could be reduced in proportion to the distance from the face of the connection, but generally it is not feasible to do so from the steel setting standpoint. It is more practical to reduce the amount of transverse reinforcement by one-third of that required at the face of the connection in each of two stages, as shown in Fig. 6-6. The

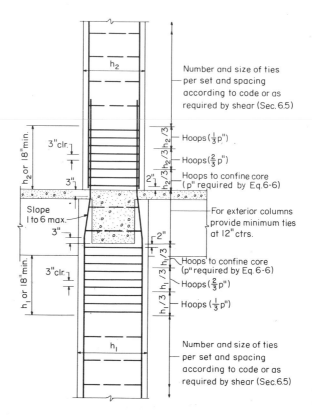

Number and size of ties per set and spacing according to code or as required by shear (Sec. 6.5)

h_2

3" clr.

h_2 or 18" min.

3"

Hoops ($\frac{1}{3}$ p")

Hoops ($\frac{2}{3}$ p")

Hoops to confine core (p" required by Eq. 6-6)

$h_2/3$ | $h_2/3$ | $h_2/3$

Slope 1 to 6 max.

3"

For exterior columns provide minimum ties at 12" ctrs.

2"

2"

$h_1/3$

Hoops to confine core (p" required by Eq. 6-6)

$h_1/3$

Hoops ($\frac{2}{3}$ p")

3" clr.

h_1 or 18" min.

$h_1/3$

Hoops ($\frac{1}{3}$ p")

h_1

Number and size of ties per set and spacing according to code or as required by shear (Sec. 6.5)

Fig. 6-6. Elevation of a column showing transverse reinforcement at a joint when confinement of the concrete is required.

transverse reinforcement can consist of helical reinforcement (spiral) in round columns or individual ties. However, in the latter case each of the ties must form a complete loop and must have adequate anchorage as indicated in Fig. 6-5. In order to differentiate them from ordinary ties that are not intended to confine the concrete, as discussed in Section 5.1 under the subheading Confined Concrete, ties utilized to confine the concrete are referred to as hoops.

If transverse reinforcement is required to confine the concrete, either circular spiral reinforcement or rectangular hoops may be used. For a circular spiral of diameter $\bar{D}$, the volumetric ratio of the transverse reinforcement provided at the section where maximum ductility and hence confinement is required (namely, at the extreme top and bottom of columns) shall be not less than indicated below, *but not less than 0.008 for cold-drawn wire, 0.010 for hard-grade bars, or 0.012 for intermediate-grade bars.*

$$p'' = 0.45(\frac{A_g}{A_c} - 1)\frac{f'_c}{f''_y} \qquad (6\text{-}6)$$

It should be noted that the above requirement to provide adequate ductility is the same as the requirements for spiral reinforcement in the ACI code.

For a rectangular or square column of gross area A_g, the permissible maximum length h'' of the longer side of any rectangular hoop is related to the diameter $\bar{D}$ of a circular spiral, having the same core area A_c in a circular column of the same gross area A_g, by the following equation (which takes account of the reduced efficiency of the rectangular hoop compared with a circular spiral):

$$\frac{h''}{\bar{D}} = \frac{1}{2} \frac{A''_{sh}}{\frac{1}{4} p'' \bar{D} a} \frac{f''_{yh}}{f''_y}$$

or

$$h'' = \frac{2 A''_{sh} f''_{yh}}{p'' a f''_y} \tag{6-7}$$

where

a = center-to-center spacing of hoops

p'' is given by equation (6-6) but is not less than 0.008 for cold-drawn wire, 0.010 for hard-grade bars, or 0.012 for intermediate-grade bars

A''_{sh} = area of cross-section of transverse hoop

f''_y = useful limit stress of transverse spiral reinforcement, to be taken as the yield stress for intermediate and hard-grade steel and as the stress corresponding to a strain of 0.005 for cold-drawn wire or high-strength steel not having a definite yield stress

f''_{yh} = useful limit stress of hoop reinforcement defined in same way as f''_y

TABLE 6-2 Longer Dimension (h'') of Rectangular Hoops*

p''	0.004	0.005	0.006	0.008	0.010	0.012	0.016	0.020	0.024	0.032
Bar size					h'', in.					
#3	18	15	12	9	7	6				
#4	33	27	22	17	13	11	8	7	6	
#5	52	41	34	26	21	17	13	10	9	6
#6	73	59	49	37	29	24	18	15	12	9
#7			67	50	40	33	25	20	17	13
#8				66	53	44	33	26	22	16

*a = 3 in.

Table 6-2 gives maximum lengths h'' of rectangular hoops as determined by equation (6-7) for a center-to-center spacing of $a = 3$ in., various percentages p'' [from equation (6-6)] and sizes of transverse reinforcement. For other values of a, the length h'' can be obtained by direct ratio.

Where the length h'' is less than the length of a side of a rectangular or square column, a sufficient number of overlapping hoops must be provided in order to avoid exceeding the limiting value of h'' given by equation (6-7). The clear spacing between spirals or hoops should not exceed 3 in. (maximum $a = 4$ in. center to center) nor be less than $1\frac{3}{8}$ in. (minimum $a = 1\frac{3}{4}$ in. center to center) or $1\frac{1}{2}$ times the maximum size of coarse aggregate used. The minimum diameter of transverse hoops of intermediate or hard-grade steel should be $\frac{3}{8}$ in.

Supplementary ties in addition to the perimeter hoops are shown in Fig. 6-5 because under extreme circumstances they may be required for shear or by local code requirements. However, supplementary ties are not considered necessary to prevent buckling because of the close spacing of the hoops, which are designed to be equivalent to a spiral.

The transverse reinforcement in the column should be checked to see if it is adequate to resist the shear that may be imposed on the column during an earthquake. This can be done by satisfying the following expression:

$$A_v f_y \frac{d}{s} = V_u - V_c \tag{6-8}$$

where

$A_v =$ [for circular transverse reinforcement (spiral)] two-thirds of the cross-sectional area

$\quad\ =$ [for rectilinear transverse reinforcement] the projection of the cross-sectional area on a plane perpendicular to the direction in which the shearing force acts

The transverse reinforcement that can be considered effective to resist shear must extend continuously over the depth of the section from one extreme layer of vertical reinforcement to the other in the direction being considered; hoops that overlap and enclose in common no less than two column bars to which the hoops are securely wired, however, may be considered effective as a single stirrup in the longitudinal direction and as a double stirrup in the transverse direction, as shown in Fig. 6-5.

$f_y =$ yield stress of the transverse reinforcement

$d =$ effective depth of the section (as in a beam section)

$s =$ spacing of the transverse reinforcement along the height of the column

$$V_u = \frac{M_c^B + \frac{1}{2}M_b}{H'} \quad \text{but not more than} \quad \frac{M_c^B + M_c^T}{H'}$$

$$V_c = 1.9 b' d \sqrt{f_c'} \left(1 + \frac{P}{16 A_{tr} \sqrt{f_c'}} \right) \quad \text{for rectangular sections}$$

$$\quad\ = 1.9 A_c \sqrt{f_c'} \left(1 + \frac{P}{16 A_{tr} \sqrt{f_c'}} \right) \quad \text{for nonrectangular sections}$$

$P =$ minimum axial compressive load expected on the column during an earthquake

$A_{tr} =$ uncracked transformed area of total column cross-section

$A_c =$ area of concrete enclosed by well-anchored ties, hoops or spiral

M_c^B = moment capacity of the column at the bottom connection

M_c^T = moment capacity of the column at the top connection

$\frac{1}{2}M_b$ = maximum sum of the moment capacities of the beams framing into the top connection. This is the sum of the "negative" moment capacity of one beam and the "positive" moment capacity of the other at the faces of the column. The factor $\frac{1}{2}$ should be dropped if only one column frames into the top connection

H' = clear height of column

If the axial load on the column is tensile, the term V_c should be based on equation (5-21) in Chapter 5.

Details of Transverse Reinforcement in Columns

When design conditions do not call for confined concrete, the vertical reinforcement should be tied as specified by the prevailing building code. It is recommended, however, that the concrete in all columns be confined by hoops or spirals over the length of column within 6 in. of the beam-column connections, as indicated in Fig. 6-7.

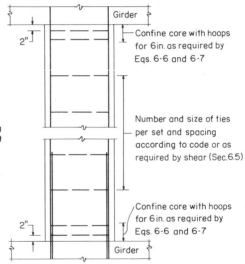

Fig. 6-7. Elevation of a column showing transverse reinforcement when confinement of the concrete is not required.

Girder

Confine core with hoops for 6in. as required by Eqs. 6-6 and 6-7

2"

Number and size of ties per set and spacing according to code or as required by shear (Sec.6.5)

Confine core with hoops for 6in. as required by Eqs. 6-6 and 6-7

2"

Girder

When a continuous spiral is provided to confine the concrete at a beam-column connection, it should be anchored by two complete turns of the spiral rod or wire at each end of the spiral. Individual rectangular hoops should be anchored by bending the ends of the hoop around a vertical reinforcing bar and extending them at least 10 diameters. Details of such reinforcement are shown in Fig. 6-5. Provided good welding practice is followed, rectangular hoops may be shop welded when approved by the structural engineer. Vertical spacers for all spirals should be provided in accordance with the prevailing code, and each hoop or tie must be securely wired to the vertical reinforcement in the proper position and to prevent subsequent displacement.

Splicing of Vertical Reinforcement in Columns

Since the columns are expected to resist large bending moments and may be subjected to axial tension in some cases, splices in column reinforcement are much more critical in earthquake-resistant structures than in ordinary construction. The common procedure of splicing column reinforcement is to extend the bars of the lower column into the upper column or, where there is an unusual change in the size of columns, dowel bars may be used. Since it is only these bars that are continuous at the face of the joints, they are the bars that will resist the stresses induced by bending. Bars should be anchored in the upper column, or in both the upper and lower columns if dowels are used, so that the stress in the bars, which may reach the yield stress, can be developed at the face of the joint. This can be done by extending these bars into the upper column for at least 30 bar diameters, but not less than the distance required to develop the yield stress in the bar by anchorage at 1.75 times the normal bond stress

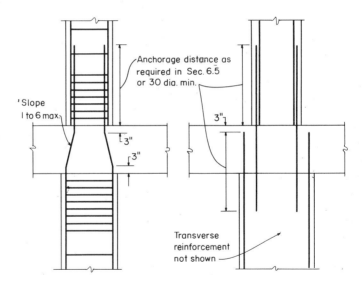

Fig. 6-8. Elevation of a column showing anchorage requirements for vertical reinforcement and dowels.

permitted by the ACI code (see Table 6-1). Continuity may be effected by welding when approved by the structural engineer and providing not more than every fourth bar is welded at any level and the vertical distance between welds of adjacent bars is not less than 12 in.

It is recommended that bars extending into the upper or lower column not be bent at the face of the connection, but at a point at least 3 in. inside the face of the connection as shown in Fig. 6-8.

6.6 Recommended Arrangement of Reinforcement in Walls

It can be said categorically that no wall in an earthquake-resistant building is an unimportant wall whether it is classified as a curtain wall or a shear wall. Reinforcing details in every wall must receive careful attention, not only to ensure against unsightly cracking but also to make optimum use of the inherent energy-absorbing capacity of the wall even though its contribution to the lateral strength of the building is ignored in the computations. Of course the contribution of walls to the stiffness of a structure should be taken into consideration in the determination of shears.

Minimum Wall Reinforcement

Minimum wall reinforcement should be provided in accordance with the requirements of the ACI building code. The following arrangements of wall reinforcement are offered as a guide.

TABLE 6-3 · Minimum Wall Reinforcement Requirements

Wall thickness, in.	Horizontal reinforcement spacing, in.		Vertical reinforcement spacing, in.	
	#3	#4	#3	#4
6	7	13	12	16
8	5	10	9	16
10*	9	16	12	16
12*	7	13	12	16

*Spacing in each of two curtains.

Of course every wall must be properly designed for seismic forces or shears normal and parallel to its plane.

Welded wire fabric may be used for wall reinforcement in accordance with the requirements of the ACI building code.

Wall Reinforcement at Corners and Junctures

It is particularly important that the corners and junctures of intersecting walls be adequately tied together to ensure unity of action.

Recommended reinforcing details are shown in Fig. 6-9. It should be noted

163

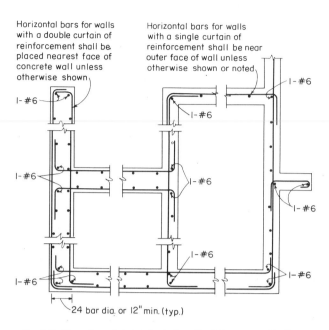

Horizontal bars for walls
with a double curtain of
reinforcement shall be
placed nearest face of
concrete wall unless
otherwise shown

Horizontal bars for walls
with a single curtain of
reinforcement shall be near
outer face of wall unless
otherwise shown or noted

1-#6

1-#6

1-#6

1-#6

1-#6

1-#6

1-#6

1-#6

1-#6

1-#6

24 bar dia. or 12" min. (typ.)

Fig. 6-9. Plan view showing typical wall reinforcement details.

that all horizontal bars extend nearly to the far face of the joining wall when they are bent in a right angle around a No. 6 vertical bar and extended 24 bar diameters but not less than 12 in.

Wall Reinforcement Around Openings

Additional reinforcement should be provided at the sides and corners of openings in walls similar to that in floors, as shown in Fig. 6-10. If the area of reinforcement in either direction interrupted by the opening is greater than the area of the trimmer bars, additional bars should be provided to equal the area of the interrupted bars and should be extended beyond the sides of the opening not less than 30 diameters or 16 in.

Splices for Wall Reinforcement

Where necessary to splice wall bars, they should be lap spliced a minimum of 24 diameters or 12 in. Splices in adjacent bars should be staggered a minimum of 18 in. Recommended details for splicing wall reinforcement at vertical and horizontal construction joints are shown in Fig. 6-11.

Shear Wall Reinforcement

The minimum amount of reinforcement in walls designed to resist shearing forces caused by earthquake motions should be 0.25 per cent of the wall cross-section in both the vertical and horizontal directions and the spacing of the bars should not exceed that given in Table 6-3. If welded wire fabric or other high-strength reinforcement is used, this minimum may be reduced by 25 per cent.

The maximum design bending moment and shear, which occurs at the bottom of the wall unless large openings exist in the lower stories, should be increased

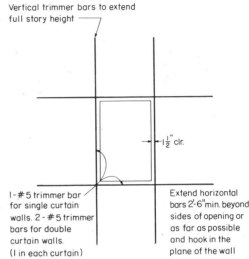

Vertical trimmer bars to extend full story height

$1\frac{1}{2}$" clr.

Fig. 6-10. Supplementary reinforcement to be provided at wall openings.

1-#5 trimmer bar for single curtain walls. 2 - #5 trimmer bars for double curtain walls. (1 in each curtain)

Extend horizontal bars 2'-6"min. beyond sides of opening or as far as possible and hook in the plane of the wall

Note: Provide extra bars (not shown) parallel to sides of opening equal to area of interrupted wall reinforcement less area of trimmer bars

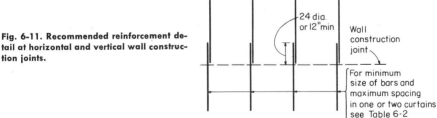

Fig. 6-11. Recommended reinforcement detail at horizontal and vertical wall construction joints.

24 dia. or 12"min.

Wall construction joint

For minimum size of bars and maximum spacing in one or two curtains see Table 6-2

by a factor of 1.5 and compared with the resistance at cracking of the uncracked wall estimated from the following expressions:

$$M_{cr} = 6\frac{I}{c}\sqrt{f'_c} \qquad (6\text{-}9)$$

$$V_c = 4bL\sqrt{f'_c} \qquad (6\text{-}10)$$

165

where

M_{cr} = flexural cracking moment
I = moment of inertia of shear wall
c = distance from neutral axis to extreme fiber in tension
V_c = cracking shear
b = minimum width of wall
L = length of wall in the horizontal direction (subtract length of openings, if any)

If the cracking resistance of the wall is not sufficient to counteract $1\frac{1}{2}$ times the design moment and/or shear, special reinforcement should be provided in the wall (not in addition to the minimum) such that the following expressions yield the desired shear and moment.

where

$$M = \tfrac{1}{3} A_s f_y L \qquad (6\text{-}11)$$

A_s = total cross-sectional area of the vertical reinforcement distributed over the length of the wall

and

where

$$V = 1.9bL\sqrt{f_c'} + A_s f_y \qquad (6\text{-}12)$$

A_s = total cross-sectional area of the horizontal reinforcement distributed uniformly over a height of the wall equal to half its length (length measured in the horizontal direction)

It should be pointed out that the amounts of reinforcement indicated above may be reduced in accordance with the values of design moments and shears along the height of the wall to the minimum of 0.25 per cent. The vertical reinforcement may be distributed nonuniformly along the length of the wall in accordance with the principles discussed in Chapter 5, provided the reinforcement ratio is not less than 0.25 in any part of the wall.

6.7 Expansion and Construction Joints

Construction joints are stopping places in the process of placing concrete and are required because it is impractical to place concrete in a continuous operation except for very small structures or special types of structures built with slipforms. Construction joints should not be confused with expansion joints, which, if considered necessary to allow for free movement of parts of a building because of size or shape, should be designed for complete separation in accordance with Section 4.6. On the other hand, construction joints should be so designed and built as to prevent movement and to be essentially as strong as where there is no joint.

The most desirable locations for construction joints should be determined in the design, and the joints should be detailed by the engineer and shown on the drawings. If a joint is to be exposed in the finished structure, it is assumed that its location will be agreed upon by the architect and the engineer.

Generally, it is impracticable to place concrete to a height greater than one story; this fact should be recognized when locating horizontal construction joints. For buildings in which the concrete walls are to be exposed, joints may be located at bands of ornamentation, ledges, rustications, or other architectural details. It is generally convenient to locate horizontal joints at the floor line or in line with window sills or heads, or both.

Vertical construction joints are required in buildings of large area and sometimes must be provided even in relatively small buildings because of an emergency work stoppage.

When a substantial time elapses before placing new concrete adjacent to a construction joint, considerable shrinkage of the concrete will have taken place, thereby minimizing the tendency of walls or floors to crack. For construction joints to be effective in this manner, however, they should be spaced at not more than 60 ft., and preferably not more than 40 ft. apart. It is best to avoid locating construction joints at or near the corners of the building, since their presence may make it difficult to tie the corners together securely.

Continuous or intermittent keyways in either vertical or horizontal construction joints are not recommended. They contribute little resistance to faulting or working of the joints, they may contribute to spalling, and they interfere with getting the best quality of concrete and maximum strength at the joint. When the concreting procedures described in Section 8.3 are followed, the bond between old and new concrete can be made good enough to provide tensile and shear resistance equivalent to that of concrete placed monolithically.

CHAPTER 7

Design of a 24-Story Building

7.1 Introduction

The preceding chapters have discussed earthquake motions, dynamic response of structures, the history of seismic design, and various codes that have evolved. This chapter presents an example of a 24-story office building designed in accordance with the *Recommended Lateral Force Requirements* of the Structural Engineers Association of California (reprinted in Appendix C)*, the 1958 Uniform Building Code [82] prepared by the International Conference of Building Officials, for wind forces and live-load reductions, and the ACI Building Code Requirements for Reinforced Concrete [76]. In the design the lateral forces are assumed to be resisted by the frame alone.

Figs. 7-1 and 7-2 show schematic elevations and a plan of the structural frame. In plan the building is 100x175 ft. center to center of exterior columns and rises 310 ft. above ground level. The columns are spaced 20x25 ft. on centers. All story heights are 12 ft. except the first story and basement, which are 15 ft., the two top stories, which are 14 ft., and the penthouse, which is 15 ft. To achieve greater re-use of the forms, and to simplify construction, the size of the girders and columns has been changed only at every third story. The spacing of the columns and the live load assumed is greater than that normally used in apartment buildings and somewhat larger than that required in many major

---

*The earthquake design requirements of the 1961 Uniform Building Code are essentially the same as the SEAOC requirements.

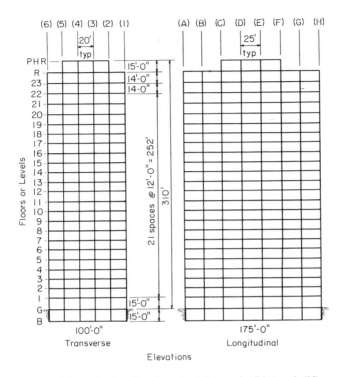

Fig. 7-1. Schematic elevation of structural frame of a 24-story building.

cities for office buildings today. The trend in office buildings because of the demand of owners, however, is toward greater column-free areas. For this reason, the spacing is more liberal than might generally be used.

The vertical and wind loadings and the strength of materials used in the design are as follows:

DESIGN LOADING

Office floors	80 psf
Partitions	20 psf
Mechanical floors	150 psf (23rd and 24th floors)
Roof	20 psf
Wind	15 psf (0 to 60 ft. above grade)
	20 psf (more than 60 ft. above grade)

MATERIALS

Concrete (150 lb. per cubic foot) = 5,000 psi

Reinforcing steel: intermediate grade (f_y = 40,000 psi) for all except vertical column bars; hard grade (f_y = 50,000 psi) for column bars

The selection of a uniform concrete strength for the entire building is purely a device for the purposes of this example and does not necessarily represent current or desirable practice. Usually a higher concrete strength is specified for

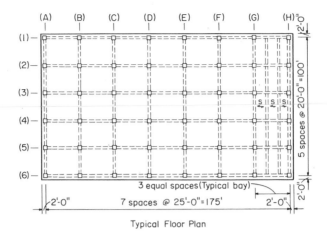

Typical Floor Plan

Fig. 7-2. Schematic plan of structural frame of a 24-story building.

columns than for the floor system in order to reduce their size. Concrete strength lower than 5,000 psi would be more appropriate for the floor system. The use of a lower-strength concrete in the floor system and also in the columns where the size of the columns is not a major factor in the architectural requirements does not significantly reduce the energy-absorbing capacity of the structure. Tests [147] show that there is no reduction in column strength when the strength of concrete in the columns does not exceed 1.4 or 1.5 times the strength of the concrete in the floor for exterior and interior columns, respectively. It was deemed desirable to use the same strength and hence the same modulus of elasticity for all the members in the frame to eliminate a variable that might tend to obscure the description of the design procedure.

Because a multistory building is an indeterminate structure, the sizes of the members cannot be determined directly on the basis of allowable stresses. It is usually necessary to select trial sizes, analyze the building for moments, shears, and thrusts, and then compare the stresses produced with the allowable stresses. Consequently, the complete design involves repeated trials until a satisfactory agreement between computed and allowable stresses is obtained. Since in most cases the same procedure is used for the various trials, with perhaps simplifying assumptions used in the earlier stages, only the computations for one trial will be shown.

7.2 Seismic Shear and Overturning Moment

Although the determination of the seismic shears and overturning moments involves simple steps, because of the number of operations required it will be found that a tabular organization of the work as indicated in Table 7-1 is often

TABLE 7-1   Earthquake Lateral Forces and Overturning Moment

In accordance with SEAOC recommendations

Period $T = 0.1\,N = (0.1)\,(25) = 2.5$ sec.   Coef., base shear $C = \dfrac{0.05}{\sqrt[3]{T}} = \dfrac{0.05}{\sqrt[3]{2.5}} = 0.0369$

Force factor $K = 0.67$ Coef., base moment $J = \dfrac{0.5}{\sqrt[3]{T^2}} = \dfrac{0.5}{\sqrt[3]{2.5^2}} = 0.272 < 0.33$ min.

Floor or story	Height to level z	Weight at level z		Lateral force at level z	Story shear	Story ht.	Cantilever moment		Overturning moment	Overturning moment / Cantilever moment
	h_z^* ft.	w_z kips	$w_z h_z$ ft.kips	$F_z = \dfrac{V}{\Sigma wh} w_z h_z$ kips	$\Sigma F_z = V_z$ kips	H_s ft.	$\Sigma H_s V_z$ ft.kips	$H - h_z^\dagger$	$M_z = \dfrac{H - h_z}{H} M$ ft. kips	$\dfrac{H - h_z}{H}$
(1)	(2)	(3)	(4)	(5)	(6)	(7)	(8)	(9)	(10)	(11)
P.H.R.	310	492	153,000	25.9	26	15				
Roof	295	3,083	909,000	153.9	180	14	390	15	390	1.00
23	281	4,175	1,173,000	198.6	378	14	2,910	29	2,910	1.00
22	267	2,973	794,000	134.4	513	12	8,200	43	8,200	1.00
21	255	2,957	754,000	127.6	640	12	14,400	55	14,400	1.00
20	243	2,974	723,000	122.4	763	12	22,000	67	22,000	1.00
19	231	3,170	732,000	123.9	887	12	31,200	79	31,200	1.00
18	219	3,170	694,000	117.5	1000	12	41,800	91	41,300	0.99
17	207	3,215	666,000	112.7	1120	12	53,800	103	46,800	0.87
16	195	3,259	636,000	107.7	1220	12	67,300	115	52,200	0.78
15	183	3,259	596,000	100.9	1330	12	81,900	127	57,600	0.70
14	171	3,299	564,000	95.5	1420	12	97,900	139	63,100	0.65
13	159	3,436	546,000	92.4	1510	12	115,000	151	68,500	0.60
12	147	3,436	505,000	85.5	1600	12	133,000	163	74,000	0.56
11	135	3,465	468,000	79.2	1680	12	152,000	175	79,400	0.52
10	123	3,493	430,000	72.7	1750	12	172,000	187	84,900	0.49
9	111	3,493	388,000	65.6	1820	12	193,000	199	90,300	0.47
8	99	3,555	352,000	59.6	1880	12	215,000	211	95,800	0.45
7	87	3,820	332,000	56.2	1930	12	238,000	223	101,000	0.43
6	75	3,820	287,000	48.5	1980	12	261,000	235	107,000	0.41
5	63	3,848	242,000	41.0	2020	12	285,000	247	112,000	0.40
4	51	4,097	209,000	35.4	2060	12	309,000	259	118,000	0.38
3	39	4,097	160,000	27.1	2080	12	334,000	271	123,000	0.37
2	27	4,368	118,000	20.0	2100	12	359,000	283	128,000	0.36
1	15	4,635	70,000	11.8	2120	15	384,000	295	134,000	0.35
G					2120	15	416,000	310	141,000	0.34
B							447,000	325	148,000	0.33
Σ		85,589	12,501,000							

Base shear $V = KCW = (0.67)(0.0369)(85,589) = 2,120$ kips

Lateral force at any floor $F_z = \dfrac{V}{\Sigma wh} w_z h_z = \dfrac{2,120}{12,501,000} w_z h_z$

Overturning moment at base of structure $M = J\Sigma F_z h_z = (0.33)(447,000) = 148,000$ ft.kips

Overturning moment at any story, use the smaller of

$$M_z = \frac{H - h_z}{H} M = \frac{H - h_z}{325}\,(148,000) \text{ or } M_z = \Sigma H_s V_z \text{ [From col. (8)]}$$

*h_z measured from grade.   †h_z and H measured from basement level.

desirable. For the sake of completeness, some of the formulas contained in the SEAOC recommendations are restated at the top of the table. The computations involved by these formulas are obvious so no explanation is necessary. The coefficient $K = 0.67$ is selected from Table 23-C of the SEAOC code because a ductile reinforced concrete frame is considered to provide all the resistance to the seismic forces. If shear walls had been provided to help resist the seismic forces and the frame could resist 25 per cent or more of the specified lateral forces, the value of $K = 0.8$ would have been used.

After the height to each floor level has been established and tabulated in col. (2), the next step is to determine the weight at each floor level.

Normally, the height of the building H and the heights to the various levels should be measured from the base of the frame. However, in this example, it was found that measuring h_z from the grade gave slightly larger story shears. Consequently, because of this and the rigidity of the exterior basement walls, it is assumed that the columns are fixed against translation at the ground floor but only restrained against rotation; therefore, h_z was measured from grade. In the computation of w_z, not only the total dead load at each floor must be included and all walls and partitions (usually calculated between midheights of stories), but also any permanent live load attached to the building, such as mechanical equipment. These values are tabulated in col. (3). Col. (4) represents the product of cols. (2) and (3) for each floor. After this step, the base shear V and the numerical coefficient for determining F_z is computed as shown in the lower portion of the table. In col. (5) the lateral seismic force acting on each floor is computed as the product of the values in col. (4) and the previously computed coefficient. The story shear V_z shown in col. (6) is the summation of the values in col. (5). These values will be used in subsequent tables to determine the shear and bending moments acting on the individual columns.

For ease in computing the cantilever moment produced by the lateral forces at any elevation, the height of each story is tabulated in col. (7). In col. (8), the cantilever moment at an elevation is computed by adding the product of the story shear and the corresponding story height to the moment at the floor above. Thus the moment at the 15th floor is

$$M = 67,300 + 1,220 \times 12 = 81,900 \text{ ft.kips}$$

The moment at the basement level, 447,000 ft.kips, equals the $\sum F_z h_z (\sum F_x h_x$ of the SEAOC code). From this, the overturning moment at the base of the structure is obtained as the product of J times the cantilever moment. The values of $H - h_z$ are tabulated in col. (9). For the determination of overturning moment, H and h_z are measured from the basement level. The overturning moment at any elevation computed according to the SEAOC code is tabulated in col. (10). In this example, the overturning moments above the 18th floor, as computed by the formula given in the heading of col. (10), are greater than the cantilever moments. Consequently, in this range, the cantilever moments are used.

For the computation of axial loads due to overturning moment, it will be helpful to use the ratio of the overturning moment to the cantilever moment as discussed further in Section 7.4. Values of this ratio are tabulated in col. (11) of Table 7-1.

If the building is not symmetrical, it is desirable to extend Table 7-1 to include computations involving horizontal torsional moments. Two columns could be added in which the horizontal distances between the center of mass of a given story and a reference plane, preferably near the center of rigidity of the total structure, would be tabulated. The torsional moment above the reference plane can then be obtained as the summation of the product of the horizontal distances and the lateral forces.

7.3 Frame Analysis

It is not the purpose of this example to demonstrate frame analysis; it is assumed that the reader is well versed in such procedures. The building used in this example is quite symmetrical and lends itself well to an approximate method of analysis, except for the lower stories where the effect of the ground floor resistance against translation requires a more precise analysis.

In the previous section, the total seismic force acting at each floor level was determined. The next step is to determine by elastic analysis the proportion of shear carried by each column. Because the selected building is quite regular, the method of analysis outlined in Chapter 4 or the joint coefficient method outlined in reference 83 can be used. For the purpose of consistency, the procedure outlined in Chapter 4 will be used here, but a more irregular frame may require a more precise method. Since the procedure is the same for the transverse and longitudinal directions, the calculations for the purpose of illustration will be limited to the transverse direction.

The first step in the analysis is determination of the relative stiffnesses of the members. For this purpose, with the size of the columns and girders already established from a previous trial analysis, the stiffnesses of the members, assuming that the far end of each member is fixed, are first tabulated in cols. (3) to (6) of Table 7-2A. The stiffness of each girder includes 50 per cent of the stiffness of each of the beams immediately adjacent to the girder. The effect of the flanges of the T-sections are also taken into account, which can be accomplished readily as shown in reference 83. Selection of the effective flange width may be based on the ACI code recommendations. For computing deflection and rotation absolute values are needed, but since the term $4E_c$ is common to all the relative stiffnesses, needless computations can be avoided by using the value of $K_c/4E_c$ = I_c/H_s rather than K_c, and $K_g/4E_c = I_g/L$ instead of K_g. If the modulus of elasticity of the columns E_c is not the same as the modulus of elasticity of the girders E_g, the expression $K_g/4E_c = (I_g/L)(E_g/E_c)$ should be used instead of K_g. For ready identification in the table, the stiffnesses of the columns and the

TABLE 7-2A Exterior Frame—Computation of Relative Stiffness of Columns

(1) Floor	(2) Story	(3) Ext. col. $K_c/4E_c = I_c/H_s$	(4) Ext. girder $K_g/4E_c = (I_o/L)\frac{E_c}{E_c}$	(5) Int. col. $K_c/4E_c = I_c/H_s$	(6) Int. girder $K_g/4E_c = (I_o/L)\frac{E_c}{E_c}$	Exterior column (7a) $\Sigma K_j/4E_c$ or $\Sigma K'_j/4E_c$	(8a) Top $K_c/\Sigma K_j$	(9a) Bottom $K'_c/\Sigma K'_j$	(10a) $\frac{\lambda}{\lambda_{int}} \cong 1-\left(\frac{K_c}{\Sigma K_j}+\frac{K'_c}{\Sigma K'_j}\right)$	(11a) $\lambda = (10a)\times\frac{12E_c}{H_s^2}$	Interior column (7b) ΣK_j or $\Sigma K'_j$	(8b) Top $K_c/\Sigma K_j$	(9b) Bottom $K'_c/\Sigma K'_j$	(10b) $\frac{\lambda}{\lambda_{int}} \cong 1-\left(\frac{K_c}{\Sigma K_j}+\frac{K'_c}{\Sigma K'_j}\right)$	(11b) $\lambda = (10b)\times(5)\,\frac{12E_c}{H_s^2}$
Rf.	24	52	81	52	81	133	0.391	0.216	0.393	20	214	0.243	0.138	0.619	32
23	23	52	137	52	137	241	0.216	0.208	0.576	30	378	0.138	0.134	0.728	38
22	22	61	137	61	137	250					387				
4	5	773	407	773	407	1,953	0.396	0.396	0.208	161	2,360	0.328	0.328	0.344	266
3	4	773	407	773	407	1,953	0.396	0.355	0.249	192	2,360	0.328	0.296	0.376	291
2	3	773	433	773	433	2,178	0.446	0.446	0.108	105	2,611	0.372	0.372	0.256	249
1	2	972	433	972	433	2,180	0.356	0.386	0.258	200	2,613	0.297	0.315	0.388	301
G	1	775	455	775	455	2,005					2,460				
	B	775		775											

girders are staggered. Thus the stiffness of the first-floor girders at a connection, $K_g/4E_c = 433$, is shown on the floor line while that of the first-story column, $K_c/4E_c = 775$, is shown on the story line. The summation of stiffnesses about a joint is next computed and tabulated in col. (7a). For the joint at the top of the exterior column at the first floor, the summation designated in equation (4-3) as $\sum K_j$ is

$$\frac{\sum K_j}{4E_c} = 433 + 972 + 775 = 2{,}180$$

The value of $\sum K_j'$ for the base of the second-story column is the same as $\sum K_j$ for the top of the first-story column. The ratios of $K_c/\sum K_j$ and $K_c'/\sum K_j'$ tabulated in cols. (8a) and (9a) are computed by using values in cols. (3) and (7a). The values in col. (8a) are obtained by dividing the column stiffness in col. (3), by $\sum K_j/4E_c$ in col. (7a). For the first story, the numerical value is

$$\frac{775}{2{,}180} = 0.356$$

The values in col. (9a) represent the condition at the base of the columns. For the first story, the value is

$$\frac{775}{2{,}005} = 0.386$$

Col. (10a) contains values of $\lambda/\lambda_{\text{inf}}$ obtained as the sum of values in cols. (8a) and (9a) subtracted from 1 (unity) in accordance with equation (4-3). Since

$$\lambda_{\text{inf}} = \frac{12E_c I_c}{H_s^3} = \frac{12E_c}{H_s^2} \cdot \frac{I_c}{H_s}$$

and the ratios of $\lambda/\lambda_{\text{inf}}$ are given in col. (10a),

$$\frac{H_s^2}{12E_c}\lambda = \text{col. (3) times col. (10a)}$$

$H_s^2/12E_c$ is common to all columns at a given story, therefore only the values of $(H_s^2/12E_c)\lambda$ are obtained and recorded in col. (11a) to save needless computations.

In a similar manner, the values of $(H_s/12E_c)\lambda$ for the interior columns are obtained by means of cols. (7b) to (10b) together with col. (5) and are recorded in col. (11b). Should there be other size columns in the same frame, the procedure would be repeated.

In order to obtain the summation of the relative stiffnesses of the columns at a given story, the calculations indicated for the exterior frame, Table 7-2A, need to be carried out for all different frames in the building. Table 7-2B shows the calculations required for a typical interior frame.

After the relative stiffnesses have been obtained for all columns in each frame, the total stiffness at a story is obtained by summing the values. For convenience

TABLE 7-2B Interior Frame—Computation of Relative Stiffness of Columns

(1) Floor	(2) Story	(3) Ext. col. $K_c/4E_c = I/H_s$	(4) Ext. girder $K_g/4E_c = (I/L)\frac{E_c}{E_g}$	(5) Int. col. $K_c/4E_c = I/H_s$	(6) Int. girder $K_g/4E_c = (I/L)\frac{E_c}{E_g}$	Exterior column					Interior column				
						(7a) $\frac{\Sigma K_i}{4E_c}$ or $\frac{\Sigma K'_i}{4E_c}$	(8a) Top $\frac{K_c}{\Sigma K_i}$	(9a) Bottom $\frac{K'_c}{\Sigma K'_i}$	(10a) $\frac{\lambda_{int}}{\lambda} \cong 1 - \left(\frac{K_c}{\Sigma K_i} + \frac{K'_c}{\Sigma K'_i}\right)$	(11a) $\lambda = (10a)\times(3)\ \frac{12E_c}{H_s^2}$	(7b) ΣK_i or $\Sigma K'_i$	(8b) Top $\frac{K_c}{\Sigma K_i}$	(9b) Bottom $\frac{K'_c}{\Sigma K'_i}$	(10b) $\frac{\lambda_{int}}{\lambda} \cong 1 - \left(\frac{K_c}{\Sigma K_i} + \frac{K'_c}{\Sigma K'_i}\right)$	(11b) $\lambda = (10b)\times(5)\ \frac{12E_c}{H_s^2}$
Rf.	24	52	109	116	109	162	0.321	0.184	0.495	26	334	0.347	0.201	0.452	52
23	23	52	172	116	172	276	0.184	0.182	0.634	33	576	0.201	0.195	0.604	70
22	22	61	172	135	172	285					595				
4	5	773	468	1,482	468	2,014	0.384	0.384	0.232	179	3,900	0.380	0.380	0.240	356
3	4	773	468	1,482	468	2,014	0.384	0.347	0.269	208	3,900	0.380	0.349	0.271	402
2	3	773	481	1,482	481	2,226	0.437	0.434	0.129	125	4,246	0.424	0.427	0.149	268
1	2	972	491	1,802	491	2,238	0.346	0.375	0.279	216	4,224	0.341	0.368	0.291	419
G	1	775	519	1,440	519	2,069					3,918				
	B	775		1,440											

in computing, the relative stiffnesses are retabulated in cols. (2) to (5) of Table 7-3. With four identical interior columns and two identical exterior columns in each of the two exterior frames and, similarly, four identical interior and two identical exterior columns in six interior frames, the total story stiffness equals the sum indicated in the heading of col. (6).

At this point either of two procedures can be used to determine column shears and moments. In the first, the total shear at any floor level acting at each frame is computed as the ratio of the sum of the relative stiffnesses of the columns in the frame to the story stiffness times the story shear. The frame shear is then distributed to the individual columns by frame analysis. In the second procedure the proportion of shear carried by each column is obtained directly from the ratio of the relative stiffness of the column to the story stiffness. For the portion of the building between the top three stories and the three lower stories, each method will give approximately the same results. The first method gives slightly more accurate values in the upper and lower stories. Such accuracy may be justified when the base is fixed, and for that condition use of equation (4-10) is helpful. For partial fixity, it is questionable whether the accuracy of the first method is consistent with the basic assumptions. In the chosen example, because some rotation can occur at the base of the first-story columns, it is considered sufficiently accurate to distribute the story shear by the second procedure.

For ease in computation, the values of $(H_s^2/12E_c)\Sigma\lambda$ from Table 7-3 and V_z and H_s from Table 7-1 are retabulated in cols. (3), (4), and (5) in Table 7-4A. The $(H_s^2/12E_c)\lambda$ values are transferred from Table 7-2A to col. (6a). The shear acting on the exterior column is then computed in col. (7a). The sums of the moments at the base and top of the columns are then obtained from a consideration of statics and are recorded in col. (8a). For the major portion of

TABLE 7-3 Computation of Story Stiffness

	Relative column stiffness, $\dfrac{H_s^2}{12E_c}\lambda$				Story stiffness
	Exterior frame		Interior frame		$\dfrac{H_s^2}{12E_c}\Sigma\lambda =$
Story	Ext. col.	Int. col.	Ext. col.	Int. col.	$2[2 \times (2) + 4 \times (3)]$ $+ 6[2 \times (4) + 4 \times (5)]$
(1)	(2)	(3)	(4)	(5)	(6)
24	20	32	26	52	1,896
23	30	38	33	70	2,510
4	161	266	179	356	13,460
3	192	291	208	402	15,240
2	105	249	125	268	10,340
1	200	301	216	419	15,860

TABLE 7-4A Exterior Frame—Computation of Column Shears and Moments, and Girder Moments

Floor (1)	Story (2)	Story stiffness $\frac{H_s^2}{12E_c}\Sigma\lambda$ (3)	Story shear V_s (4)	Story ht. H_s (5)	Exterior column							Interior column						
					$\frac{H_s^2}{12E_c}\lambda$ (6a)	$V=\lambda\frac{\Sigma}{\Sigma_s}$ (7a)	$VH_s=M_T+M_B$ (8a)	$\frac{M_T}{M_B}$ (9a)	M_T (10a)	M_B (11a)	M_G (12a)	$\frac{H_s^2}{12E_c}\lambda$ (6b)	$V=\lambda\frac{\Sigma}{\Sigma_s}$ (7b)	$VH_s=M_T-M_B$ (8b)	$\frac{M_T}{M_B}$ (9b)	M_T (10b)	M_B (11b)	M_G (12b)
Rf.	24	1,896	180	14	20	1.9	27	1.1	−14	−13	14	32	3.0	42	1.1	−22	−20	11
23	23	2,510	378	14	30	4.5	63	1.1	−33	−30	46	38	5.7	80	1.1	−42	−38	31
22	22																	
⋮	⋮	⋮	⋮	⋮	⋮	⋮	⋮	⋮	⋮	⋮	⋮	⋮	⋮	⋮	⋮	⋮	⋮	⋮
4	5	13,460	2,060	12	161	24.6	295	1.0	−148	−148	297	266	40.7	488	1.0	−244	−244	239
3	4	15,240	2,080	12	192	26.2	314	0.90	−149	−165	292	291	39.7	476	0.96	−233	−243	270
2	3	10,340	2,100	12	105	21.3	256	0.99	−127	−129	248	249	50.6	607	0.96	−297	−310	267
1	2	15,860	2,120	15	200	26.7	401	0.42	−119	−282	104	301	40.2	603	0.59	−224	−310	103
G	1								+178	+89						+174	+87	
	B																	

the building $M_T/M_B = 1$. For the lower stories Figs. 4-12 and 4-13 can be used to obtain reasonable values of M_T/M_B.

In the exterior frame, all the columns in any one story are the same size. The first story height $H_1 = 1.25H_s$ and

$$\frac{I_c}{H_s} = 972$$

$$\left(\frac{E_g}{E_c}\right)\left(\frac{I_g}{L}\right) = 433$$

$$\frac{E_c I_c L}{E_g I_g H_s} = \frac{972}{433} = 2.24$$

The average of the values obtained from Fig. 4-12 ($H_1 = H_s$) and Fig. 4-13 ($H_1 = 1.5H_s$), with 2.24 as the abscissa, is

$$\frac{M_T}{M_B} = 0.42$$

This is entered in col. (9a). By equation (4-9)

$$M_B = \frac{V_z H_s}{1 + \dfrac{M_T}{M_B}} = \frac{401}{1.42} = 282 \text{ ft.kips}$$

and

$$M_T = 282 \times 0.42 = 119 \text{ ft.kips}$$

The computed values are recorded in cols. (11a) and (10a), respectively. The girder moments at any column-girder connection equal the sum of the column moments about the joint. For the first floor

$$M_g = 119 + 129 = 248 \text{ ft.kips}$$

The moment at the bottom of the first-story column is resisted by the basement wall pilaster or column and the adjoining beams. A reasonable assumption is that the magnitude of the moments induced in each member is a function of the relative stiffnesses. On this basis, the moment at the top of the basement column can be considered to be

$$M_T = \frac{282 \times 775}{775 + 455} = 178 \text{ ft.kips}$$

and

$$M_B = 178 \times \tfrac{1}{2} = 89 \text{ ft.kips}$$

By statics

$$M_g = 282 - 178 = 104 \text{ ft.kips}$$

The interior columns of the exterior frames are treated in a similar manner; however, the sum of the column moments above and below a floor are distributed to two girders.

For the lower stories of an interior frame, the procedure for determination of the column moments is identical to that for the exterior frames except that Fig. 4-11 only is used to obtain the M_T/M_B ratios.

To investigate the accuracy obtained by the use of Figs. 4-11, 4-12, and 4-13, a more precise solution of an interior frame was made. The proportion of the story shear carried by an interior frame was based on the ratio of the sum of the relative stiffnesses of the joints in the frame to the sum of the stiffnesses of the joints for the entire story. Hence the shear acting on an interior frame at the first story is, from Table 7-2B cols. (11a) and (11b), Table 7-3 col. (6), and Table 7-1 col. (6),

$$\left(\frac{2 \times 216 + 4 \times 419}{15,860}\right) 2,120 = 282 \text{ kips}$$

The frame shears were obtained for the lowest 10 stories and an analysis made according to the Maney-Goldberg modified slope deflection method [39]. In the analysis, the ground floor was assumed fixed against translation and the bottom of the basement columns were considered fixed. The resulting exact moments are shown at the left and the shears at the right in Fig. 7-3 in italic lettering. The approximate moments and shears from Table 7-4B are shown in roman lettering. Because the columns at the ground floor are only partially restrained, the moments in the columns at the bottom of the first story, as computed by the use of Figs. 4-11, 4-12, and 4-13, are slightly larger than those given by the more

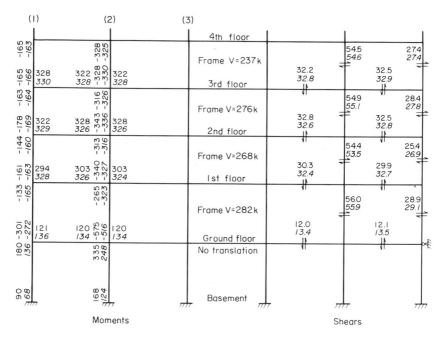

Fig. 7-3. Exact moments and shears shown in italic lettering and approximate moments and shears shown in roman lettering for lower stories of an interior frame of building design example.

TABLE 7-4B Interior Frame—Computation of Column Shears and Moments, and Girder Moments

(1) Floor	(2) Story	(3) Story stiffness $\frac{H_s^2 \Sigma\lambda}{12E_c}$	(4) Story shear V_z	(5) Story ht. H_s	Exterior column							Interior column						
					(6a) $\frac{H_s^2\lambda}{12E_c}$	(7a) $V = \lambda\frac{V_z}{\Sigma\lambda}$	(8a) $VH_s = M_T + M_B$	(9a) $\frac{M_T}{M_B}$	(10a) M_T	(11a) M_B	(12a) M_G	(6b) $\frac{H_s^2\lambda}{12E_c}$	(7b) $V = \lambda\frac{V_z}{\Sigma\lambda}$	(8b) $VH_s = M_T + M_B$	(9b) $\frac{M_T}{M_B}$	(10b) M_T	(11b) M_B	(12b) M_G
Rf.	24	1,896	180	14	26	2.5	35	1.1	−18	−17	17	52	4.9	69	1.1	−36	−33	18
23	23	2,510	378	14	33	5.0	70	1.1	−37	−33	54	70	10.5	147	1.1	−77	−70	55
22	22																	
4	5	13,460	2,060	12	179	27.4	329	1.00	−165	−165		356	54.5	655	1.00	−328	−328	322
3	4	15,240	2,080	12	208	28.4	341	0.92	−163	−178	328	402	54.9	659	0.92	−316	−343	328
2	3	10,340	2,100	12	125	25.4	305	0.90	−144	−161	322	268	54.4	653	0.92	−313	−340	303
1	2	15,860	2,120	15	216	28.9	434	0.44	−133	−301	294	419	56.0	840	0.46	−265	−575	120
G	1								+180	+90	121					+335	+168	

precise analysis. For the same reason, the moments at the top of the columns are somewhat less. The columns will therefore tend to be overdesigned by the approximate solution since the size and reinforcement of the columns will be controlled by the larger moment. The girder moments shown in Table 7-4B are slightly smaller than those given by the precise solution, but the difference is not large enough to affect the design. The major difference between the two solutions occurs in the moments at the top of the basement columns. Here again, the

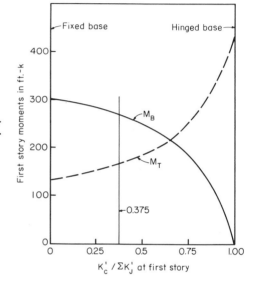

Fig. 7-4. Moment-stiffness relationship for columns with fixed or hinged bases in building design example.

controlling moment for the reinforcement is at the bottom of the ground-floor columns. Hence the difference has no practical meaning.

The approximate agreement between the two solutions indicates that a direct interpolation between Fig. 4-11 (full fixity) and Fig. 4-14 (zero fixity) cannot be made on the basis of $K'_c/\sum K'_j$ of the first-story columns because the final moments are affected by translation as well as rotation of the joints. In general, it will be found that the moment-stiffness relationship will be similar to that shown in Fig. 7-4. Although Fig. 7-4 applies only to this example, the form of the curves would be essentially the same for other multistory frames. If considered necessary, an adjustment of the column moments could be made as indicated by the curves.

Torsional Effects

The effects of horizontal torsion can be determined by the procedure presented in Section 4.9. The example building is symmetrical, with regard to both mass and rigidity; thus both the centers of mass and rigidity are known without calculation and they coincide. However, the SEAOC code requires that the frame at any story shall be designed for an accidental torsion equal to the story shear multiplied by 5 per cent of the maximum building dimension.

The shear produced by torsion is distributed to the resisting elements in proportion to their stiffness and distance from the center of rigidity by means of the expressions presented in Section 4.9. The relative column stiffnesses in both directions are known from previous analysis. The evaluation of the moments in individual columns due to horizontal torsion for the first story is shown in Table 7-5.

The relative stiffnesses $(H_s^2/12E_c)\lambda$ in the transverse direction, taken from Tables 7-2A and 7-2B, are retabulated in cols. (2) and (3). The calculations of the column stiffnesses in the longitudinal direction are not shown but they are determined in a manner similar to the stiffnesses in the transverse direction and are recorded in the bottom half of Table 7-5. The distances from the center of rigidity to the respective frames $\bar{X}_{cr}$ and $\bar{Y}_{cr}$, shown in col. (4), are obtained from Fig. 7-2. The quantity $[(H_s^2/12E_c)\Sigma\lambda_y]\bar{X}_{cr}^2$ for each frame is entered in col. (6). As shown at the bottom of the table, the rotational stiffness for the story I_p is obtained by summing all the values in col. (6), both in the transverse and longitudinal direction, and multiplying by 2 to include the effects of all the frames. The results of the distribution of the torsional shear are entered in col. (7a). The remaining computation procedure is identical to that presented in Tables 7-4A and 7-4B and consequently the same ratios (M_T/M_B) are used. It should be noted that the moments due to accidental torsion are not considered to reduce the direct moments.

The computation of column shears and moments due to accidental torsion need be made at every story only when there are large differences in the location of the centers of rigidity and mass from story to story or when the stiffnesses of the resisting elements change. For buildings such as the example building, it is sufficient to perform the computations only for levels at which the columns and girder stiffnesses change. The values at intermediate floors may then be obtained in proportion to the story shears.

7.4 Column Loads Due to Overturning Moment

Before proceeding with the design of sections, it will be necessary to compute the axial loads in the columns due to the overturning moment. The axial loads are obtained by summing the girder shears obtained in the seismic analysis modified by the ratio of overturning to cantilever moment shown in col. (11) of Table 7-1. For example, the exterior girder shear in the first interior frame shown in Fig. 7-3 at the ground floor of the frame is $12.1k$ and the contribution to axial load at the exterior column due to overturning is $(12.1)\ 0.34 = 4.1k$. At the interior column the contribution due to overturning is $(12.1 - 12.0)\ 0.34 = 0.03k$. This procedure is repeated at each floor and the results summed down to the floor under investigation. The seismic and static axial loads are combined

TABLE 7-5   Accidental Torsion—1st Story Column Shears and Moments

							Exterior column					Interior column				
Frame	$\dfrac{H_s^2}{12E_c}\lambda_y$ Exterior column	$\dfrac{H_s^2}{12E_c}\lambda_y$ Interior column	$\bar{X}_{cr}$	$\bar{X}_{cr}^2$	$\left[\dfrac{H_s^2}{12E_c}\Sigma\lambda_y\right]\bar{X}_{cr}^2 =$ $[2\times(2)+4\times(3)]\times(5)$	$V'_y = \dfrac{\bar{M}_{cr}}{I_p}\lambda_y\bar{X}_{cr}$	$V'_y H_s'' = M_T + M_B$	$\dfrac{M_T}{M_B}$	M_T	M_B	$V'_y = \dfrac{\bar{M}_{cr}}{I_p}\lambda_y\bar{X}_{cr}$	$V'_y H_s'' = M_T + M_B$	$\dfrac{M_T}{M_B}$	M_T	M_B
(1)	(2)	(3)	(4)	(5)	(6)	(7a)	(8a)	(9a)	(10a)	(11a)	(7b)	(8b)	(9b)	(10b)	(11b)
A&H	200	301	87.5	7,660	12,280,000	5.0	75	0.42	−22	−53	7.5	113	0.59	−42	−71
B&G	216	419	62.5	3,910	8,230,000	3.8	57	0.44	−17	−40	7.6	114	0.46	−36	−78
C&F	216	419	37.5	1,410	2,960,000	2.3	35	0.44	−11	−24	4.5	68	0.46	−21	−47
D&E	216	419	12.5	156	330,000	0.8	12	0.44	−4	−8	1.5	23	0.46	−7	−16
Σ					23,800,000										

Transverse direction

Table 7-5 (Continued)

	$\dfrac{H_s^2}{12E_c}\lambda_x$					Exterior column					Interior column				
Frame	Exterior column	Interior column	$\bar{r}_{cr}$	$\bar{r}_{cr}^2$	$\left[\dfrac{H_s^2}{12E_c}\Sigma\lambda_x\right]\bar{r}_{cr}^2 = [2\times(2)+6\times(3)]\times(5)$	$V'_x = \dfrac{\bar{M}_{cr}}{I_p}\lambda_x\bar{r}_{cr}$	$V'_xH_s = M_T+M_B$	$\dfrac{M_T}{M_B}$	M_T	M_B	$V'_x = \dfrac{\bar{M}_{cr}}{I_p}\lambda_x\bar{r}_{cr}$	$V'_xH_s = M_T+M_B$	$\dfrac{M_T}{M_B}$	M_T	M_B
(1)	(2)	(3)	(4)	(5)	(6)	(7a)	(8a)	(9a)	(10a)	(11a)	(7b)	(8b)	(9b)	(10b)	(11b)
1 & 6	210	315	50	2,500	5,780,000										
2 & 5	222	431	30	900	2,730,000										
3 & 4	222	431	10	100	300,000										
Σ					8,810,000										

Longitudinal direction

Total rotational stiffness
$$I_p = \Sigma(\lambda_y\bar{X}_{cr}^2 + \lambda_x\bar{r}_{cr}^2) = \frac{12E_c}{H_s^2}\left[23,800,000 + 8,810,000\right] = 65,220,000\,\frac{12E_c}{H_s^2}$$

Eccentricity
$$e = (0.05)(175) = 8.75 \text{ ft.}$$

Story shear
$$V_z = 2,120 \text{ kips}$$

Torsional moment
$$\bar{M}_{cr} = eV_z = (8.75)(2,120) = 18,550 \text{ ft.kips}$$

Column shears
$$V'_y = \lambda_y\bar{X}_{cr}\frac{\bar{M}_{cr}}{I_p} = \lambda_y\bar{X}_{cr}\frac{18,550}{65,220,000}\frac{H_s^2}{12E_c} = (0.284\times10^{-3})\frac{H_s^2}{12E_c}\lambda_y\bar{X}_{cr} = 0.284\times10^{-3}\text{ col. (2)}\times\text{col. (4)}$$

$$V'_x = (0.284\times10^{-3})\frac{H_s^2}{12E_c}\lambda_x\bar{r}_{cr}$$

Story height
$$H_s = 15 \text{ ft.}$$

to give the axial loads for which the columns must be designed, unless it is found that the wind loads control. The increase in axial load due to overturning is minor in this example.

While the stresses due to the axial load resulting from overturning are minor, they produce a differential elongation or shortening of adjacent columns, which is most marked at the upper stories. This differential deformation is resisted by the stiffness of the frame girders and consequently the axial load as computed above for the exterior column is somewhat relieved and transmitted to the interior column. The amount of such redistribution depends on the stiffness of the girders. If the frame acts in the elastic range, a reasonable value for the stiffness of the girders can be assumed and therefore, while difficult, the amount of redistribution can be computed. However, in the inelastic range, such as occurs in providing the resistance to seismic motions, the stiffness of the girders is reduced by the formation of plastic hinges and consequently the amount of redistribution of axial load is decreased. It is questionable whether increased accuracy is obtained by further computations.

7.5 Wind Analysis

The determination of the moments and shears created by wind load follows the same procedure as outlined for seismic forces except that the intensity and vertical distribution of the loads will differ. However, since the M_T/M_B values are quite insensitive to the variation in the lateral loading, the column moments produced by wind can be determined directly as the product of the ratio of the wind story shear to the seismic story shear and the seismic column moment. The wind story shears are less than half the seismic story shears in this example. The wind moments in the frame will therefore also be less than half the seismic moments.

The wind overturning moment at the base is about 16 per cent higher than the overturning moment shown in Table 7-1 because of the reduction factor J applied to the cantilever moment due to seismic forces. Above the third floor, the wind overturning moment becomes less than that due to the seismic forces. The increase in axial load on the columns caused by overturning due to wind will still be negligible when compared with that due to dead and live loads. It is evident that consideration of wind forces in this example may be significant only in computations for drift.

7.6 Vertical Loads

The frame analysis to determine moments and shears due to vertical loads may be performed in accordance with the ACI code by applying the live load to the floor under consideration and assuming the far ends of the columns fixed. The

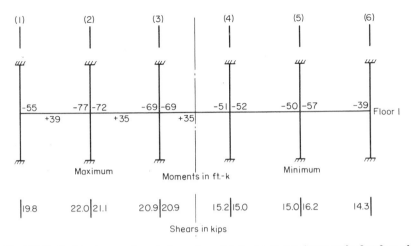

results of such an analysis for an interior transverse frame at the first floor are shown in Fig. 7-5.

7.7 Proportioning of Sections

After the frame moments and shears have been computed in the transverse and longitudinal directions, further refinement of member sizes and reinforcement can be made. This work being of a routine and general nature and not necessarily specific to seismic design, only an example of final values is given. Because of the repetitive nature of the calculations, tabular forms similar to Tables 7-6 to 7-8 often may be used advantageously.

Girders

In Table 7-6, the values in cols. (1) to (11), with the exception of col. (4), have been previously determined or established. For example, the end moment in girder 1-2 of frames B and G at the exterior column due to seismic forces as recorded in col. (5) is obtained from col. (12a) in Table 7-4B. The accidental torsional moment at the same section, recorded in col. (6), is equal to the sum of the torsional moment $M_T = -17$ in the first-story column obtained from col. (10a) in Table 7-5 and the similarly computed, but not shown, torsional moment $M_B = -19$ in the second-story column. The torsional moments in the girders at the interior columns are the sums of the torsional moments in the columns above and below divided by 2. The vertical load moments in girder 1-2 given in cols. (7) and (8) are obtained from Fig. 7-5. Col. (4) is obtained readily as the product of cols. (1) and (3) and is included for ready comparison

TABLE 7-6 Girder Design Moments—Interior Transverse Frames B and G

Floor	Column	Dimensions b in. (1)	h in. (2)	d in. (3)	$F* = \dfrac{bd^2}{12{,}000}$ (4)	Seismic lat. ft.k. (5)	Seismic tor. ft.k (6)	End Vertical max. ft.k (7)	End Vertical min. ft.k (8)	Sum (max.) neg. ft.k (9)	Sum (max.) pos. ft.k (10)	Midspan max. pos. ft.k (11)	End max. neg. 1.33F (12a)	End max. neg. A_s sq.in. (13a)	End max. neg. reinf. (14a)	End max. pos. 1.33F (12b)	End max. pos. A_s sq.in. (13b)	End max. pos. reinf. (14b)	Midspan F (12c)	Midspan A_s sq.in. (13c)	Midspan reinf. (14c)
P H R	1																				
	2																				
1	1	24	34	31.5	1.99	±294	±36	−55	−39	−385	+291	39	0.98	6.35	7−#9	—	4.81	5−#9	0.1	3.80†	4−#9
	2	24	34	31.5	1.99	±303	±39	−77	−57	−419	+285		1.07	6.92	7−#9	—	4.71	5−#9			
	3																				

*See ACI Reinforced Concrete Design Handbook
†Minimum required $p = 0.005$

TABLE 7-7 Girder Design Shears—Interior Transverse Frames B and G

Floor	Column	Dimensions			Seismic		Shears							Stresses			
							Vertical		Sum (max.)		v (max.)				Σₒ		u	
		b in.	h in.	d in.	lat. kips	tor. kips	max. kips	min. kips	pos. kips	neg. kips	pos. psi	neg. psi	$v-v_c$ psi	top in.	bot. in.	top psi	bot. psi
		(1)	(2)	(3)	(4)	(5)	(6)	(7)	(8)	(9)	(10)	(11)	(12)	(13)	(14)	(15)	(16)
P	1																
H	2																
R	2																
1	1	24	34	31.5	±29.9	±3.7	+19.8	+14.3	+53.4	−19.3	82	29	0	24.8	17.7	79	40
	2	24	34	31.5	±29.9	±3.7	+22.0	+16.2	+55.6	−17.4	85	26	0	24.8	17.7	82	36
	2																
	3																

with the required F values computed and tabulated in col. (12a). By using these values, the amount of reinforcement needed at critical sections can be obtained readily.

It will be noted that the girder dimensions appear to be substantially greater than necessary for the design moments as indicated by the actual and required F values. There are several reasons for providing a larger cross-section than in the usual design for vertical loads and wind. Among the reasons are: (a) larger girders and, hence, greater stiffness reduce the critical column moments in the lower stories; (b) girder stiffness usually is the most economical way to control drift; (c) small-size girders do not necessarily reflect economy in construction and heavily reinforced sections result in poor connection details and difficulty in concrete placement.

In Table 7-7, the shear computations have been arranged similarly to the moment calculations in Table 7-6. The values in col. (4) are taken from Fig. 7-3 and those in col. (5) can be obtained from Table 7-6 by adding the torsional moments at the ends of girder 1-2 and dividing the sum by the span length. The values in cols. (6) and (7) are taken directly from Fig. 7-5, and those in cols. (13) and (14) are based on the number of bars determined in Table 7-6. Other values in the table are obvious. Although in most cases the investigation of bond stresses for the bottom reinforcement to satisfy positive moment requirements is not needed, columns are provided in the table for completeness.

Columns

Table 7-8 suggests a convenient arrangement for collecting the data necessary for the design of columns. Because a succession of computations is required to determine the adequacy of columns, this tabulation is restricted to axial load and moment values only. Investigations of ductility and shear will be considered later. If it is assumed that column $3D$ is reinforced with 16 No. 18 bars then, following the procedure outlined in the ACI code, 318-56,

$$F_a = 1.48 \text{ ksi}$$

$$F_b = 2.25 \text{ ksi}$$

and for vertical loads only

$$f_a = 1.47 \text{ ksi}$$

$$f_b = 0.044 \text{ ksi}$$

and consequently

$$\frac{f_a}{F_a} + \frac{f_b}{F_b} = \frac{1.47}{1.48} + \frac{0.044}{2.25} = 1.013$$

For vertical and lateral loads

$$f_a = 1.47$$

$$f_b = 0.514$$

$$\frac{f_a}{F_a} + \frac{f_b}{F_b} = \frac{1.47}{1.48} + \frac{0.514}{2.25} = 1.22$$

Because a one-third increase in allowable stress is permitted for combined dead, live, and earthquake load, it is evident that the combination of dead and live load controls. The column is so slightly underdesigned that from a practical point of view it can be considered adequate.

TABLE 7-8 Summary of Column 3D Axial Loads and Moments in the First Story

Axial Load, kips				Moments, ft.kips					
DL	DL+LL	Over-turning	Total	Direction	DL+LL	Seismic		Eccen-tricity*	Seismic + eccentricity
						Lateral	Torsional		
2,080	2,590	0	2,590	Trans.*	15	575	16	39	630
				Long.†	44	550	12	39	601

*Due to an assumed deflection of $0.002H$.
†Computations not shown

An important point that should be considered in seismic design is the degree of safety against seismic forces alone, especially when combined bending and axial load are involved. Unfortunately, the use of allowable stresses and working loads obscures this relationship. For this purpose the ultimate-strength design procedure must be employed. If U is designated as the ultimate capacity of the column and D, L, and E are the effects, respectively, of dead, live, and earthquake forces, then the factor of safety for seismic forces is

$$F.S. = \frac{U - (D + L)}{E}$$

Because of the interrelationship between moment and thrust, investigations generally have to be made with respect to both maximum thrust and maximum moment to determine the factor of safety for combined bending and axial load. In this example, however, because the seismic forces do not contribute appreciable axial thrust to column $3D$ and therefore are assumed to be zero, only the maximum moment capacity that can be sustained with the axial load due to dead and live load need be determined. This could be done by solving for e, the eccentricity in either equation (A9) or (A11) of the Appendix to the ACI code, 1956. Fortunately, graphic solutions of these equations are readily available [51], from which Figs. 7-6 and 7-7 are reproduced in part for convenience in illustrating their use.

Given: $P_u = 2{,}590$ kips; $b = t = 42$ in.; $d = 38.38$ in.;
$A_s = 64$ in.^{2}; $f'_c = 5{,}000$ psi and $f_y = 50{,}000$ psi

If it is assumed that all the steel is concentrated at the two faces, then

$$p_t m = \frac{64}{42 \times 42} \times \frac{50{,}000}{0.85 \times 5{,}000} = 0.427$$

$$\frac{P_u}{btf'_c} = \frac{2,590}{42 \times 42 \times 5.0} = 0.294$$

and

$$\frac{d}{t} = \frac{38.38}{42} = 0.914$$

Interpolating between Fig. 7-6 with $d/t = 0.95$ and Fig. 7-7 with $d/t = 0.90$ gives

$$\frac{P_u e'}{bt^2 f'_c} = \frac{M_u}{bt^2 f'_c} = 0.25$$

If it is considered that the steel is distributed equally on four sides, but on the sides perpendicular to the axis of bending is ineffective, then

$$p_t m = \frac{64 - 16}{42 \times 42} \times \frac{50,000}{0.85 \times 5,000} = 0.32$$

Interpolating again between Figs. 7-6 and 7-7, with $P_u/btf'_c = 0.294$, gives

$$\frac{M_u}{bt^2 f'_c} = 0.21$$

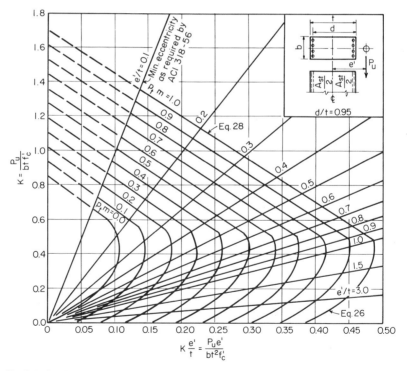

Fig. 7-6. Graphic solutions for equation (A9) and equation (A11) of Appendix to ACI code, 1956—d/t=0.95, rectangular sections with symmetrical reinforcement. (Adapted from reference 51, ACI.)

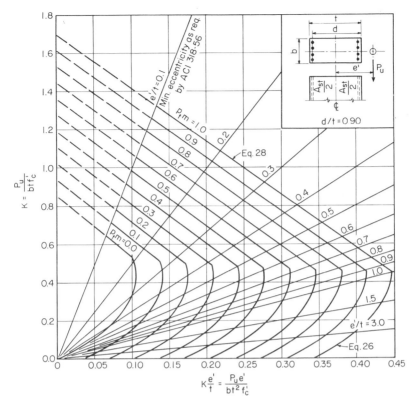

Fig. 7-7. Graphic solutions for equation (A9) and equation (A11) of Appendix to ACI code, 1956—d/t = 0.90, rectangular sections with symmetrical reinforcement. (Adapted from reference 51, ACI.)

Since the side reinforcement will be effective to some degree, it is reasonable to assume that the actual value will be about midway between the extreme conditions. On this basis

$$\frac{M_u}{bt^2f_c'} = \frac{0.25 + 0.21}{2} = 0.23$$

and consequently

$$M_u = 0.23 \times 42^3 \times 5.0 = 85{,}200 \text{ in.kips} = 7{,}100 \text{ ft.kips}$$

Assuming conservatively that the effects of vertical loads in the longitudinal and transverse direction are additive and using $E = 630$ ft.kips, then

$$F.S. = \frac{7{,}100 - 59}{630} = 11.1$$

This high value of the factor of safety against the design earthquake forces will not be constant throughout the structure because the ratio of the effects of static and lateral forces is not uniform. However, at the location under consideration, the static loads control the column design as illustrated.

It is interesting to note that even with $P_u/btf'_c = 0.294$, the capacity of the column as shown in Figs. 7-6 and 7-7 is controlled by tension. The high factor of safety in the column as contrasted to a value of about 1.9 in the adjoining girders, calculated in a similar manner, indicates that when subject to a seismic shock of an intensity of about 1.9 times the design seismic forces, yielding will first occur in the girders. Furthermore, because of frame action and the high factor of safety in the column, successive formation of hinges in the girders in a number of floors above will have to occur before the capacity of this column is approached.

The exact number of hinges that will be formed before the column capacity is reached depends to a major extent on the reserve capacity of the girders. If all of the girders were to form hinges simultaneously at a seismic shock of an intensity of 1.9 times the design seismic force, then column 3D would act as a free cantilever. Even under this extremely improbable condition, the column would carry about 2.5 times the seismic load before yielding of the steel would occur. But under such a condition, with hinges forming simultaneously in every girder, deflection of the top floor would be roughly 30 times that of the elastic frame. As previously discussed, the effect of an excursion into the plastic range by a structure subject to seismic motion is to decrease the forces developed. Therefore, it is most unlikely that column 3D will ever go into the plastic range.

This difference between the factor of safety in the column and girder, which is typical of the behavior in the lower stories, points up the desirability of increasing somewhat the reserve capacity of some of the girders. This is especially true at those sections in which the vertical load moment and seismic moment are of opposite direction. Increasing the capacity of some of the girders reduces the number of hinges formed and enables the structure to behave as a more flexible elastic frame with hinge action limited to certain floors.

7.8 Detailing for Ductility

Girders

In addition to the computations in Tables 7-6 and 7-7, check calculations should be made to determine that the amount of reinforcement in the girders conforms to recommendations made in Chapter 6 in order to ensure adequate ductility.

For the first floor girder 1-2 designed in Tables 7-6 and 7-7,

$$f'_c = 5 \text{ ksi}; f_y = 40 \text{ ksi}; b = 60 \text{ in.}; b' = 24 \text{ in.};$$
$$d = 31.5 \text{ in.}; d' = 2.5 \text{ in.}; A_s = 7.0 \text{ in.}^2; A'_s = 5.0 \text{ in.}^2$$

Consequently, checking the permissible percentages of reinforcement, top $\qquad p = A_s/bd = 7.0/24 \times 31.5 = 0.0093 < 0.025$ max.

bottom $\qquad p' = A_s'/bd = 5.0/24 \times 31.5 = 0.0066 < 0.025$ max.

Furthermore
$$q_u = \frac{pf_y}{0.70f_c'} = \frac{0.0093 \times 40}{0.70 \times 5} = 0.106$$

$$q_u' = \frac{pf_y'}{0.70f_c'} = \frac{0.0066 \times 40}{0.70 \times 5} = 0.076$$

hence
$$q_u - q_u' = 0.106 - 0.076 = 0.03 < 0.25 \text{ max.}$$

From the above, it is apparent that the recommendations with respect to steel percentages are fully satisfied to ensure that the capacity of the girder will be controlled by tension in the reinforcement and it will have adequate ductility.

The maximum possible shear that can be induced will be determined on the basis of the flexural capacity of the two ends of the girder (see Fig. 6-1). The ultimate capacity of the section as given by equations (6-2) and (6-3), respectively, is

$$M_u = A_s f_y d(1 - 0.4q_u) \qquad (6\text{-}2)$$

and

$$M_u = (A_s f_y - A_s' f_y')d[1 - 0.4(q_u - q_u')] + A_s' f_y'(d - d') \qquad (6\text{-}3)$$

In accordance with equation (6-3), the ultimate negative moment resistance is

$$M_u = - \left[(7.0 - 5.0)\frac{31.5}{12}(1 - 0.4 \times 0.03) \right.$$
$$\left. + 5.0 \times \frac{31.5 - 2.5}{12} \right]40 = 691 \text{ ft.kips}$$

At column 2, the tension reinforcement (bottom) for positive moment consists of five No. 9 bars and the top reinforcement consists of seven No. 9 bars. Because the percentage of tension reinforcement is low, a check should be made to determine where the neutral axis occurs. Furthermore, considering T-beam action, the beam width equals the effective flange width or $b = 60$ in., hence

$$p = \frac{A_s}{bd} = \frac{5.0}{60 \times 31.5} = 0.0026$$

$$q_u = \frac{pf_y}{0.70f_c'} = \frac{0.0026 \times 40}{0.70 \times 5} = 0.030$$

$$k_u d = q_u d = 0.030 \times 31.5 = 0.95 \text{ in.}$$

Since this is less than d', the top reinforcement is not in compression at ultimate and by equation (6-2) the positive moment capacity at the column, neglecting strain hardening, is

$$M_u = 5.0 \times 40 \times \frac{31.5}{12}(1 - 0.4 \times 0.030) = 519 \text{ ft.kips}$$

and the ratio of positive to negative capacity is

$$\frac{519}{691} = 0.751 > 0.75 \text{ min.}$$

With the dead and live load equal to 2.08 kips per foot, the total shear due to vertical loads is

$$V = \frac{2.08 \times 20}{2} = 20.8 \text{ kips}$$

The maximum shear that can be induced is therefore

$$V_u = 20.8 + \frac{691 + 519}{20} = 81.3 \text{ kips}$$

The shear capacity of the beam without web reinforcement is

$$1.9bd\sqrt{f'_c} = 1.9 \times 24 \times 31.5\sqrt{5{,}000} = 102{,}000 \text{ lb.}$$

Since the shear resistance is adequate, the amount of web reinforcement to be used is given by equation (6-5). The minimum area required can be provided by No. 3 U-stirrups spaced 6 in. on centers for a distance equal to four times the effective depth from each end of the beam, except that stirrup-ties of the type shown in Fig. 6-2(c) must be used near the beam-column connections as indicated in Fig. 6-3. The determination of the number and spacing of stirrups along a girder in which the shear reinforcement required is more than the minimum can be accomplished by standard procedure with Diagram 17 in the ACI *Reinforced Concrete Design Handbook* [50].

Throughout the building for which the design is illustrated in this chapter, the percentage of longitudinal reinforcement in all girders is well below the maximum permitted and, therefore, the desired ductility and energy-absorption capacity of the girders is provided. An indication of the toughness of girder 1-2 can be obtained from Fig. 5-14. For the condition of negative end moment for this girder, $p'/p = 0.71$ and $q_u = 0.106$. By entering the figure with these values it is found that ϕ_u/ϕ_y or, in other words, the ratio of maximum possible rotation to yield rotation, is more than 28.0.

Columns

Two additional investigations must be made for columns. The first applies solely to the ends of the columns and deals with confinement of the concrete. The second investigation deals with shear requirements. The design of transverse reinforcement for confinement (hoops) is governed by the maximum axial load expected to act on the column during an earthquake. On the other hand, the design of stirrup-ties to resist shear is governed by the minimum axial load during an earthquake. The range of these maximum and minimum axial loads depends primarily on the compressive or tensile contribution to axial load due to overturning. In this example, because of the equal spans and regular layout, this contribution in the elastic range manifests itself at the exterior columns only. The axial load $P = 2,590$ kips for column $3D$, for which the loads and moments are summarized in Table 7-8, is not affected by overturning. The computations that follow are, therefore, based on a constant axial load. In order to produce a maximum and minimum fluctuation artificially, a vertical component of acceleration* may be assumed.

For column $3D$, confinement is necessary over a length of 42 in. since

$$\frac{P}{A_g f'_c} = \frac{2,590}{1,764 \times 5.0} = 0.294 > 0.12$$

From equation (6-6), with $f'_c = 5,000$ psi, $f''_y = 40,000$ psi,

$$p'' = 0.45\left[\left(\frac{42}{39}\right)^2 - 1\right]\frac{5,000}{40,000} = 0.009$$

which is less than the 0.012 specified for intermediate-grade bars in Chapter 6 as minimum at the face of the connection. In this example, the size of bar will be chosen so that only one hoop is necessary†. With $h'' = 39$ in., $a = 3$ in., and the required minimum $p'' = 0.012$, the size required by Table 6-1 is No. 8 at the face of the connection.

The bar size of the hoop reinforcement can be reduced at 14 in. from the bottom of the girder to No. 6 and at 28 in. to No. 5, as shown in Fig. 7-8. Where hoops are provided for confinement of the concrete, as illustrated, it is considered that there is no more possibility of buckling of the vertical bars than in a spiral column, because the design of the hoops is predicated on being equivalent to a spiral. Therefore, no interior ties are shown in Section A-A. Local codes may nevertheless require interior ties.

As in the case of the girder, the shear resistance of the column will be based on the assumption that both ends of the column reach their ultimate flexural capacity or restraint. With an axial load of $P = 2,590$ kips, the moment capacity as indicated on page 193 is 7,100 ft.kips. This capacity can be assumed at top and bottom since the same arrangement of reinforcement is used at both places. From the previous girder computations the sum of the moments on each side of the column is

$$M_b = 691 + 519 = 1,210 \text{ ft.kips}$$

In accordance with recommendations in Chapter 6, the ultimate shear is given by the lesser of the two

$$V_u = \frac{M_c^B + \frac{1}{2}M_b}{H'}$$

---

*±0.25g has been recorded.

†Multiple hoops could be of smaller bar diameter but may result in greater total weight of steel.

or

$$V_u = \frac{M_c^B + M_c^T}{H'}$$

Since $\frac{1}{2}M_b$ is less than M_c^T, then with $H' = 12.17$ ft.

$$V_u = \frac{7,100 + 605}{12.17} = 633 \text{ kips}$$

The shear capacity of the column without web reinforcement has been given in Chapter 6 as

$$V_c = 1.9b'd\sqrt{f_c'}\left(1 + \frac{P}{16A_{tr}\sqrt{f_c'}}\right)$$

in which A_{tr} equals uncracked transformed area of total column cross-section. Hence, with

$$A_{tr} = A_c + (n - 1)A_g = 1,764 + 5 \times 64 = 2,084 \text{ in.}^2$$

$$V_c = 1.9 \times 42 \times 38.4\sqrt{5,000}\left(1 + \frac{2,590,000}{16 \times 2,084 \times \sqrt{5,000}}\right)$$

$$= 456,000 \text{ lb.} = 456 \text{ kips}$$

Substituting these values in equation (6-8),

$$A_v f_v \frac{d}{s} = 633 - 456 = 177 \text{ kips}$$

or with $f_y'' = 40,000 \text{ psi} = 40 \text{ ksi}$ and $d = 38.4$ in.

$$\frac{A_v}{s} = \frac{177}{40 \times 38.4} = 0.115$$

Considering that No. 5 ties will be used throughout the central portion of the column beyond the confined end, as shown in Fig. 7-8, $A_v = 4 \times 0.31 = 1.24$ sq.in. in each direction and the resulting tie spacing is

$$s = \frac{1.24}{0.115} = 10.8 \text{ in.}$$

The tie spacing is less than ACI code requirements.

The ductility factor for the column can be checked by means of Fig. 5-17:

$$q'' = \frac{A_{sh}'' f_{yh}''}{ah'' f_c'} = \frac{0.79 \times 40,000}{3.0 \times 39.0 \times 5,000} = 0.054$$

$$(1 + 4.1q'')\frac{b''}{b} = \left[1 + 4.1 \times 0.054\right]\frac{39.0}{42} = 1.14$$

$$\frac{p'}{p} = 1$$

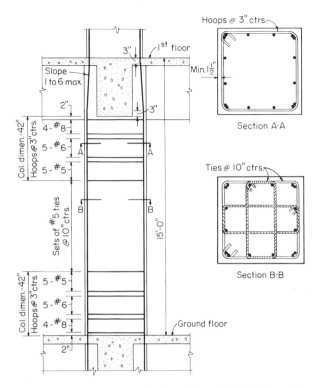

Fig. 7-8. Reinforcement details for column 3D of building design example.

$$\frac{P}{f'_c bd} = \frac{2,590}{5 \times 42 \times 38.4} = 0.32$$

Because $p'/p = 1$, the ductility of the column is independent of q and therefore Fig. 5-17 is entered at the intersection of the $P/f'_c bd$ curve with the ordinate scale. From this point, one proceeds horizontally to a value of $(1 + 4.1q'')b''/b = 1.14$. From this point, proceeding downward, a value of ϕ_u/ϕ_y equal to about 6 is indicated. As with beams, it is not necessary to compute the ductility, but the computations and chart have been included to provide a better understanding of the effect of the various factors.

If a vertical component of acceleration of $0.25g$ had been assumed, the axial load in column $3D$ would be $P = 2,590 \pm 650$ kips and the shear requirements of the column would be investigated for these conditions.

For $P = 2,590 + 650 = 3,240$ kips

$M_u = 7,200$ ft.kips

$V_u = 641$ kips

$V_c = 514$ kips

and $A_v f_v \dfrac{d}{s} = 641 - 514 = 127$ kips

The shear, therefore, is not critical for the above condition.

For $\quad P = 2,590 - 650 = 1,940$ kips

$\quad\quad\quad M_u = 6,700$ ft.kips

$\quad\quad\quad V_u = 600$ kips

$\quad\quad\quad V_c = 395$ kips

and $\quad A_v f_y \dfrac{d}{s} = 600 - 395 = 205$ kips

The shear to be resisted by the ties acting as stirrups when the axial load is reduced because of vertical acceleration, in this example, is greater than that used to design the ties for the assumption of no vertical acceleration. Thus, for an assumed fluctuation in axial load of $0.25g$, the spacing of No. 5 ties is $s = 9.3$ in. The quantity $P/f_c'bd$ will range from 0.40 to 0.24 and the corresponding values of ϕ_u/ϕ_y from Fig. 5-17 are about 5 to 9.

7.9 Frame Displacement or Drift

The desirability of determining the approximate drift or deflection was pointed out in Chapter 4, even though lateral displacement is seldom critical in a multistory reinforced concrete building. The computations can be readily made from previously calculated values. Since by definition the stiffness λ is the force required to produce a unit displacement, the lateral displacement of a single story in the elastic range due to the shear in that story is

$$u = \frac{V_z}{\sum \lambda} \tag{7-1}$$

The total displacement u_z at any level z being equal to the sum of the displacement of all the stories below is therefore

$$u_z = \sum_{\text{base}}^{z} \frac{V_z}{\sum \lambda} \tag{7-2}$$

A portion of the calculations required for the structure under consideration is shown in Table 7-9. The values in cols. (3), (4), and (5) are taken directly from col. (6) of Table 7-3 and cols. (6) and (7) of Table 7-1, respectively. The values in col. (6) represent the displacement of a floor relative to the next lower floor and are calculated from equation (7-1). In col. (7), the total deflection is obtained by summing the values starting from the bottom.

As noted above, the total displacement at the roof level as determined in Table 7-9 is the displacement in the elastic range. It was suggested in Chapter 4 that this value be increased by a factor of 2 in order to account for possible excursions into the plastic range.

In general, it will be found that the approximate procedure as used here will give accurate values except when the girders are relatively flexible compared to

Frame Displacement or Drift

TABLE 7-9 Lateral Displacement

Floor	Story	Story stiffness $\dfrac{H_s^2}{12E_c}\Sigma\lambda$	Story shear V_z kips	Story height H_s ft.	Story displacement $\dfrac{(4)}{(3)}\cdot\dfrac{(5)^2}{12E_c}$ in.	Total displacement $\Sigma(6)$ in.
(1)	(2)	(3)	(4)	(5)	(6)	(7)
Rf.						1.816*
	24	1,896	180	14	0.045	
23						1.771
	23	2,510	378	14	0.071	
22						1.700
4						0.242
	4	13,460	2,060	12	0.053	
3						0.189
	3	15,240	2,080	12	0.047	
2						0.142
	2	10,340	2,100	12	0.070	
1						0.072
	1	15,860	2,120	15	0.072	
G						0

*With $H=295$ ft., the roof displacement $=\dfrac{1.816H}{12\times295}=0.0005H$

the columns. In the range where $E_cI_cL/E_gI_gH_s = 2.0$ and the base is fixed, no appreciable difference could be found between a more accurate solution and the proposed procedure. However, in the range of $E_cI_cL/E_gI_gH_s = 10.0$ the approximate procedure overestimated the deflection by as much as 60 per cent. The reason for this is that the approximate procedure assumes that equal rotation occurs at both ends of the columns. This condition often is not fully satisfied near the base. Hence, when the points of inflection in the columns depart considerably from midheight, the approximate procedure may not give an accurate indication of the displacement.

In most cases, because the lateral displacement is small, the discrepancies between the approximate and more accurate procedures are of minor significance. However, when the lateral displacement as computed by the approximate procedure exceeds limiting values, which should occur only when the girders are quite flexible compared to the columns, a more exact procedure is recommended. If it is desired merely to determine the displacement at one level with respect to the base, the following formula based on the moment area principle applied to the moments in a single column stack is suitable when the base is fixed.

$$u_z = \sum_{\text{base}}^{z} \frac{H_s^2}{6E_cI_c}\left[3\left(M_B - M_T\right)\left(\frac{a}{H_s}\right) + 2M_B - M_T\right] \qquad (7\text{-}3)$$

in which the summation is to be taken from the base to the level under consideration, and a equals the distance from the level for which the displacement is being determined to the top of the respective stories. If the base of the column rotates, the total displacement equals the value of u_z as given by equation (7-3) plus the product of the rotation times the distance from the base to the level under consideration.

When it is desired to know the displacement along the entire height, a more convenient form of equation (7-3) is

$$u_z = u_{z-1} + \frac{H_{s(z)}^2}{6EI}\left(2M_B - M_T\right) + H_{s(z)}\sum_{\text{base}}^{z-1}\frac{H_s}{2E_cI_c}(M_B - M_T) \qquad (7\text{-}4)$$

in which the summation is to be taken from the base to the floor below that under consideration. The H_s and E_cI_c values should be those associated with the M_B and M_T at each story. $H_{s(z)}$ is the height of the z story.

CHAPTER **8**

Construction and Inspection

8.1 Codes and Standards

Building construction must usually meet requirements set forth in a city, county, or state building code; compliance is enforced by law. Federal agencies generally have their own standard requirements that have much the same purpose as building codes. The purpose of building codes is to protect life, health, property, and the public welfare by controlling the design, construction, quality of materials, and use of buildings. Certain sections of building codes, particularly those relating to the structural parts of buildings such as the foundation, frame, floors, roof, and walls, often are patterned after the recommendations of committees of technical societies and industry organizations that have given special study to problems of design and construction. Those having responsibility for adequate design and proper construction should be thoroughly familiar with code requirements, recognized standards of good practice, and pertinent recommendations in reports of technical organizations, a number of which are listed among the references in Appendix D. Designers and specification writers should also know inspection and testing procedures. It is specifically to the construction and inspection of the structural parts of reinforced concrete buildings in seismic areas that this chapter is directed.

Meeting the requirements of codes and also the standards of recognized good practice begins with the plans and specifications of the architect and engineer. They must be based on thorough knowledge of site conditions and all other conditions and circumstances that will influence the design or construction of the building and its behavior throughout its existence.

8.2 Responsibility for Quality

It is generally considered that responsibility rests with the contractor to construct the buildings in strict accordance with adequate plans and specifications as prepared by the architect and structural engineer. Frequently, compliance with the plans and specifications is stipulated in the specifications or the contract, or in both, to be the legal responsibility of the contractor. Reputable contractors, just as professional architects and engineers, conscientiously endeavor to deliver to the owner a building that will give economical, satisfactory performance as designed and specified. In seismic areas it is particularly important that all requirements of plans and specifications be observed meticulously and that all workmanship be of high quality, because the possibility of earthquake damage is greatly increased by any construction deficiencies. It is a truism of building construction that good workmanship cannot be written into the specifications. Good workmanship is the result of employment of skilled, conscientious workmen working under vigilant and constant supervision by competent foremen and by the contractor's superintendent.

Supervision

It is not sufficient to leave supervision of workmanship and other job operations entirely to the contractor and his organization. The structural engineer, who has had the responsibility for determination of site conditions and the preparation of plans and specifications for the structural parts of a building to resist the effects of earthquake motions, should be retained to supervise the construction in the interest of the owner, the safety of the public, the professional reputation of the architect and engineer, and also the reputation of the contractor. In a paper concerning the performance of structures in the Kern County earthquake [84] it was said, "To construct earthquake resistant structures, the prime requisite is to provide for adequate engineering services both in the design and in the field supervision. Neither portion of the service is adequate alone. Too many engineers feel that if the design is adequate, the field construction will take care of itself. Experience has proven that nothing could be further from the truth."

Although the engineer as agent for the owner does not guarantee the work of the contractor, and in no way relieves the contractor of his responsibilities under the contract of which the plans and specifications are a part, the engineer must endeavor by general supervision to guard the owner against defects and deficiencies in the work. When in the engineer's judgment the intent of the plans and specifications is not being followed and he has been unable to secure compliance by the contractor, the owner should be notified so that appropriate measures may be taken to ensure compliance.

Supervision by the structural engineer should include continuous on-site inspection [85] during the construction of all structural parts of the building by one or more competent, technically qualified, and experienced inspectors employed by the owner on the recommendation of the structural engineer. The inspectors should be under the structural engineer's supervision and direction and should report directly to him or through the resident engineer, if the project is large enough to require one. It is the responsibility of the inspector to be sure that all details of the structural engineer's design drawings, and shop drawings and bar-placing plans when provided and approved by the structural engineer, are constructed exactly as shown, that all requirements of the specifications are met, and that workmanship and construction practices are of high standard. The structural engineer should make sure that all mechanical and electrical installations required are thoroughly coordinated with the structural design so that the strength and stiffness of members will not be affected unless taken into account in the design. The inspector should make sure as the job progresses that the mechanical and electrical installations are in accordance with drawings approved by the structural engineer and that any other nonstructural items do not adversely interfere with structural elements.

Supervision by the structural engineer and by the job inspector are quite different—particularly in one very important respect. The inspector should have no authority to change plans or specifications or to make his own interpretations, even though he may be and preferably should be a structural engineer with design as well as construction experience. If any question of interpretation arises, if there is a disagreement of understanding between the inspector and the contractor, or if any possibility of error or deviation from good practice should be noticed, it should immediately be brought to the attention of the structural engineer for decision. Professional supervision, on the other hand, includes authority to modify the plans and specifications consistent with the contracts, between the owner and the engineer (sometimes through an architect) and between the owner and the contractor, if job conditions indicate a change would be in the interest of improvement of the structure or otherwise justified and consistent with the sound design principles followed in the original design.

Inspector's Authority

Certain specific authority should be given to the inspector in order that he may function effectively; the contractor should be made cognizant of that authority by the structural engineer. The inspector should be authorized to:

1. Prohibit concreting until all preliminary preparations have been made and approved, including construction of forms and placing and securing of reinforcement, inserts, pipes, and other items that are to be embedded in the concrete.

2. Forbid the use of materials, equipment, or methods that have not been approved by the structural engineer or do not conform to specifications or will result in improper construction or inferior workmanship.
3. Stop any work that is not being done in accordance with the plans and specifications.
4. When specifically authorized by the structural engineer, require the removal or repair of faulty construction or of construction completed without inspection that cannot be inspected subsequently.

Stopping work or requiring the removal of completed work and reconstruction should be very carefully considered before being ordered, but should not be avoided if the safety of the structure is involved or the quality of the work is definitely inferior to that specified.

It is essential that the job inspector and those in responsible charge of work for the contractor are experienced in concrete construction and have a thorough knowledge of the fundamentals of high-quality concrete. Attention, however, will be directed in this manual to construction details and practices considered particularly significant in the construction and performance of buildings in seismic areas, even though some may be common to good construction in general. It should not be construed that factors and practices not specifically mentioned are unimportant. For further information a list of references (Appendix D) includes manuals and standards of the American Concrete Institute, standards of the American Society for Testing Materials, and selected publications of the Concrete Reinforcing Steel Institute, the National Ready Mixed Concrete Association, the Portland Cement Association, and the Wire Reinforcement Institute. The inspector should be familiar with and should have available for use on the job at least references 76, 78, 85, 86, 87, 88, 89, 90, 91, and 92.

8.3 Concrete

Either job-mixed or ready-mixed concrete is satisfactory for use in buildings in seismic areas, providing equivalent standards of quality control are observed. Selection of the method of producing the concrete depends upon job-site conditions, availability of ready-mixed concrete known to meet high standards of quality, the contractor's organization, and other factors primarily of concern to the contractor, who should therefore be free to decide how the concrete will be produced.

If ready-mixed concrete is to be used, certain requirements not common to job-mixed concrete should be included in the specifications or included by reference to the current ASTM specifications for ready-mixed concrete [93] unless such requirements conflict with other provisions of the specifications.

Inspector's Facilities

Whether concrete is purchased by the contractor from a ready-mix producer or batched and mixed at the job site, tests of the concrete must be made. The job inspector takes samples of the concrete, makes slump tests, and molds cylinders and cures them up to the time for shipment to a commercial laboratory for testing or tests them at the job in a testing machine of sufficient capacity and properly verified by means of standard calibrating devices in accordance with ASTM methods [94]. If the concrete is made at the job site, aggregate specimens must be taken and tested for grading, surface moisture, and impurities as well as for other properties. All tests should comply with the methods of tests recommended by the American Society for Testing Materials. In order that all such operations can be made under conditions conducive to good job control, the inspector should be provided with a laboratory equipped with work benches, sink, supply cabinet, specimen storage tank, and whatever other built-in facilities may be needed, at the contractor's expense. The size of the laboratory and the kind and

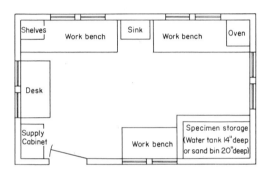

Fig. 8-1. Plan of inspector's laboratory and office for moderate-size building project. (Adapted from reference 86, ACI.)

amount of equipment will depend upon the job (see Fig. 8-1). Equipment, such as a set of standard sieves, scales, hot plate, slump cone, and other tools required for making ASTM tests, is generally provided by the employer of the inspector. A list of equipment often available to a job inspector is given in the American Concrete Institute *Manual of Concrete Inspection* [86].

Durability

Often the requirements of exposure rather than the strength will determine the maximum amount of mixing water. Tables giving water-cement ratios for various types of construction and exposure conditions are given in numerous publications [87, 88, 95]. Except for unusual conditions of exposure, the water-cement ratio for concrete in the interior of buildings and below grade should be selected on the basis of strength requirements. For thin concrete sections exposed to outside air in severe climate, not more than 5.5 gal. of water per sack of cement should be used. In mild climate, a 6-gal. mix is satisfactory. For foundations in soil or ground water containing sulfate concentrations of more than 0.2 per cent, not more than 4.5 gal. of mixing water should be used. Under such conditions, Type V sulfate-resisting portland cement should be used, if available; otherwise Type II or Type IIA portland cement, or Type IS-MS or Type IS-A-MS portland blast-furnace slag cement should be used. An air-entraining admixture should be used with Type II and Type IS-MS cements to give added resistance to sulfate attack.

Strength Control

The design strength of concrete used in the frame, floors, and walls of buildings should be as recommended elsewhere in this manual. It is particularly important in earthquake-resistant construction that the strength of the concrete should not fall below the specified design strength, because the design philosophy takes into consideration the dynamic behavior of the structure and also the inelastic characteristics of reinforced concrete even though it is only in the extreme emergency that deformations will be in the plastic range. This does not mean that because a single specimen or even a test (usually considered to be the average of two or more specimens from the same batch), occasionally falls below the specified strength, the strength of the structure is in jeopardy. It is commonly recognized [96] that "random variations and occasional failures to comply with strength requirements are inevitable. Accordingly, flexible strength requirements are realistic and control of the *pattern* of results, rather than individual values, is the most appropriate basis for both specifications and the general assessment of results."

Consistent with the working stress method of design, which is used in this manual and is commonly used in the design of earthquake-resistant structures, the ACI code [76], Section 304(c), specifies that "the average strength of laboratory-cured specimens representing each class of concrete as well as the average of any five consecutive strength tests (a test is the average of three specimens) representing each class of concrete shall be equal to, or greater than, the specified strength, and not more than one strength test in ten shall have an average value less than 90 per cent of the specified strength."

In order to satisfy the requirements of the code, the required average strength, according to statistical methods of analysis, for which the concrete must be proportioned must be somewhat higher than the design strength as determined by the following equation:

$$f'_r = \frac{0.9f'_c}{1 - \bar{t}\bar{V}} \qquad (8\text{-}1)$$

where

f'_c = assumed design strength or the minimum strength below which not more than one test in a given number may fall

$\bar{t}$ = a constant depending on the proportion of tests that may fall below $0.9f'_c$ and the number of samples used to establish $\bar{V}$ (see Table 8-1)

$\bar{V}$ = forecasted value of the coefficient of variation expressed as a fraction ($\bar{V}$, for good control, is 0.10 to 0.15).

By substituting the values of $\bar{t} = 1.282$ and $\bar{V} = 0.15$ in equation (8-1), the required average concrete strength for which a mix must be designed will be

$$f'_r = \frac{0.9f'_c}{1 - 1.282 \times 0.15} = 1.11f'_c$$

As noted above, the coefficient of variation $\bar{V}$ is 10 to 15 per cent for good

TABLE 8-1   Values of t^*

No. of samples minus 1	Chances of falling below lower limit		
	1.5 in 10	1 in 10	1 in 20
1	1.963	3.078	6.314
2	1.386	1.886	2.920
3	1.250	1.638	2.353
4	1.190	1.533	2.132
5	1.156	1.476	2.015
6	1.134	1.440	1.943
7	1.119	1.415	1.895
8	1.108	1.397	1.860
9	1.100	1.383	1.833
10	1.093	1.372	1.812
15	1.074	1.341	1.753
20	1.064	1.325	1.725
25	1.058	1.316	1.708
30	1.055	1.310	1.697
∞	1.036	1.282	1.645

*Adapted from reference 96, ACI.

control as established by experience from a large number of projects. A value of $\bar{V} < 0.10$ indicates excellent control, and $\bar{V} > 0.15$ indicates fair to poor control. $\bar{V}$ should be specified to be not greater than 0.15, and the value representative of the quality of control maintained by the job plant or the ready-mix plant supplying the job should be established on the basis of test results.

The quality of control currently maintained by a ready-mix plant should be readily determinable from records of most recent tests of not less than 100 standard cylinder specimens of concrete made of essentially the same materials and specified to have approximately the same strength as that specified for the job. If the calculated coefficient of variation is less than 0.15 and the lower value is maintained, as shown by 7-day tests (28-day extrapolated strengths) of 15 or more specimens of the job concrete, then the lower value may be used in calculating the required average strength f'_r for which the mix is designed. The job inspector should periodically make similar checks based on accumulated results of tests of concrete being delivered to the job, but no value of $\bar{V} < 0.10$ should be used in the calculation of f'_r.

When job-mixed concrete is to be used, an initial value of $\bar{V}$ may have to be assumed, but contractors who generally set up a job plant should have records representative of the quality of control maintained on other projects from which a calculated value could be determined. Such data may be used to establish an initial coefficient of variation, but a value less than 0.15 should not be used in the calculation of f'_r until such a value can be established by sufficient tests of

TABLE 8-2 Factors for Computing Within-Test
Standard Deviations*

Number of specimens	c	$\dfrac{1}{\bar{c}}$
2	1.128	0.8865
3	1.693	0.5907
4	2.059	0.4857
5	2.326	0.4299
6	2.534	0.3946
7	2.704	0.3698
8	2.847	0.3512
9	2.970	0.3367
10	3.078	0.3249

*Adapted from reference 96, ACI.

the job concrete. When 7-day test results from 15 specimens made on the job are available, the value of $\bar{V}$ should be determined. If it exceeds 0.15, measures should be taken to improve quality control and the required average strength f'_r should be increased in accordance with the calculated value of $\bar{V}$ until test results from an additional 15 specimens are accumulated, when a recalculation of $\bar{V}$ should be made. In the event the value of $\bar{V}$ is less than 15 per cent based on 30 specimens, no reduction in f'_r should be made unless equal or better quality control is shown by results of tests on a total of 100 specimens. Under no circumstances should a value of $\bar{V} < 0.10$ be used in the calculation of f'_r.

The value of $\bar{V}$ is determined [96] as

$$\bar{V} = 100\frac{\sigma}{\bar{X}} \tag{8-2}$$

in which

σ = the standard deviation or root-mean-square deviation of the strengths from their average

$\bar{X}$ = average strength of all cylinders used to establish $\bar{V}$

It is evident that it is economical to establish the best possible quality control. By reducing $\bar{V}$ from 0.15 to 0.10, the required average strength for which the mix must be designed is reduced from $1.11f'_c$ to $1.04f'_c$.

Variations in strength tests are due to: (a) the properties of the concrete, and (b) differences in making and curing specimens and in testing methods. It is desirable to distinguish between these primary causes of apparently large strength variations so that proper corrective measures may be taken and a higher-than-necessary average strength f'_r will not be required. It is reasonable to assume that a test sample of concrete is uniform and hence the within-test variation based upon the range of strength of companion specimens can be considered due to causes other than the properties of the concrete. Experience shows that with good job control the within-test coefficient of variation should be between 4 and 5 per cent [96]. If the calculated value based on 20 or more specimens is greater than 5 per cent, measures should be taken to conform more closely to the ASTM standard method of sampling fresh concrete [97], making and curing compression test specimens in the field [98], and testing molded concrete cylinders [99].

The within-test coefficient of variation can be determined [96] as follows:

$$\sigma_o = \frac{1}{c}\bar{R} \qquad (8\text{-}3)$$

$$\bar{V}_o = 100\frac{\sigma_o}{\bar{X}} \qquad (8\text{-}4)$$

in which

σ_o = within-test standard deviation

$\frac{1}{c}$ = a constant depending upon the number of companion specimens made from each test sample (see Table 8-2)

$\bar{R}$ = average range of groups of companion specimens

$\bar{V}_o$ = within-test coefficient of variation

$\bar{X}$ = average strength of all specimens

It is recommended that a job curve be established showing the relationship between the water-cement ratio and compressive strength at 28 days for the specific materials to be used, rather than selecting the water-cement ratio from average strength curves or a table of arbitrary values in which a very conservative allowance has been made for variations in materials and the quality of control. Having established a job curve that reflects the quality of control previously established, the water-cement ratio should be selected for the required average strength f'_r as computed above. In the event the water-cement ratio required for durability is less than that determined for f'_r from the job curve, the lower water-cement ratio should be used in proportioning the mix. It is also advantageous to establish the 3-, 7-, and 14-day water-cement ratio-strength curves as an indication of rate of strength gain in the event it should be desired to make tests at an earlier age than 28 days (as for the establishment of the value of $\bar{V}$) during the progress of the job.

Having prepared trial mixes with which to establish the job or plant curve, it is a simple matter to determine the proportions of fine and coarse aggregate that will give the desired strength and slump for a given water-cement ratio. The procedure for proportioning by trial mixes is thoroughly explained in *Design and Control of Concrete Mixtures* [87]. Table 8-3 is adapted from that publication. (See also references 88 and 95.)

Even though the concrete proportions are established by trial mixes, it is desirable to specify certain maximum or minimum values of water and cement content, slump, and size of coarse aggregate. Taking into consideration required

TABLE 8-3 Suggested Trial Mixes for Concrete of Medium Consistency (3-in. Slump*)

Maximum size of aggregate, in.	Water, gal. per sack of cement	Water, gal. per cu.yd. of concrete	Cement, sacks per cu.yd. of concrete	Fine agg., per cent of total agg.	Fine agg., lb. per sack of cement	Coarse agg., lb. per sack of cement	Fine agg., lb. per cu.yd. of concrete	Coarse agg., lb. per cu.yd. of concrete	Yield, cu.ft. concrete per sack of cement
\multicolumn{10}{With fine sand—fineness modulus 2.20–2.60}
$\frac{3}{4}$	5	38	7.6	43	170	230	1,290	1,750	3.56
1	5	37	7.4	38	160	255	1,185	1,890	3.65
$1\frac{1}{2}$	5	35	7.0	34	150	300	1,050	2,100	3.86
$\frac{3}{4}$	$5\frac{1}{2}$	38	6.9	44	195	250	1,345	1,725	3.91
1	$5\frac{1}{2}$	37	6.7	39	180	285	1,205	1,910	4.03
$1\frac{1}{2}$	$5\frac{1}{2}$	35	6.4	35	175	320	1,120	2,050	4.22
$\frac{3}{4}$	6	38	6.3	45	225	275	1,420	1,730	4.29
1	6	37	6.2	40	205	305	1,270	1,890	4.36
$1\frac{1}{2}$	6	35	5.8	36	200	355	1,160	2,060	4.66
$\frac{3}{4}$	$6\frac{1}{2}$	38	5.9	46	245	288	1,445	1,700	4.58
1	$6\frac{1}{2}$	37	5.7	41	230	330	1,310	1,880	4.74
$1\frac{1}{2}$	$6\frac{1}{2}$	35	5.4	37	225	380	1,215	2,050	5.00
\multicolumn{10}{With medium sand—fineness modulus 2.60–2.90}
$\frac{3}{4}$	5	38	7.6	45	180	220	1,370	1,670	3.56
1	5	37	7.4	40	165	250	1,220	1,850	3.65
$1\frac{1}{2}$	5	35	7.0	36	160	290	1,120	2,030	3.86
$\frac{3}{4}$	$5\frac{1}{2}$	38	6.9	46	205	240	1,415	1,655	3.91
1	$5\frac{1}{2}$	37	6.7	41	190	275	1,270	1,840	4.03
$1\frac{1}{2}$	$5\frac{1}{2}$	35	6.4	37	185	315	1,185	2,015	4.22
$\frac{3}{4}$	6	38	6.3	47	235	265	1,480	1,670	4.29
1	6	37	6.2	42	215	295	1,335	1,830	4.36
$1\frac{1}{2}$	6	35	5.8	38	210	345	1,220	2,000	4.66
$\frac{3}{4}$	$6\frac{1}{2}$	38	5.9	48	255	280	1,505	1,650	4.58
1	$6\frac{1}{2}$	37	5.7	43	240	320	1,370	1,825	4.74
$1\frac{1}{2}$	$6\frac{1}{2}$	35	5.4	39	235	370	1,270	2,000	5.00
\multicolumn{10}{With coarse sand—fineness modulus 2.90–3.20}
$\frac{3}{4}$	5	38	7.6	47	185	210	1,370	1,595	3.56
1	5	37	7.4	42	175	240	1,295	1,775	3.65
$1\frac{1}{2}$	5	35	7.0	38	170	280	1,190	1,960	3.86
$\frac{3}{4}$	$5\frac{1}{2}$	38	6.9	48	215	230	1,480	1,585	3.91
1	$5\frac{1}{2}$	37	6.7	43	200	265	1,340	1,775	4.03
$1\frac{1}{2}$	$5\frac{1}{2}$	35	6.4	39	195	305	1,250	1,950	4.22
$\frac{3}{4}$	6	38	6.3	49	245	255	1,540	1,610	4.29
1	6	37	6.2	44	225	285	1,395	1,770	4.36
$1\frac{1}{2}$	6	35	5.8	40	225	335	1,305	1,945	4.66
$\frac{3}{4}$	$6\frac{1}{2}$	38	5.9	50	265	265	1,560	1,560	4.58
1	$6\frac{1}{2}$	37	5.7	45	250	310	1,425	1,765	4.74
$1\frac{1}{2}$	$6\frac{1}{2}$	35	5.4	41	250	355	1,350	1,920	5.00

*Increase or decrease water per cu.yd. of concrete by 3 per cent for each increase or decrease of 1 in. in slump, then recalculate quantities of cement and aggregates to maintain the quality of concrete. For stone sand, increase percentage of sand by 3 and water by 15 lb. per cu.yd. of concrete.

strength, consistency and aggregate size for good placeability, and normal exposure and shrinkage, the following values are recommended:

Water content, maximum	6.0 gal. per sack
Cement content, minimum	5.5 sacks per cubic yard*
Slump, maximum	4.0 in.
Maximum size of aggregate for frame members, floors, and walls	1.0 in.
Maximum size of aggregate for foundations and other massive work	1.5 in.

When durability requirements control, a lower maximum water content per sack of cement should be specified as discussed under Durability on page 207. Consequently, a somewhat higher minimum cement content will be needed to produce concrete of the same slump as that with a higher water content.

Acceptance of Materials and Field Control Tests

If ready-mixed concrete is to be used, the producer (or a designated laboratory satisfactory to the engineer, producer, and purchaser) should be required to furnish a statement to the purchaser, with a copy to the job inspector, giving the proportions by dry weight of cement and fine and coarse aggregate that will be used in the manufacture of each class of concrete ordered. He should also furnish evidence satisfactory to the purchaser and the job inspector that the proportions selected and the materials to be used will produce concrete of the quality specified. Such evidence should include test reports showing that the cement complies with the designated ASTM specification for cement [100, 101, 102, 103]. Certification of compliance with one of the standard cement specifications shown by mill tests is usually acceptable.

Concrete aggregates must also meet the requirements of ASTM specifications [104, 105] as to grading, deleterious substances, and soundness. The job inspector should conduct necessary tests to determine the quality of the aggregate to be used or should base his acceptance of the material on testing laboratory reports.

Some aggregates contain elements that may be destructively reactive with the alkalies (sodium and potassium oxide) in portland cement. Such aggregates should not be used in concrete that is subject to frequent wetting or extended exposure to humid atmosphere or that is in contact with moist ground if it can be avoided. If aggregate shown to be nonreactive by experience or laboratory tests according to ASTM methods [106, 107, 108, 109] is not available and an aggregate known to be reactive must be used, it should be used with a cement containing less than 0.6 per cent alkalies or with the addition of a material (pozzolan) that has been shown to prevent harmful expansion. Caution should be exercised in

---

*In nearly all cases more than this minimum amount of cement will be needed to obtain the desired slump without exceeding the maximum allowable water content per sack. The final mix design, including the necessary cement content to meet the other stated requirements, should be approved by the job inspector as a representative of the engineer. In some areas, the minimum allowable cement content is used for bidding purposes and an extra is charged for cement used in excess of the minimum requirement.

the use of pozzolans because their properties vary widely and some may introduce undesirable properties into the concrete. It is advisable before acceptance to test a pozzolan with the cement and aggregate to be used on the job. Sea water or other water containing salts of sodium and potassium should not be used in concrete containing reactive aggregate.

If at any time there should be a question as to the quality of the materials being used or of the concrete produced, the job inspector should be permitted to obtain samples of materials at the producer's plant on which to make appropriate tests.

The ready-mix producer's delivery tickets issued with each load delivered should contain as a minimum the following information:

1. Class of mix
2. Actual weight of cement in the mix
3. Yardage delivered
4. Identifying number
5. Transit or central mixed

When there is difficulty in maintaining the specified quality of the concrete, it may be desirable to require additional information on the delivery ticket, such as weight of surface-dry fine and coarse aggregate, weight of water including moisture in the fine aggregate, amount of admixture (if any), and slump.

If job-mixed concrete is to be used, the job inspector should develop for himself information similar to that required of the ready-mixed concrete producer to establish that the concrete is in every way the quality specified. He should also make slump tests [110] at such intervals as may be necessary to be sure that the concrete going into the forms has the specified consistency, just as he would do with ready-mixed concrete. During the progress of the work he should also make and cure compression test specimens complying with applicable ASTM specifications [97, 98]. Not less than three specimens should be made for each test, nor less than one test for each 250 cu.yd. of concrete of each class, but in no case should there be less than one test for each day's concreting.

The age of tests should normally be 28 days, but it is recommended that 7-day tests as well be made during the early stages of the job. When this is done the relationship between 7- and 28-day strengths of the concrete should have been established previously by tests for the materials and proportions used. As already noted, it may be desirable to make occasional specimens for 3- and 14-day tests to be sure that the rate of gain in strength is satisfactory and that the strength of concrete in place is adequate for stripping forms.

Lightweight-Aggregate Concrete

Concrete made with lightweight aggregate of the expanded shale and clay type (also expanded slag), is satisfactory for use in buildings subject to earthquake motions, providing the particular aggregate selected will produce a concrete having structural properties generally comparable to that made with sand and gravel, crushed stone, or slag. Various lightweight concretes, even those containing aggregates produced by similar processes, show substantial variations in such structural properties as strength, modulus of elasticity, creep, shear, bond, and shrinkage. It is therefore important that individual producers conduct investigations to provide reliable design data for specific materials. The structural engineer should obtain such information before proceeding with his design or before acceptance of a specific aggregate to be sure its use will produce a concrete of the properties assumed in the design.

It is pointed out by a subcommittee of ACI Committee 613 that: "The principles of normal weight concrete proportioning as established by ACI Standard 'Recommended Practice for Selecting Proportions for Concrete (ACI 613-54)' apply directly to lightweight-aggregate concretes, but generally the application of these principles is difficult. However, conventional procedures may be used with good results for such lightweight aggregates generally characterized by rounded particle shape, coated or sealed surfaces, and relatively low values of absorption." [111]

The principal difficulty in proportioning lightweight-aggregate concrete by the procedure of trial mixes, based on the water-cement ratio and the absolute volumes of the materials, is that the amount of mixing water absorbed by the aggregate and the amount that remains to occupy space in the concrete cannot be determined accurately. Furthermore, because of the large amount of water that is absorbed by some aggregates and because absorption continues at an appreciable rate and for variable lengths of time, it is difficult to obtain correct values of the specific gravity of the aggregates [111]. For these reasons, the net water-cement ratio of most lightweight-aggregate concretes cannot be established accurately; therefore, a series of trial mixes proportioned on a cement content basis at the required consistency should be made to establish lightweight-aggregate concrete mixes as recommended in the subcommittee report [111]. The job inspector should be thoroughly acquainted with this trial mix procedure as distinguished from that for concrete made with sand and gravel or crushed stone aggregates [87].

Tests have been made to determine the structural properties of lightweight-aggregate concrete in comparison with sand-and-gravel or other normal-weight concrete. Anyone contemplating design of a building using lightweight-aggregate concrete, and the job inspector, should read the full text of references 113 and 114 and technical data supplied by manufacturers of specific aggregates.

Hot-Weather Concreting

Consistent production of concrete complying with the requirements recommended on page 208 necessitates taking into consideration the effects of high temperatures on concrete strengths [115]. Although hot weather presents special problems in manufacture, placement, and curing of concrete, they are readily met by observation of a few known principles and following certain practical procedures at the mixing plant and on the job. During the season of the year when the temperature of concrete as normally produced and placed may go above 85 deg. or 90 deg. F., provision should be made, *in advance of the need*, to maintain a more desirable temperature. Difficulties such as accelerated setting, reduced slump, greater mixing water demand (see Fig. 8-2), improper placement and finishing, and larger volume changes resulting from high temperatures at time of placement can seldom be controlled by hurried improvisations.

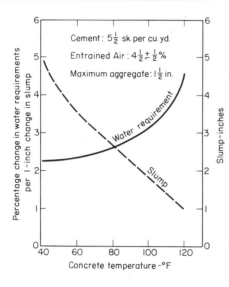

Fig. 8-2. Effect of concrete temperature on slump and on water required to change slump. (Average of data for Types I and II cements.)

Tests [116] indicate that the optimum temperature during the early life of concrete with regard to strength at later ages is somewhat influenced by cement type. For Types I and II this temperature is 55 deg. F. and for Type III it is 40 deg. F., as shown in Fig. 8-3. These optimum temperatures of concrete at time of placement are lower than can generally be attained in hot weather [117]. A temperature of 60 deg. F., or lower, is desirable and a temperature above 90 deg. F. at time of placement should not be permitted.

The most effective means of maintaining the placement temperature of concrete within permissible limits is by cooling the ingredients, particularly the water because of its high specific heat. Sprinkling the aggregate stockpiles results in cooling by evaporation, especially when the relative humidity is low, and therefore aids materially in reducing the temperatures of the concrete because of the volume of aggregate involved. It is a simple matter to calculate quite accurately the temperature of the concrete as mixed knowing the temperatures and quantities of the ingredients in a batch [115].

The cement temperature also contributes to the temperature of the concrete. However, the influence of the cement temperature on the final temperature of the concrete is relatively small because of its low specific heat and the small amount of cement compared to the other ingredients. Strength tests [116] of con-

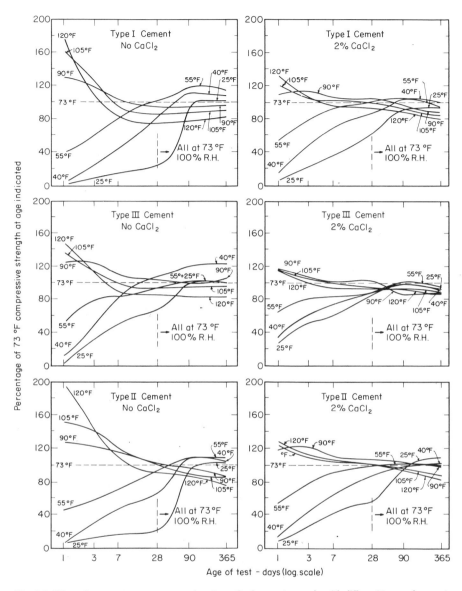

Fig. 8-3. Effect of temperature on compressive strength of concretes made with different types of cement. (All specimens—Cement: 5½ sacks per cubic yard. Entrained air: 4½ ± ½ per cent)

crete made with cement at three different temperatures, 74, 148, and 177 deg. F., show that the cement temperature in itself exerts no significant influence on the strength of the concrete so long as the comparison is made on the basis of equal concrete temperatures. This fact is illustrated in Fig. 8-4. In other words, high temperature of the cement has no detrimental effects on the concrete ex-

217

cept as it contributes to raising the temperature of the concrete.

During hot weather, concrete for floors should be placed and finished as rapidly as possible consistent with good workmanship. The inspector should be sure that there are sufficient men and materials available to complete the work without delay. He should also be sure that means have been provided to control

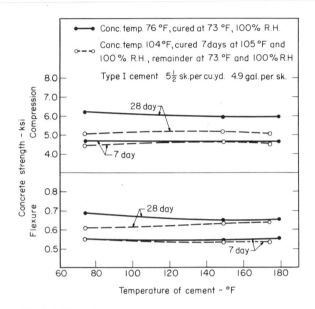

Fig. 8-4. Effect of temperature of cement on concrete strength.

excessive surface evaporation before starting to place concrete. The use of a fog spray, windbreaks, and sunshades will reduce surface evaporation. After concrete is placed and is still plastic and workable, moisture appears on the surface due to normal bleeding as the aggregate and cement tend to settle. When the rate of evaporation exceeds the rate at which bleeding water rises to the surface, plastic shrinkage and cracking are likely to occur because the surface of the concrete has attained some initial rigidity, but has not developed sufficient strength to withstand the tensile stress due to rapid volume change. The effect of variations in concrete and air temperature, relative humidity, and wind speed on rate of evaporation is clearly shown in Table 8-4 [118].

Curing of concrete in floors or other flat surfaces immediately following final finishing is particularly important, especially in hot, dry, windy weather. Curing with water is the preferred method and is strongly recommended during the first 24 hours. To prevent damage to the surface, a very fine fog or mist spray should be used for the first few hours after finishing. A film of moisture should be on the surface continuously because intermittent wetting and drying may ac-

TABLE 8-4 Effect of Variations in Concrete and Air Temperatures, Relative Humidity, and Wind Speed on Drying Tendency of Air at Job Site

Case No.	Concrete temp., deg. F.	Air temp., deg. F.	Relative humidity, %	Dewpoint, deg. F.	Wind speed	Drying tendency, lb. per sq. ft. per hr.
(1) Increase in wind speed						
1	70	70	70	59	0	.015
2	70	70	70	59	5	.038
3	70	70	70	59	10	.062
4	70	70	70	59	15	.085
5	70	70	70	59	20	.110
6	70	70	70	59	25	.135
(2) Decrease in relative humidity						
7	70	70	90	67	10	.020
8	70	70	70	59	10	.062
9	70	70	50	50	10	.100
10	70	70	30	37	10	.135
11	70	70	10	13	10	.175
(3) Increase in concrete and air temperatures						
12	50	50	70	41	10	.026
13	60	60	70	50	10	.043
14	70	70	70	59	10	.062
15	80	80	70	70	10	.077
16	90	90	70	79	10	.110
17	100	100	70	88	10	.180
(4) Concrete at 70 deg. F.; decrease in air temperature						
18	70	80	70	70	10	.000
19	70	70	70	59	10	.062
20	70	50	70	41	10	.125
21	70	30	70	21	10	.165
(5) Concrete at high temp.; air at 40 deg. F. and 100% R. H.						
22	80	40	100	40	10	.205
23	70	40	100	40	10	.130
24	60	40	100	40	10	.075
(6) Concrete at high temp.; air at 40 deg. F.; variable wind						
25	70	40	50	23	0	.035
26	70	40	50	23	10	.162
27	70	40	50	23	25	.357
(7) Decrease in concrete temp.; air at 70 deg. F.						
28	80	70	50	50	10	.175
29	70	70	50	50	10	.100
30	60	70	50	50	10	.045
(8) Concrete and air at high temp.; 10% R. H.; variable wind						
31	90	90	10	26	0	.070
32	90	90	10	26	10	.336
33	90	90	10	26	25	.740

centuate craze cracking. Where continued moist curing after the first 24 hours is impractical, reinforced waterproof paper with all edges sealed should be applied immediately and before the surface shows evidence of drying. A white-pigmented, sprayed-on, membrane curing compound can be used, but it does not afford as positive protection for the surface as a tough waterproofed paper. Any traffic on the floor must be prohibited during the curing period.

The job inspector should be particularly vigilant during hot weather to check:
1. temperature of concrete at time of placement,
2. slump,
3. water-cement ratio,
4. cement factor,
5. early curing and protective measures to minimize temperature of concrete and moisture evaporation, and
6. effect of admixture, if specified for use at normal temperatures.

The inspector must exercise special care to protect test cylinders. Even though the cylinders are in molds, they should not be exposed to the sun and should be covered with damp sand or wet burlap or kept in a fog spray to minimize temperature and to ensure retention of water in the specimens. Acceptance test specimens at the age of 1 day should be transferred from the job to the laboratory or to a location where they will receive continuous moist curing at specified temperatures until tested in accordance with ASTM specifications [98], [99].

Cold-Weather Concreting

Special precautions must also be taken during and after placing concrete in cold weather [119]. Plastic shrinkage cracks, for example, may occur if the temperature of the concrete is high when the air temperature is low, even though the relative humidity may be 100 per cent and the wind velocity quite low. With lower humidity and comparatively high wind velocity, which often occurs in winter, the condition is still further aggravated (see Table 8-4).

Strength of the concrete in the structure may be considerably less than desired if the concrete is placed at too high a temperature or allowed to become overheated because of proximity to a source of heat during curing. Thermal shrinkage cracks can also result from withdrawing protection from the concrete too rapidly, thus exposing it to a sudden drop in temperature.

The inspector should make sure that preparations are made, *in advance of the need*, to heat the concrete materials and to protect the concrete from freezing after it is placed. To assure freedom from freezing until protection can be provided, the temperature of the concrete after placing and for 72 hours thereafter should not be less than shown in line 7 of Table 8-5.

At no time should materials be heated to the extent that the fresh concrete is above 80 deg. F. because of the adverse effects on the plastic and hardened concrete as previously mentioned. It is not difficult to maintain concrete as mixed at temperatures not more than 10 deg. F. above the minimums recommended in Table 8-5. The desired temperature is readily maintained by adjusting the temperature of the mixing water; it seldom needs to be heated above 140 deg. F. The temperature of the mixture of aggregates and water should rarely exceed 80 deg. F. at the time the cement is added to the batch to avoid the possibility of flash set.

TABLE 8-5 Effect of Temperatures of Materials
on Temperature of Various Freshly Mixed Concretes**

Line			For thin sections							
1	Approx. max. size rock, in.		¾				1½			
2	Approx. per cent sand		40				35			
3	Wt. of sand for batch, lb.		1,200				1,100			
4	Wt. of rock for batch, lb.		1,800				2,100			
5	Wt. of water for batch, lb.		300				250			
6	Wt. of cement for batch, lb.		600				500			
7	Min. temp. fresh concrete after placing and for first 72 hours, deg. F.		55				50			
8	Min. temp. fresh concrete	Above 30 F.	60				55			
9	as mixed, for weather,*	0 to 30 F.	65				60			
10	deg. F.	Below 0 F.	70				65			
11	Min. temp. of materials	Cement†	35	10	10	−10	35	10	10	−10
12	to produce indicated temp.	Added water	140	140	140	140	140	140	140	140
13	of freshly mixed concrete,	Aggr. water‡	38	95	50	61	35	100	46	55
14	deg. F.	Sand	38	95	50	61	35	100	46	55
15		Rock	38	10§	50	61	35	10§	46	55
16	Temp. freshly mixed concrete, deg. F.		60	65	65	70	55	60	60	65
17	Max. allowable gradual drop in temp. throughout first 24 hours after end of protection, deg. F.		50				40			

*For colder weather a greater margin in temperature is provided between concrete as mixed and required minimum temperature of fresh concrete in place.
†Cement temperature has been taken as the same as that of average air and of unheated materials.
‡The amount of free water in the aggregate has been assumed equal to ¼ of the mix water.
§Rock at temperatures below freezing is assumed to be surface-dry and free of ice.

$$\text{Temperature of fresh concrete} = \frac{0.2(T_a W_a + T_c W_c) + T_w W_w}{0.2(W_a + W_c) + W_w}$$

T = temperature a = aggregate w = water
W = weight c = cement
**Adapted from reference 119, ACI.

Concrete made with other than high-early-strength cement, and which contains entrained air in the amounts noted on page 223 and 1 per cent calcium chloride, should be maintained at or above the minimum recommended temperature (line 7, Table 8-5) after placing for the first 3 days and above freezing for the next 3 days. For concrete made with high-early-strength cement and containing entrained air, the minimum recommended temperatures after placing should be maintained for 2 days and above freezing for the next 2 days. Concrete that does not contain entrained air and concrete made with other than high-early-strength cement and without calcium chloride must be protected to maintain the temperature of the concrete at the minimum recommended (line 7, Table 8-5) twice as long as that with entrained air and calcium chloride. Maintenance of 50-deg. protection longer than 6 days is unnecessary whether or not the concrete contains entrained air or calcium chloride. Calcium chloride should never be used in amounts greater than 2 per cent by weight of the cement. It should not be used at all: (1) when sulfate-resisting concrete is needed, (2) when there is a possibility of alkali-aggregate reaction, or (3) in prestressed concrete where it could come in contact with the prestressing steel.

Rapid chilling of the surface of mass concrete when protection is removed while the interior is substantially above atmospheric temperature may cause serious cracking. Even in relatively thin sections such as floors, columns, and walls, objectionable (although not serious) surface cracking may result. Protection should be withdrawn gradually so the maximum drop in temperature throughout the first 24 hours will not be more than that given in line 17 of Table 8-5.

There are a number of ways of protecting concrete to maintain the "as placed" temperature for the prescribed length of time. If adequate precautions are taken to conserve the heat of hydration so that the temperature at the edges and corners of the concrete does not fall below the required minimum, it is often not necessary to provide additional heat. When heat must be provided, it is best to use exhaust steam at moderate temperature to furnish moisture as well. Protective measures, including the use of insulation materials, are described in detail in various publications [119]. The job inspector should be thoroughly acquainted with such measures and the adequacy of those employed. He should keep records of outside and inside air temperatures at several places and the temperature of the concrete surface taken at a number of points. The record should include maximum and minimum outside temperatures each 24 hours, wind velocity, relative humidity, and other weather conditions that may influence the condition of the concrete. Before concrete is placed, the inspector should make sure that all surfaces against which concrete is to be deposited are free from ice and snow and that the temperaure of the surface is above freezing.

Air Entrainment

The effectiveness of air entrainment to increase the durability of concrete exposed to freezing and thawing and other severe exposure conditions has been firmly established. Air entrainment is also beneficial to the protection of concrete from damage during the first few days after placement in cold weather, while protective measures against freezing are being used. It improves the placeability and cohesiveness of concrete and reduces segregation. Such concrete is more readily worked through and around reinforcement, thereby ensuring the assumed bond, shear, and flexural strength.

To assure protection against deterioration of concrete subject to severe exposure and to be beneficial during the first few days after placement, the mix should be designed for an air content of 5 per cent for 1½-in. maximum size aggregate and 6 per cent for 1-in. aggregate. A tolerance of plus or minus 1 per cent is generally allowed. Whenever intentionally entrained air is specified, the job inspector should make frequent tests to determine the amount of air in the concrete as it is placed. A number of methods for measuring air content of fresh concrete are in use. There are ASTM standard or tentative methods of tests for the gravimetric [120], volumetric [121], and pressure [122] methods. The pressure method can be carried out somewhat more readily in the field than the other methods. Fig. 8-5 illustrates three steps in the use of pressure-method equipment for measuring the air content of fresh concrete:

1. The bowl is slightly overfilled in three rodded layers and struck off.
2. The cone-shaped cover is clamped to the bowl flange and the space above the concrete is then filled with water to the zero mark on the graduated glass tube.
3. Pressure is applied to concrete by pumping air into the space over the water column until the pressure gage indicates predetermined operating pressure.

All steps, including final determination of apparent and actual air content, must be made in accordance with ASTM Method of Test C 231[122]. While air entrainment reduces strength as compared to non-air-entrained concrete, its effect in this respect is automatically taken into account in the job curve giving

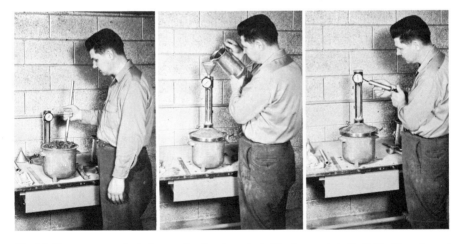

Fig. 8-5. The pressure method of measuring the air content of fresh concrete in the field with equipment illustrated is comparatively simple. All steps including final determination of apparent and actual air content must be made in accordance with ASTM Method of Test C 231.

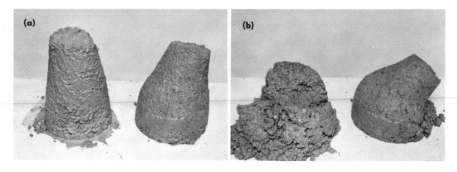

Fig. 8-6. (a) The non-air-entrained, lightweight-aggregate concrete at the left is harsh as shown by the appearance near the bottom and by the water draining from the sample. The better workability and cohesiveness of the sample at the right, which contains about 7 per cent purposely entrained air, is clearly evident. **(b)** The same samples after being struck several times with a tamping rod show even more vividly the improvement in workability and cohesiveness of the mix through air entrainment.

the relationship between water-cement ratio and strength for the materials used and the specified air content.

The use of entrained air is recommended in lightweight concrete whether or not it is required for durability or protection in cold weather concreting. Some lightweight aggregates are quite angular and tend to produce harsh mixes. Air entrainment is the most effective means of producing workable concrete without increasing the water requirement. It also tends to reduce the percentage of fine material in the mix and correspondingly minimizes the cement required for a specified slump. Its influence on cohesiveness and workability is illustrated in Fig. 8-6, which shows two mixes containing identical proportions of cement, lightweight aggregate, and water. It is recommended that all lightweight-aggregate concrete contain not less than 6 per cent purposely entrained air. Of the several methods for measuring the air content of fresh concrete, the best results with lightweight-aggregate concrete are generally obtained by the volumetric method [121].

Admixtures

An admixture is defined as any material used as an ingredient of concrete that is introduced at the mixer other than the accepted cements, aggregate, and water. Such materials, even though added to one of the three principal ingredients of the concrete and introduced into the mixer with that ingredient, are considered admixtures. There are admixtures intended for many purposes including accelerators, retarders, water-reducing and air-entraining agents, and others.

Some admixtures such as air-entraining agents [123] and certain accelerators such as calcium chloride [124] are covered by ASTM specifications. Certification of compliance with the applicable ASTM specification by the manufacturer or supplier of those admixtures for which there are such specifications is usually considered satisfactory evidence of quality and uniformity of the product.

Many other admixtures intended for use in concrete are not covered by ASTM specifications. When such materials are proposed or considered for use in concrete, the manufacturer or supplier should be required to supply data so that the admixture may be identified physically and chemically and may be accepted without the necessity of making physical property tests of the concrete for each lot of the admixture. In lieu of basing acceptance on duplication of physical and chemical properties of the admixture already proven of merit in concrete to the purchaser's satisfaction, the purchaser may require that a sample of each lot be tested in concrete [125] to prove the merit of the individual lot of the admixture.

An acceptance test procedure should be provided by the admixture manufacturer that will enable the purchaser to determine readily a complete chemical analysis of the material. The manufacturer should also furnish the chemical limitations on the composition of the admixture. Acceptance tests, complying with ASTM methods of testing, should show the effect of the material on (1) the autoclave expansion [126] and time of setting of neat cement pastes [127, 128], and on (2) the air content [129] and tensile [130] and compressive strengths [131] of portland cement mortar.

Evidence should be furnished that concrete containing the proposed admixture in the specified amounts possesses the property for which the admixture is recommended. In addition, the concrete should possess in all other respects (as demonstrated by ASTM methods of testing) essentially the same or better physical properties as similar concrete without the admixture. The mix design of the concrete without the admixture should be the optimum obtainable with the job ingredients. Similar concretes in which the effectiveness of the proposed admixture is determined should be concretes made with the same cement and aggregate and having the same cement content, workability, and air content when over 2 per cent.

When the admixture is delivered in packages, the name and brand of the manufacturer and the classification or purpose of the admixture should be plainly indicated thereon. Similar information should be provided in shipping advices accompanying the shipment of packaged or bulk admixtures.

The inspector should periodically check any automatic dispensing equipment for admixtures to ensure that the proper amounts are being used.

Handling, Transporting, and Placing Concrete

Proper handling, transporting, and placing of concrete is just as essential to developing the desired strength in the structure as proper proportioning and mixing. The basic requirements for moving concrete from the mixer into the forms in buildings in seismic areas are the same as for high-quality construction anywhere. This means "that at all points from the mixer to concrete in place, only those methods and arrangements of equipment should be used which will reduce to a minimum any separation of coarse aggregate from the concrete (Figs. 8-7 and 8-8). . . No part of any concrete handling and placing equipment should be accepted if it requires, for efficient operation, mixes containing larger

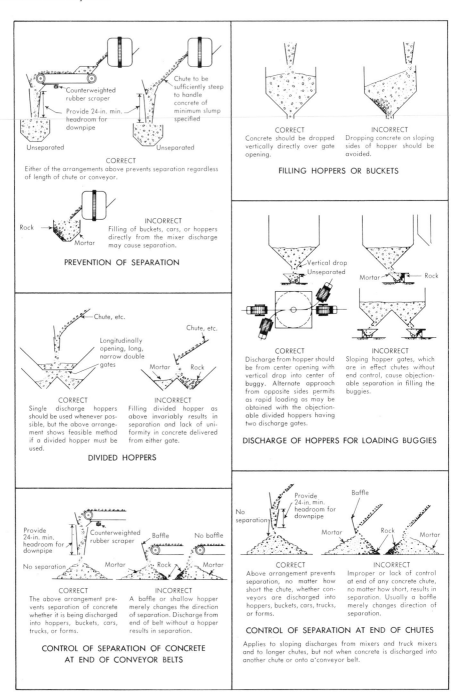

Fig. 8-7. Correct and incorrect methods of handling and transporting mixed concrete. (Adapted from reference 132, ACI.)

proportions of sand, cement and water, or smaller coarse aggregate than are practicable in mixes consolidated by vibration." The preceding quotation is from a report [132] of ACI Committee 614. The job inspector should be thoroughly familiar with this report.

Segregation at the point of discharge from the mixer can be prevented by providing a down pipe at the end of the chute so that the concrete will drop vertically into the center of the receiving bucket, hopper, or buggy. Similar provision should be made at the ends of all other chutes or conveyors. Buckets and hoppers should be provided with a vertical drop at the discharge gate. When discharge is at an angle, the larger aggregate is thrown to the far side of the container being charged and the mortar is thrown to the near side. The resulting segregation may not be corrected upon further handling of the concrete.

Tall hoist towers and long chutes should not be permitted and short chutes should be designed so that the concrete will travel fast enough to keep the chute clean but not so fast that the materials will segregate. A slope that is not flatter than 1 to 3 and not steeper than 1 to 2 is often recommended, but there is no objection to using a steeper slope for stiff mixes. The criterion for the slope of a chute is the condition of the concrete as it is discharged.

Buggies are preferred for placing concrete in walls and beams of the dimensions common in building construction because the rate of placing and distribution can be readily controlled and coordinated with the consolidation of the concrete in the forms. Buckets can be used satisfactorily, however, if of moderate size and provided with gates that can be regulated to control the flow of concrete and can be closed after only part of the load has been deposited. Regardless of the equipment used for transporting the concrete to the forms, care should be taken to prevent jarring and shaking to minimize any tendency to segregate.

The inspector should confer with the job superintendent before placing of concrete is to begin. There should be complete understanding and agreement on the methods, equipment, tools, and manpower required for handling, transporting, placing, consolidating, finishing, and curing of the concrete. Special consideration should be given to transporting the concrete to areas remote from the place of delivery and to the placement of concrete in areas of unavoidable steel congestion and high vertical drops. If this is done, time and expense will be saved and the quality of the work improved.

Before placing concrete for a foundation, the inspector should make sure that the excavation has been made to the specified elevation and that all surfaces against which concrete is to be placed have been properly trimmed. In general, all such surfaces should be horizontal and vertical, not sloping. Where the foundation material is rock, all loose material should be removed and all contact surfaces, whether rock or soil, should be moist when the concrete is placed, but there should be no standing pools of water or muddy conditions of the soil. If deemed necessary by the engineer, the adequacy of the foundation bearing capacity should be verified.

Forms should be clean, tight, adequately braced, and constructed of ma-

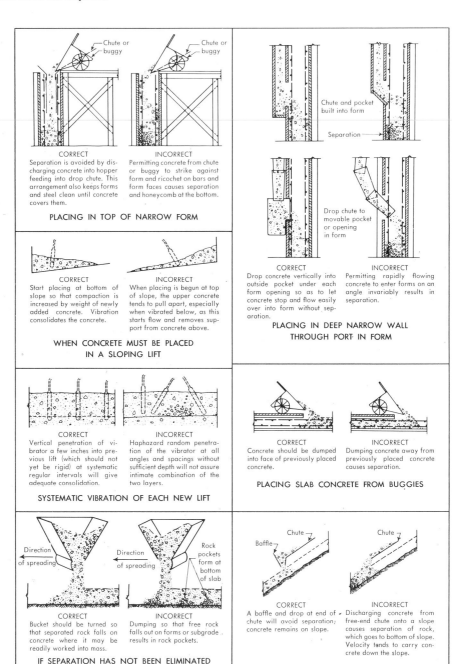

Fig. 8-8. Correct and incorrect methods of placing concrete. (Adapted from reference 132, ACI.)

terials that will impart the desired texture to the finished concrete. The inspector should determine that water, sawdust, chips, nails, and all other debris have been removed from spaces to be concreted before permitting any placing operations to be started in the vicinity. Forms should be oiled or moistened before placing concrete. If they have been exposed to the sun for some time, it may be necessary to saturate the wood thoroughly to tighten joints and to prevent absorption from the concrete. Plywood forms are sometimes lacquered instead of being wetted or oiled. All reinforcement, electrical conduits, piping, and other embedded items should be carefully checked before permitting any concrete to be placed.

Placing procedures have much to do with the durability and strength of a structure. Concrete should be placed as nearly as practicable in its final position and should not be allowed to run or be pushed from one place to another. Whenever the concrete runs or is pushed, the mortar tends to flow ahead of the coarse aggregate, resulting in segregation, stone pockets, and weak sections in the structure. Sloping planes, which are unsightly if the concrete is left exposed, often result from improper placement; even more important, the strength of the member or element is impaired.

Concrete should be deposited vertically in forms and should not be allowed to drop freely more than 3 or 4 ft. Rubber or metal drop chutes should be provided for higher walls and columns to prevent segregation and splashing of forms and reinforcement. Concrete should be placed in layers as nearly horizontal as possible and generally of uniform thickness of 12 to 24 in. in reinforced members. The rate of placing concrete and the thickness of each layer will depend upon the width between forms, the amount of reinforcement, the ability to thoroughly consolidate the concrete around the reinforcement, and the requirement that each layer must be placed before the previous one stiffens. In addition, the rate of placement should not be faster than that for which the forms were designed.

All concrete should be of such consistency as to require vibration for proper consolidation. The use of vibrators should begin immediately with the placement of concrete. Planes of weakness, such as cold joints in shear walls which occur when concrete already in place has stiffened to the degree that it will not become plastic under vibration when the next layer of concrete is placed, should be avoided. By placing concrete in layers not over 2 ft. deep and by letting the vibrator penetrate vertically a few inches into the previously placed layer which is still soft enough to become plastic, the succeeding layers will be thoroughly consolidated and will develop the full strength of the concrete. Vibrators should be inserted at points about 18 to 30 in. apart so that vibration for 5 to 15 seconds at each point will suffice to plasticize the mass. Longer vibration will tend to separate the ingredients in the mix, particularly if the consistency is near the limit for vibration, which is indicated by a slump of 3 to 4 in. Proper consolidation with vibrators is essential to obtain structural integrity and satisfactory surface appearance [133, 134].

Interaction between beams and the supporting walls and columns is generally assumed in design. To obtain a strong joint at the top of walls and columns, the placing of the concrete in floor slab and beams should be delayed as long as possible to permit shrinkage or settlement of the deep concrete to take place. Similarly, the placing of slab concrete over deep beams should be delayed to allow shrinkage of the concrete in the beam stem. The delay should not be so long, however, that the concrete in place will not become plastic when penetrated by the vibrator as the floor concrete is placed. When the weather is hot and dry and the wind is blowing, it should be remembered that concrete stiffens more rapidly than on a cool day with relatively high humidity and little or no wind. Vigilance on the part of the concrete foreman and the inspector is important to be sure the concrete in place becomes thoroughly plastic and shows some further settlement upon vibration just before the final concreting is done. Care should be exercised to be sure concrete does not spill or slough over on the floor forms or reinforcement when placing concrete in walls or beams. Likewise, when placing concrete in columns, the concrete should not be allowed to splash on the beam forms or reinforcement.

Curing

Protection and curing of concrete after placing in hot and cold weather have already been discussed. Additional information on curing under such weather conditions is contained in the ACI committee reports on hot [115] and cold [119] weather concreting. Not only is curing of concrete important under extremes of weather conditions, but also when atmospheric conditions are considered quite normal or average [86, 135].

Concrete increases in strength with age so long as drying of the concrete is prevented. When the concrete is permitted to dry, the chemical reactions cease. It is, therefore, desirable to keep the concrete moist as long as possible. Fig. 8-9 shows that concrete kept constantly moist has much higher strength than concrete allowed to dry. It also shows that when moist curing is discontinued, the strength increases for only a short period and then does not increase further to any extent. However, if moist curing is resumed even after a long period of drying, the strength will again increase under laboratory conditions where resaturation can be accomplished, but because resaturation of the concrete in the field after a period of drying is difficult, it is uncertain just how much additional strength will be gained. It is therefore essential to moist-cure continuously from the time the concrete is placed until it has attained the desired quality. It is recommended that moist curing be maintained for at least 5 days after placement of concrete, except that for high-early-strength concretes, moist curing should be provided for at least 2 days. Alternate curing methods with waterproof coverings or sprayed-on membrane should be provided for about twice as long as the recommended moist curing periods.

Forms left in place afford some protection against drying of the concrete, but this practice alone is not adequate. Wood forms should be kept wet continually during the curing period or covered with moisture-retaining covers such as burlap or cotton quilts. Whether or not forms are left in place, the inspector should check at frequent intervals to make sure that all concrete surfaces are covered and kept constantly wet. When drying conditions are severe, water should be applied to the top surfaces and allowed to run down between the forms and the concrete.

Following the normal period of moist curing for concrete exposed to hot sun, very low humidity, or strong wind, the rate of surface evaporation should be minimized by providing sunshades, covers, or windbreaks.

Curing is an operation that is often neglected or inadequately done. Its importance cannot be overemphasized.

Construction Joints

The strength of horizontal construction joints can be equal to the strength of the construction where there is no joint, if proper precautions are observed [136, 137]. First of all, good quality low-slump concrete should be used. In walls or columns of considerable height where a 4-in.-slump concrete must be used at the bottom, it is desirable to reduce the slump of the concrete in stages to as little as 1 in. near the top of the placement (or as a construction joint is approached) in order to minimize water gain, which would result in a layer of poor-quality concrete and a weak joint.

If the concrete is of the proper consistency, there should be very little water gain or settlement of the concrete. It is advisable, however, to allow some time for settlement to take place before striking off the concrete to the bottom edge of a grade strip tacked to the form as illustrated in Fig. 8-10.

It may not always be practical to reduce the slump of the concrete by several

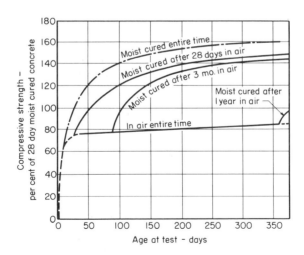

Fig. 8-9. Strength of concrete continues to increase as long as moisture is present to promote hydration of the cement—even though curing is temporarily interrupted, providing resaturation is attained.

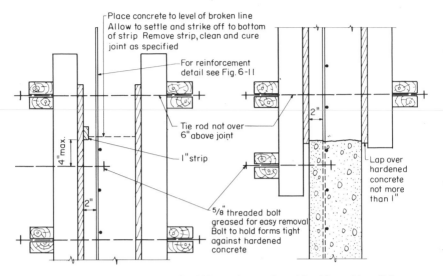

Fig. 8-10. Horizontal construction joints should be made straight and level by striking off the concrete at the top of the form or at a grade strip nailed to the inside surface of the outside form.

stages; it may even be necessary to use only one slump for the full height of the placement. Under such circumstances the lowest practical slump should be used for the full height and the form should be overfilled and struck off to the level of the joint. This will remove most laitance and concrete that may contain some excess water. Excessive use of vibrators or puddlers or any operation that tends to overwork the concrete near construction joints should be avoided; overworking contributes to the formation of planes of weakness and increases the difficulty of cleaning the joint effectively.

The joint surface should be moist-cured, preferably with a layer of sand that is kept wet, until just before closing in the forms above the joint. At that time the surface of the joint should be thoroughly wet-sandblasted to remove dirt and loose particles and to cut away laitance or surface film. The blasting should be followed by washing, thereby exposing firmly embedded aggregate. Unless new concrete is to be placed while the joint surface is still wet, moist curing should be resumed with wet sand or other effective measure until concrete is placed. This is the recommended procedure and is generally the most economical as well as the most effective.

When the wet-sandblasting procedure is done properly just before closing the forms, an initial cleaning of the joint surface during the interval between initial and final set is not necessary. In the event wet-sandblasting is completely impractical for a specific job, which is rarely true, an initial cleanup with a high-velocity air-water jet (at a time when coarse aggregate particles will not be dislodged) should give good results providing the surface is again cleaned with the air-water jet just before placing concrete.

Wire brushing may be used as an initial cleanup procedure but it requires more labor than the air-water jet and closer supervision to be sure the work is done well. An initial cleanup by wire brushing should be followed by a final cleaning with an air-water jet. The objective, whatever joint cleaning procedure is used, is to expose a clean surface of hard, sound concrete with a slightly rough texture to receive new concrete.

If a final inspection immediately before placing new concrete shows that curing sand has not been removed or that sawdust, dirt, or other material has collected on the surface of the concrete, it should be blown to clean-out ports and removed. To assure sufficient mortar at the juncture of the hardened and the newly-placed concrete, a 2-in.-thick layer of concrete containing only one-half the amount of coarse aggregate in the regular mix should be deposited through a chute against the previously placed concrete. This should be followed immediately by the regular mix.

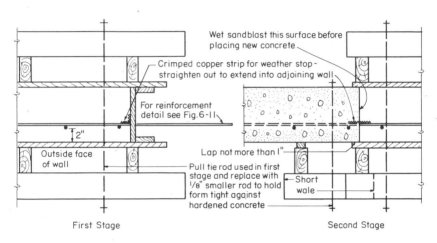

Fig. 8-11. Before closing forms adjacent to a vertical construction joint, the surface of the concrete against which the new concrete will be placed should be wet-sandblasted and washed clean.

The end surface of the concrete at a vertical construction joint should be wet-cured, as nearly as possible, up to the time of placing the adjoining concrete. Just prior to closing the forms for the second stage (Fig. 8-11), the joint surface should be wet-sandblasted and all sand, sawdust, or other material should be removed from the forms before depositing concrete.

If there should be any question as to the adequacy of the bond between the old and new concrete, the reinforcement crossing the construction joint should be supplemented by dowels. The length of the dowels should be at least twice the anchorage length shown in Table 6-1 or long enough to permit tying the dowels to two main reinforcement bars, whichever length is the greater. Dowels must not be placed by driving them into plastic concrete.

0

8.4 Forms

The forms for a reinforced concrete building are essentially the same wherever the building may be constructed [89, 90, 158]. They should be so constructed and supported that all structural members will have the dimensions called for on the drawings. Forms must be designed to have adequate strength and must be adequately tied, braced, shored, and anchored to hold all concrete members in proper position without excessive deflection, distortion, or displacement. The concrete as it hardens must not be stressed by swelling, shrinking, sagging, or bulging of the forms. Forms should be detailed and built so they can be tightened prior to placing concrete in order that members will not be weakened by loss of mortar, or formation of rock pockets because of seepage, or by shifting of the forms due to pressure of concrete or the effects of vibration. In brief, forms must be so constructed that they will in no way impair the strength of the finished structure nor detract from its appearance.

The deflection of sheathing, studs, and wales should be kept within 1/270 of the span. As a rule, the size and spacing of studs and wales will be governed by the stresses in bending and shear, but the deflection of sheathing is usually the determining factor. On the assumption that concrete in walls will be placed at a rate of about 2 ft. an hour and the temperature may be 50 deg. F. or somewhat lower, studs should not be spaced more than 16 in. on centers when used with 1-in. sheathing or $^{11}/_{16}$-in. structural-grade plywood. Wales should not be more than 24-in. on centers; ties having a minimum working strength of 3,000 lb., when fully assembled, should be spaced not more than 27-in. on centers when used with double 2x4-in. wales.

The pressure of fresh concrete on forms is influenced principally by the following factors:

1. Method of compaction, whether by hand spading or by vibration
2. Rate of filling the forms
3. Temperature of the concrete

Other factors, such as consistency and proportions of the mix, size and shape of the forms, and amount and disposition of the reinforcing, have some effect but generally may be neglected.

The ACI Committee 622—Pressures on Formwork, after an extensive study of test reports and other sources of information, has tentatively recommended [138] the equation

$$p_l = 150 + \frac{9,000\bar{r}}{\bar{T}} \tag{8-5}$$

in which

p_l = maximum lateral pressure in psf
$\bar{r}$ = rate of placing in feet per hour
$\bar{T}$ = temperature of concrete in degrees F.
150 = unit weight of concrete in pounds per cubic feet

The committee considers the above formula sufficiently conservative for design of forms for all values of $\bar{r} \leqq 10$ ft. per hour and considering vibration through-

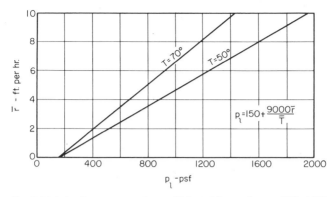

Fig. 8-12. Lateral pressures on forms. (Adapted from reference 138, ACI.)

out the entire height of the form. Fig. 8-12 shows the lateral pressures for various rates of placing at 70 deg. and 50 deg. F. Pressures will be somewhat less than the values shown when concrete is compacted by hand, but because of the common use of vibrators and the necessity for using them to compact the low-slump concrete recommended for structures in seismic areas, the higher pressures given by equation (8-5) should be used for all form design.

Formwork, being temporary, may be designed for somewhat higher working stresses than allowed for permanent construction. Table 8-6 gives safe working stresses for form design for various kinds of lumber. [159]

For high-quality formwork, all lumber should be surfaced four sides (S4S). The use of all surfaced lumber aids considerably in the building of tight forms true to desired dimensions and alignment with the minimum of labor. Where appearance of the finished concrete is not of importance and maximum strength of individual pieces is essential, lumber S2S or S2E may be used. Table 8-7 gives the dimensions and properties of lumber sizes commonly used for form construction. [160]

Shoring of adequate strength and rigidity for floor and beam forms is particularly important in multistory construction. Shores supporting successive stories should be placed directly over those below. Only adjustable shores should be used in order that formwork can be brought to required grade and camber as shown on the plans before placement of concrete and maintained at established levels under weight of fresh concrete. A screw or other positive nonslip device should be used for adjustment of shores. Hardwood shims may be used for small adjustments. Shores bearing on the ground should be supported on mud sills or bearing blocks sufficiently large to prevent settlement. Adequate crossbracing should be provided to ensure stability of formwork. The inspector should confer with the structural engineer if there is any question of safety of form construction before permitting concrete to be placed.

Before any concrete is placed, the inspector should check all formwork to be sure it will meet the foregoing requirements and that chips, blocks, sawdust,

TABLE 8-6   Allowable Working Stresses (psi) and Moduli of Elasticity
of Various Kinds of Lumber for Form Construction*

Kind	Extreme fiber in bending	Compression perpendicular to grain	Compression parallel to grain	Horizontal shear	Modulus of elasticity
Douglas fir, coast region—construction grade	1,850	490	1,500	150	1,760,000
Hemlock, west coast—construction grade	1,850	450	1,375	125	1,540,000
Larch—structural grade	1,850	490	1,500	150	1,760,000
Pine, Norway—common structural grade	1,375	450	970	95	1,320,000
Pine, Southern—No. 1 grade	1,850	490	1,700	150	1,760,000
Redwood, Heart—structural grade	1,625	400	1,375	120	1,320,000
Spruce, Eastern—structural grade	1,625	375	1,220	120	1,320,000

*The working stresses given in this table are approximately 25 per cent greater than ordinarily used for permanent construction and for the grade and sizes (2-in. thickness or less) of lumber generally used for forms, because forms are temporary, thereby reducing the effect of time yield. (Adapted from reference 159, NLMA.)

dried mortar, or other debris have been removed, that clean-out ports have been closed, and that the forms have been oiled, wetted, or coated with other material to facilitate stripping.

Forms should be removed in such a manner as to ensure the complete safety of the structure and without damage to the surface and edges of the concrete. Where the structure is supported on shores, removable beam and girder sides and column and wall forms may be removed after 24 hours under favorable weather conditions, providing the concrete is sufficiently hard not to be injured. Leaving side forms on longer is desirable at temperatures below 60 deg. F. As mentioned under Curing, page 231, leaving forms in place is beneficial in curing the concrete providing the forms are kept wet. Under no circumstances should the supporting forms or shoring be removed until the members have sufficient strength to support safely their weight and construction loads. It is generally considered that the concrete has attained sufficient strength when field-cured cylinders have twice the strength required for the members involved under construction conditions.

8.5 Placing Reinforcement

Proper placing of reinforcement begins with the structural engineer's design drawings. Standardization in the manner of conveying construction information

TABLE 8-7 Properties of American Standard Board, Plank, Dimension, and Timber Sizes Commonly Used for Form Construction

Nominal and rough sizes in inches (b h)	American standard sizes in inches — S2S (b h)	S2E (b h)	S4S (b h)	Area of section A=bh sq.in. — rough	S2S	S2E	S4S	Moment of inertia $I=\frac{bh^3}{12}$ — rough	S2S	S2E	S4S	Section modulus $S=\frac{bh^2}{6}$ — rough	S2S	S2E	S4S	Board feet per lineal foot of piece
4x1	4x25/32	3 5/8x1	3 5/8x25/32	4.0	3.13	3.63	2.83	.33	.16	.30	.14	.67	.41	.60	.37	1/3
6x1	6x25/32	5 1/2x1	5 1/2x25/32	6.0	4.69	5.50	4.30	.50	.24	.46	.22	1.00	.61	.92	.56	1/2
8x1	8x25/32	7 1/2x1	7 1/2x25/32	8.0	6.25	7.50	5.86	.67	.32	.63	.30	1.33	.81	1.25	.76	2/3
10x1	10x25/32	9 1/2x1	9 1/2x25/32	10.0	7.81	9.50	7.42	.83	.40	.79	.38	1.67	1.02	1.58	.97	5/6
12x1	12x25/32	11 1/2x1	11 1/2x25/32	12.0	9.38	11.50	8.98	1.00	.48	.96	.46	2.00	1.22	1.92	1.17	1
4x1¼	4x1 1/16	3 5/8x1¼	3 5/8x1 1/16	5.0	4.25	4.53	3.85	.65	.40	.59	.36	1.04	.75	.94	.68	5/12
6x1¼	6x1 1/16	5 1/2x1¼	5 1/2x1 1/16	7.5	6.38	6.87	5.84	.98	.60	.89	.55	1.56	1.13	1.44	1.04	5/8
8x1¼	8x1 1/16	7 1/2x1¼	7 1/2x1 1/16	10.0	8.50	9.38	7.97	1.30	.80	1.22	.75	2.08	1.51	1.95	1.41	5/6
10x1¼	10x1 1/16	9 1/2x1¼	9 1/2x1 1/16	12.5	10.63	11.88	10.09	1.63	1.00	1.55	.95	2.60	1.88	2.47	1.79	11/24
12x1¼	12x1 1/16	11 1/2x1¼	11 1/2x1 1/16	15.0	12.75	14.38	12.22	1.95	1.20	1.87	1.15	3.13	2.26	2.99	2.16	1 1/4
4x1½	4x1 5/16	3 5/8x1½	3 5/8x1 5/16	6.0	5.25	5.44	4.76	1.13	.75	1.02	.68	1.50	1.15	1.36	1.04	1/2
6x1½	6x1 5/16	5 1/2x1½	5 1/2x1 5/16	9.0	7.88	8.24	7.21	1.69	1.13	1.54	1.03	2.25	1.72	2.07	1.58	3/4
8x1½	8x1 5/16	7 1/2x1½	7 1/2x1 5/16	12.0	10.50	11.25	9.84	2.25	1.51	2.11	1.41	3.00	2.30	2.81	2.15	1
10x1½	10x1 5/16	9 1/2x1½	9 1/2x1 5/16	15.0	13.13	14.25	12.47	2.81	1.88	2.67	1.79	3.75	2.87	3.56	2.73	1 1/4
12x1½	12x1 5/16	11 1/2x1½	11 1/2x1 5/16	18.0	15.75	17.25	15.09	3.38	2.26	3.23	2.17	4.50	3.45	4.31	3.30	1 1/2
4x2	4x1 5/8	3 5/8x2	3 5/8x1 5/8	8.0	6.50	7.25	5.89	2.67	1.43	2.42	1.30	2.67	1.76	2.42	1.60	2/3
6x2	6x1 5/8	5 1/2x2	5 1/2x1 5/8	12.0	9.75	11.00	8.94	4.00	2.15	3.67	1.97	4.00	2.64	3.67	2.43	1
8x2	8x1 5/8	7 1/2x2	7 1/2x1 5/8	16.0	13.00	15.00	12.19	5.33	2.86	5.00	2.68	5.33	3.52	5.00	3.30	1 1/3
10x2	10x1 5/8	9 1/2x2	9 1/2x1 5/8	20.0	16.25	19.00	15.44	6.67	3.58	6.33	3.40	6.67	4.40	6.33	4.18	1 2/3
12x2	12x1 5/8	11 1/2x2	11 1/2x1 5/8	24.0	19.50	23.00	18.69	8.00	4.29	7.67	4.11	8.00	5.28	7.67	5.06	2
2x4	1 5/8x4	2x3 5/8	1 5/8x3 5/8	8.0	6.50	7.25	5.89	10.67	8.67	7.94	6.45	5.33	4.33	4.38	3.56	2/3
2x6	1 5/8x6	2x5 1/2	1 5/8x5 1/2	12.0	9.75	11.00	8.94	36.00	9.25	27.70	22.55	12.00	9.75	10.05	8.19	1
2x8	1 5/8x8	2x7 1/2	1 5/8x7 1/2	16.0	13.00	15.00	12.19	85.33	69.33	70.31	57.13	21.33	17.33	18.75	15.23	1 1/3
2x10	1 5/8x10	2x9 1/2	1 5/8x9 1/2	20.0	16.25	19.00	15.44	166.67	135.42	142.90	116.10	33.33	27.08	30.08	24.44	1 2/3
2x12	1 5/8x12	2x11 1/2	1 5/8x11 1/2	24.0	19.50	23.00	18.69	288.00	234.00	253.48	205.95	48.00	39.00	44.08	35.82	2
3x6	2 5/8x6	3x5 1/2	2 5/8x5 1/2	18.0	15.75	16.50	14.44	54.00	47.25	41.50	36.41	18.00	15.75	15.10	13.24	1 1/2
3x8	2 5/8x8	3x7 1/2	2 5/8x7 1/2	24.0	21.00	22.50	19.69	128.00	112.00	105.47	92.29	32.00	28.00	28.13	24.61	2
3x10	2 5/8x10	3x9 1/2	2 5/8x9 1/2	30.0	26.25	28.50	24.94	250.00	218.75	214.34	187.55	50.00	43.75	45.13	39.48	2 1/2
3x12	2 5/8x12	3x11 1/2	2 5/8x11 1/2	36.0	31.50	34.50	30.19	432.00	378.00	380.22	332.69	72.00	63.00	66.13	57.86	3

NOTES: b = width of piece or dimension perpendicular to direction of load.
h = depth of piece or dimension parallel to direction of load.
S4S — all figures under this heading apply also to pieces S1S1E, S1S2E and S2S1E.
*Adapted from reference 160, NLMA.

237

resulting from the engineer's design to the contractor and to the reinforcement fabricator aids materially in avoiding errors of interpretation and in securing strict compliance on the job.

In some areas the structural engineer's design drawings give complete bar details and are practically shop drawings and placing plans. Where this is the practice, the actual placing of reinforcement on the job may be done directly from the engineer's design drawings, against which the inspector also checks the reinforcement. In other areas, shop drawings and placing plans are prepared by the fabricator. Standardization of such drawings is of great importance so that the workmen, foremen, and inspectors will understand exactly where each bar is to be placed, and so that the least amount of time will be required to determine the intentions of the engineer and the fabricator. Where placing plans prepared by the fabricator are provided, the steel setters on the job seldom refer to the engineer's drawings except when some alteration is made or a difference of opinion arises. Therefore, the placing plans should be meticulously checked by the engineer and each sheet should show the date when approved. The standardization of engineering drawings, placing plans, and detailing of reinforcement has been the subject of intensive study by ACI Committee 315 for a number of years. Except where special reinforcement details considered essential for structures in seismic areas are recommended in this manual, the ACI Committee 315 recommendations [77] should be observed.

The inspector should check the reinforcement as it is delivered to the job. Only steel fabricated from the structural engineer's design drawings, or from the fabricator's shop drawings and placing plans that have been checked and approved by the engineer, should be allowed on the job site. The inspector should not permit any steel to be placed except as shown on the approved placing plans or on the engineer's design drawings. He should make sure that all reinforcing materials are the kind, type, and quality specified in accordance with the designated ASTM specifications [139, 140, 141, 142, 143, 144, 145, 146]. Reinforcing bars are usually tested and inspected at the mill for acceptance. The inspector should ascertain that each shipment has been mill inspected, or otherwise inspected in accordance with the structural engineer's specifications, and has not been damaged or excessively rusted before arrival on the job. Bars should be stored on the job so as to avoid excessive rusting and in a systematic arrangement to facilitate checking and easy identification. A coating of rust that adheres tightly to the bars is not considered objectionable, but heavy, loose rust or scale should be removed from bars before being placed.

Reinforcement bars are delivered to the job by the fabricator in bundles marked with tags. The information generally given on bar tags includes the order number, number of pieces, size, length, and mark corresponding to the placing plans. The inspector should check each delivery against the placing plans and schedules to be sure the material is being received in proper sequence and correctly fabricated.

Before any reinforcement is placed, it is desirable for the inspector to confer with the job superintendent and the foreman of the steel setters to be sure that all are in agreement with the placing procedure to be followed, the manner of supporting and securing the reinforcement in place, the setting and splicing of dowels, and all other details of the work. Loose dowels driven into the plastic concrete should not be allowed.

As the work progresses, the inspector should satisfy himself that all bars have been cut and bent as shown on the engineer's drawings, placing plans, and in bar schedules within allowable tolerances. No field bending of reinforcement should be permitted unless specifically authorized by the engineer. He should make sure that all bars are located correctly with the proper spacing between bars and between bars and forms, as required by code and as shown on the engineering drawings and placing plans. Bars must be firmly supported and secured so they will not be displaced either during construction operations prior to placing concrete or when concrete is placed. Only the trades authorized to place reinforcement should move a bar for any reason or reset and secure a bar inadvertently displaced during construction.

It is particularly important that bar splices are located where shown on the plans. No other locations should be permitted without specific approval of the engineer. Wherever possible, splices should be staggered. Bars at splices should be lapped the full length shown on the drawings and pairs of lapped bars should be separated the normal amount required between parallel bars to permit concrete to surround them, or they should be in contact and securely wired. The minimum lap required in the ACI building code for column bars is 20 diameters, and for beams and girders, 24 diameters. Longer splices may be required, however, and the length of splices considered necessary by the engineer should be shown on the drawings. It is not uncommon in seismic areas to specify splices of 30 diameters or more, as indicated elsewhere in this manual.

Welded splices should be checked carefully by the inspector to be sure that the weld is of the required length and size and properly made by currently qualified welders in accordance with best welding practice, using low-hydrogen electrodes [80, 81]. A desirable practice is to require that proof welds be made and tested in a laboratory prior to job use. The inspector should then check welding procedures to be sure that field welds are in all respects comparable to the proof welds. If there is any question about the strength of field welds, tests should be made before allowing the work to proceed.

Before concrete is placed, a final inspection should be made to be sure that all reinforcement is in place as shown on the plans and is securely tied and supported to prevent displacement during construction, and that the required concrete coverage has been provided. The reinforcement must be free from oil, grease, splashings of mortar, or other foreign material that might reduce the bond between the concrete and reinforcement.

The manual, *Recommended Practice for Placing Reinforcing Bars*, 1959 [78], published by the Concrete Reinforcing Steel Institute, contains a wealth of information based upon current accepted practices in the placing of reinforcing bars and welded wire fabric. Bar setters and inspectors should be thoroughly acquainted with this manual, which is also useful to the engineer, detailer, and fabricator.

8.6 Building Separations

The need for providing space between buildings on adjoining property to prevent hammering against each other during an earthquake has been discussed in Chapter 4. Similar separations between portions of one building may also be necessary when they have greatly different structural-dynamic properties and cannot be designed to act as an integral unit to resist horizontal forces. Complete separations may be required in very long buildings, even though generally symmetrical, if provision for relief of volume-change stresses is necessary.

In order that building separations may perform the function for which they are intended, they must be kept free from construction debris such as concrete spillage, bricks, and blocks of wood. Through neglect, wall forms are sometimes left in place, thereby practically if not completely filling the space. Constant vigilance as the construction progresses is necessary to be sure nothing drops into the separation and that all formwork is removed, because as the wall height increases it becomes impossible to remove or even detect the presence of forms or debris.

Elastic Modal Analysis of a 24-Story Building

A.1 Modal Frequencies and Displacements

An analysis was made for the building designed in Chapter 7, as an elastic structure, using spring constants for the structure in the transverse direction obtained by the procedure described in reference 83. The parameters used in the analysis are summarized in Table A-1. The floor levels are identified as the number of the floor above the ground level. The base of the building, at which the input was considered, was the ground level rather than the basement floor level of Fig. 7-1. With the mass of the penthouse roof considered, the building has, in effect, 25 stories.

The mass at each floor tabulated in Table A-1 was obtained from Table 7-1 by dividing the weights shown by the acceleration of gravity—namely, 387 in. per second squared. The spring constants could have been obtained from col. (6) of a tabulation such as Table 7-3 by multiplying the tabulated values by $12E_c/H_s^2$. It should be noted that values obtained in this way may not always agree with those shown in Table A-1 because the Table 7-3 values were computed according to the approximate procedure in Chapter 4, beginning on page 77, rather than the method employed in reference 83. The differences between the stiffnesses computed by the two methods do not cause a major difference in the computed periods or mode shapes and, as a consequence, have little effect on subsequent computations of elastic and inelastic shears.

The modal displacements and frequencies were determined by the methods described in Chapter 2. Flexural deflection of the building as a whole (axial column deformation) was neglected. The first three modes were determined by the procedure of sweeping out lower modes by use of the "orthogonality" condition discussed in Chapter 2 beginning on page 26 and illustrated in Fig. 2-5. However, it was possible to set up the entire problem on a digital computer, and the modal displacements and frequencies given in Table A-1 are the final results of the computer analysis, which are somewhat more accurate than the calculations made with a desk calculator but not recorded in this appendix.

TABLE A-1   Parameters and Modal Displacements

Floor	Mass 10^3 lb. sec.^{2} per in.	Spring constant 10^6 lb. per in.	Modal displacement u_1	u_2	u_3	u_4	u_5
25	1.27	0.3	+34,577	−46,633	+72,892	−96,943	+64,859
24	7.97	4.4	+32,992	−34,298	+23,245	+ 1,926	−27,297
23	10.79	5.3	+32,237	−29,575	+13,085	+ 7,826	−16,985
22	7.68	7.2	+30,900	−21,892	+ 365	+ 8,887	+ 3,182
21	7.64	7.3	+29,558	−14,778	− 9,061	+ 7,383	+16,888
20	7.68	8.7	+27,900	− 6,794	−16,832	+ 4,039	+24,474
19	8.19	10.1	+26,242	+ 279	−20,962	+ 374	+23,588
18	8.19	10.1	+24,584	+ 6,358	−21,785	− 2,856	+16,405
17	8.31	13.3	+22,710	+12,115	−19,766	− 5,528	+ 4,757
16	8.42	14.1	+21,133	+16,014	−16,245	− 6,725	− 5,086
15	8.42	14.1	+19,509	+19,094	−11,363	− 6,887	−13,351
14	8.52	16.3	+17,758	+21,461	− 5,390	− 6,058	−18,940
13	8.88	19.5	+16,144	+22,808	+ 231	− 4,578	−20,452
12	8.88	19.5	+14,715	+23,285	+ 4,912	− 2,838	−18,590
11	8.95	21.0	+13,213	+23,100	+ 9,233	− 787	−13,886
10	9.03	21.0	+11,758	+22,313	+12,613	+ 1,198	− 7,532
9	9.03	21.0	+10,247	+20,926	+15,120	+ 3,059	− 91
8	9.19	23.2	+ 8,690	+18,977	+16,581	+ 4,603	+ 7,363
7	9.87	31.8	+ 7,242	+16,743	+16,846	+ 5,562	+13,131
6	9.87	31.9	+ 6,162	+14,788	+16,199	+ 5,845	+15,972
5	9.94	33.4	+ 5,064	+12,554	+14,747	+ 5,692	+17,145
4	10.59	39.8	+ 4,000	+10,187	+12,654	+ 5,137	+16,552
3	10.59	39.5	+ 3,095	+ 8,030	+10,356	+ 4,343	+14,577
2	11.29	42.4	+ 2,174	+ 5,724	+ 7,594	+ 3,262	+11,275
1	11.98	28.1	+ 1,310	+ 3,479	+ 4,696	+ 2,045	+ 7,191
Ground			0	0	0	0	0
ω_n^2 (radians per sec.^{2})			10.83	62.48	160.89	240.9	335.6
Frequency, f, cycles per sec.			0.524	1.258	2.019	2.470	2.916
Period, T, sec.			1.91	0.795	0.495	0.405	0.343
Participation factor, γ_n, 10^{-6}			43.998	21.510	16.980	13.745	10.308

The frequencies determined manually check those recorded in Table A-1 to nearly three significant figures in the case of the first three modes, which were the only ones computed manually.

The square of the circular frequency, the natural frequency in cycles per second, and the period in seconds of each mode are tabulated. Since the magnitude of each mode shape is arbitrary, in terms of any uniform multiplication factor, the participation factor of the mode must be used in order to determine the precise magnitude of the modal displacement component to be used in further calculations. This was determined by use of equation (2-27). If the modal shape tabulated is multiplied by the participation factor γ_n the modes will have the proper magnitude so that the sum of the algebraic values of the modal displacements at each floor value will add up to unity if all 25 modes are considered.

TABLE A-2   Selected Story Deflections and Shears

Quantity	Mode	Story between floor levels					
		G-1	1–2	9–10	16–17	23–24	24–25
Stiffness, kips per in.		28,100	42,400	21,000	13,300	4,400	300
Relative modal deflection	1	+1,310	+ 864	+1,511	+1,577	+ 755	+ 1,585
from Table A-1	2	+3,479	+2,245	+1,387	−3,899	− 4,723	−12,335
	3	+4,696	+2,898	−2,507	−3,521	+10,160	+49,647
	4	+2,045	+1,217	−1,861	+1,197	− 5,900	−98,869
	5	+7,191	+4,084	−7,441	+9,843	−10,312	+92,156
Modal deflection per inch	1	0.05764	0.03801	0.06648	0.06938	0.03322	0.06974
of spectral displacement,	2	0.07483	0.04829	0.02983	0.08387	0.10159	0.26533
in.	3	0.07974	0.04921	0.04257	0.05979	0.17252	0.84301
	4	0.02811	0.01673	0.02558	0.01645	0.08110	1.35895
	5	0.07412	0.04210	0.07670	0.10146	0.10630	0.94994
Modal shear per inch of	1	1,620	1,612	1,396	923	146	21
spectral displacement,	2	2,103	2,047	626	1,115	447	80
kips	3	2,241	2,087	894	795	759	253
	4	790	709	537	219	357	408
	5	2,083	1,785	1,611	1,349	468	285
Modal shears for spectral	1	10,200	10,200	8,800	5,800	920	132
displacement of Figure	2	5,500	5,300	1,600	2,900	1,160	208
A-1 (listed in Table A-3),	3	3,400	3,100	1,300	1,200	1,140	380
kips	4	800	700	500	200	360	408
	5	1,600	1,300	1,200	1,000	350	214
Maximum elastic shear, kips (First 5 modes only)		21,500	20,600	13,400	11,100	3,930	1,342
Probable value, elastic shear, kips		12,200	12,000	9,130	6,700	1,930	646

In order to study the shears more directly, selected stories were studied and the results tabulated in Table A-2. The relative modal deflection between each of the six sets of floor levels considered was computed from Table A-1 by taking the algebraic difference of the modal displacements tabulated there. This yields the first group of five values in Table A-2. The second group was obtained by multiplying the first group by the participation factors listed at the bottom of the columns in Table A-1. These give the modal deflections in each story level per inch of spectral displacement. The modal shears per inch of spectral displacement are the next set of quantities computed. These are obtained by multiplying the modal deflections by the stiffnesses. These values are to be multiplied by the spectral displacements for any response spectrum in order to obtain the actual modal shears at each of the stories considered.

It is of some interest to note that in the analysis of a uniform building with uniform stiffness and equal masses at all floor levels, the modal deflections in the first story per inch of spectral displacement would be approximately 0.08 for a 25-story building. The actual values in Table A-2 are approximately of this magnitude for modes 2, 3, and 5 but they are less for modes 1 and 4. The reason for this is that in the actual building for mode 1 the much smaller stiffness of the first story has an important effect and reduces the value from that applicable to a hypothetical uniform building. Mode 4 in the actual building is a little unusual because the frequency of the penthouse roof on the columns connecting it to the roof of the main structure is such that it has almost the same frequency as the frequency of the building in the fourth mode. Consequently, the penthouse roof acts as a dynamic vibration absorber in this mode and has a large deflection itself, but tends to reduce the deflection of the rest of the building. This is a circumstance that would not generally arise. It might have been avoided, if it had been desired to do so, by stiffening the columns in the supports of the penthouse roof.

A.2 Response Spectra

The response spectra that might be considered for the analysis of this building could include any spectrum obtained from actual earthquake records or any idealized spectrum the designer wishes to consider. The spectrum used in the present analysis is shown in Fig. A-1. It is an idealized spectrum obtained from the ground motion data for the El Centro earthquake of 1940, as described in Chapter 1, Section 1.4, by multiplying the maximum ground displacement of 8.3 in. by the factor unity; multiplying the maximum ground velocity of 13.7 in. per second by 1.5 (giving 20.6 in. per second), and multiplying the maximum ground acceleration of $0.33g$ by 2, giving $0.66g$. One can read from Fig. A-1 the displacements for any frequency by using the appropriate guide lines.

It should be pointed out that this idealized spectrum is not the same as the actual spectrum but it does approximate its value when moderate amounts of damping are considered; however, it does not reproduce the "wiggles" or peaks and valleys of the actual spectrum.

A.3 Modal Shears

For the modal periods determined in Table A-1, the spectral displacements obtained from Fig. A-1 are given in Table A-3. These are the values read directly

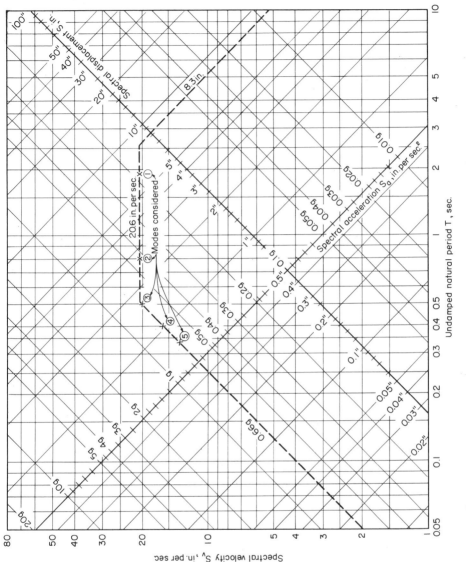

from the idealized response curve in Fig. A-1. The spectral displacements tabulated in Table A-3 are multiplied by the values of modal shear per inch of spectral displacement in Table A-2 to give the modal shears for the spectral displacements shown in the lowest group of five values in Table A-2. These values may be interpreted as the elastic shears in the selected stories for each of the first five modes, for the input ground motion considered. It is of some interest to note that for the lower stories of the building the first mode gives the largest

245

TABLE A-3 Spectral Displacements from Fig. A-1

Mode	Period T, sec.	Spectral displacement, in.
1	1.91	6.3
2	0.795	2.6
3	0.495	1.5
4	0.405	1.0
5	0.343	0.75

shears. Near the top of the building, however, larger shears are obtained in the higher mode responses. Actually, for the penthouse roof, the greatest shear is obtained in the fourth mode.

It is noted that the modal shears are tabulated without regard to sign. The relative modal deflections have both positive and negative components as shown in Table A-2. However, because the modal shear maximums may occur at different times, and be additive in different ways, only the absolute values are considered in Table A-2, in accordance with the discussion in Chapter 2.

A.4 Maximum Elastic Shears

From the modal shears shown in Table A-2, the maximum elastic shears, considering the first five modes, are obtained by direct summation of the absolute values. These values are tabulated. Higher mode responses would give only minor further increases of these sums.

The "probable" values of the maximum elastic shear, defined here as the root mean square of the values of the modal shears, are also tabulated in Table A-2. The effect of neglecting the higher mode response beyond the fifth mode would be quite negligible in these calculations because the square of the neglected values is considerably smaller than the square of the values tabulated in the first five modes.

It is noted that the values tabulated in Tables A-1 and A-2 are consistent with a modulus of elasticity for the concrete of 5,000,000 psi, which was the value used in the design of columns presented in Chapter 7. Merely as an indication of the effect of assuming a lower modulus with the same member sizes in computing the theoretical response, the effect of considering a modulus of 4,000,000 psi was taken into account by the calculation shown in Tables A-4 and A-5. Changing the modulus changes the stiffness and consequently changes the period by a ratio equal to the inverse square root of the ratio of the change in modulus or stiffness. Changing the assumed value of modulus to 4,000,000 psi from 5,000,000 will therefore lengthen the period by roughly 12 per cent. This in turn will change the spectral displacements by amounts varying from 12 to

TABLE A-4 Periods and Spectral Displacements
for $E = 4 \times 10^6$ psi

Mode	Period T, sec.	Spectral displacement, in.
1	2.14	7.0
2	0.889	2.9
3	0.553	1.8
4	0.453	1.3
5	0.383	0.94

TABLE A-5 Revised Shears for $E = 4 \times 10^6$ psi

Quantity	Mode	G-1	1–2	9–10	16–17	23–24	24–25
Modal shears, kips	1	9,100	9,000	7,800	5,200	820	118
	2	4,900	4,700	1,400	2,600	1,040	186
	3	3,200	3,000	1,300	1,100	1,090	364
	4	800	700	600	200	370	424
	5	1,600	1,300	1,200	1,000	350	214
Maximum elastic shear, kips (first 5 modes only)		19,600	18,700	12,300	10,100	3,670	1,306
Probable value, elastic shear, kips		11,100	10,700	8,100	6,000	1,790	638

25 per cent, depending on whether the spectral displacement value is on the horizontal constant velocity line or on the diagonal constant acceleration line in the response spectrum of Fig. A-1. Since the modal shapes do not change with the change in period, the modal shears are changed by the ratio of the stiffnesses; when these are multiplied by the spectral displacements, the net result is a change of the order of a maximum of 12 per cent or a minimum of zero. The zero change occurs for those modal values for which the response remains on the acceleration line for the changed conditions. The revised modal shears shown in Table A-5 are summed in the same way as those in Table A-2 to give the maximum elastic shears and the probable value of elastic shears. The probable values are reduced slightly from those in Table A-2. The reduction is less than 10 per cent, however. In the further discussion the values in Table A-2 will be used.

A.5 Comparison with Code Design Shears

The design shears computed by the SEAOC code for the conventional value of natural period of the building—namely, 2.50 seconds—are tabulated for the selected stories in line (a) of Table A-6, as taken from Table 7-1. For comparative purposes the shears could be related to the same period used in the elastic analysis. For an assumed period of 2.14 seconds, the base shear from the SEAOC code is changed from 2,120 kips to 2,230 kips, which is a relatively small change. For an assumed period of 1.91 seconds, the code base shear becomes 2,320 kips. Using a proportional change in all the other shears, the shears in the various stories for a value of T of 1.91 seconds are shown in Table A-6. These differ by less than 10 per cent from the values for $T = 2.50$ seconds, and consequently the intermediate shears for the other two values of T considered are not computed. Because the building was actually designed for the shears of line (a), further comparisons are made for those values only.

TABLE A-6 Comparison of Code Design Shears with Computed Shears

Quantity	Shears in story between floor levels, kips					
	G-1	1–2	9–10	16–17	23–24	24–25
Shears by SEAOC code						
(a) $T = 2.50$	2,120	2,100	1,750	1,120	180	26
$T = 2.40$	2,140					
$T = 2.14$	2,230					
$T = 1.91$	2,320	2,300	1,910	1,220	200	28
From Table A-2						
(b) "Maximum" shears, (First 5 modes)	21,500	20,600	13,400	11,100	3,930	1,342
(c) First mode shears	10,200	10,200	8,800	5,800	920	132
(d) "Probable" elastic shears	12,200	12,000	9,130	6,700	1,930	646
Shears proportional to "probable" shears for base shear of 2,120 kips	2,120	2,080	1,590	1,160	330	112
Ratios to SEAOC code shears, Line (a):						
Maximum shears—line (b)	10.1	9.8	7.7	9.9	21.8	52
First mode shears—line (c)	4.8	4.9	5.0	5.2	5.1	5.1
Probable shears—line (d)	5.8	5.7	5.2	6.0	10.7	25

To compare with these shears for which the building is designed, shears computed from the theoretical analysis are also summarized in Table A-6. In line (b) there are given the "maximum" shears, computed from the sum of the first five modes. The theoretical maximums would be slightly larger. In line (c) the first mode values only are given, and in line (d) the root mean square "probable" values are tabulated. All of these values are considerably greater than the code design shears.

Ratios of the theoretical shears in lines (b), (c), and (d) to the code design shears in line (a) are summarized in the table. It is apparent that, relative to the code values, the first mode shears (c) have a nearly constant ratio of 5 over the entire height of the building. The probable theoretical elastic shears are about 20 per cent higher than the first mode values in the lower stories, but increase to 11 and 25 times the code design values for the top two stories. The so-called maximum values are considerably higher, ranging from 1.5 to 2.0 times the probable values.

If shears are computed over the height of the building proportional to the first mode shears, but with the code base shear of 2,120 kips, the results would be almost exactly equal to the code design shears. However, if the computation is made for shears proportional to the probable shears, as summarized in Table A-6, the upper two stories would have shears greatly increased over the code design values, as indicated by the quantities 330 and 112 kips compared with 180 and 26 kips in the table.

If plastic action occurs first in the lower stories, it is likely that the response in the upper stories will be primarily that in a mode like the first elastic mode, rather than in any combination of elastic modes as implied by either the maximum theoretical shears or the probable theoretical shears. However, if plastic action first occurs higher in the building, then the response may be more nearly like that corresponding to the probable theoretical shears. In either case, except for the upper stories, the ratio of the theoretical value of shear to the code design value is about 5 to 6. Considering the fact that the theoretical value is to be used with yield stresses, and the code design value with augmented working stresses (working stress increased by one-third), the actual effective ratio of theoretical to code design shear is 5 or 6 divided by the ratio of yield stress to augmented working stress, which is approximately 1.5. This reasoning gives an effective ratio, for the conditions considered, of 3.3 to 4.

From these results it appears that for the conditions considered in this analysis (including the assumed response spectrum values), a design according to the recommendations in Chapter 6 at yield-point conditions will result in a resisting capacity of about one-fourth of the probable values of elastic shears, as defined here and as tabulated in Table A-6. This result is generally consistent with the observations and discussions outlined in Sections 1.5 and 1.6 of Chapter 1, and with Section 3.3 of Chapter 3. However, provision of a greater shearing strength in the upper stories of this building would be desirable.

Further studies of the building as designed have been made by the reserve energy technique described in Appendix B, Section B.1. The results of these analyses are generally comparable with the results just described, and are summarized in Section B.2.

APPENDIX **B**

Energy-Absorption Considerations

B.1 Reserve Energy Technique*

Introduction

Research efforts in recent years have demonstrated that earthquake history, including lack of damage as well as damage, usually cannot be reconciled with normal static design coefficients, elastic unit stresses, and current procedures. Inelastic action must be considered together with the capacity of the structures to dissipate energy in emergencies. Unfortunately, this tends to inject further complexity into a problem that should be simplified to obtain broad application of seismic design for public safety. Moreover, an approach to earthquake-resistant design has already been established that is difficult to change, and probably should not be changed if advances made to date are not to be lost.

In view of these considerations and the urgent need to include all basic parameters in design and analysis procedures, the technique to be described here was developed in such a way as to deal in terms that the structural designer uses in his daily work. Certain empirical relationships and approximations are employed in order to reduce the complex problem of inelasticity and energy to more general and more immediate application. The lack of a more rigorous approach and the absence of complete scientific justification is excusable, it is hoped, because of the urgent need to design much closer to the way things really are rather than how one would like them to be—for convenience and to suit traditional procedures.

---

*The text of Section B.1 following the introduction is essentially a reproduction of previous papers by John A. Blume presented to the American Society of Civil Engineers [20] and the Second World Conference on Earthquake Engineering [17], Tokyo, Japan, 1960. As presented here, certain changes from the Tokyo paper appropriate for this manual have been made, including the addition of references to recent papers of interest.

A simplified technique for design, analysis, or comparison of structures of any height, type, or combination of materials and elements in the inelastic range up to failure is described and illustrated in the following pages. The procedure utilizes the energy-absorption capacity of all building elements and considers change of natural periods, damping, energy value, damage, permanent set, etc., under increasing or repeated oscillations and deterioration from major earthquakes. The procedure also provides a practical means of reconciling static building code design coefficients with the much greater coefficients obtained from actual earthquake record analysis by elastic spectral techniques. Simple expressions for spectral velocity and acceleration are provided.

A proposed system of rating structures for inelastic energy value, drift, and the damage risk factor for specific idealized earthquake spectra is also presented.

The reserve energy technique was presented in the *Transactions* of the American Society of Civil Engineers as part of a broad consideration of structural dynamics [20], certain elements of the method have been discussed further in references 18 and 21, and a detailed presentation solely on the technique has been given in reference 17. Some additional refinements have been developed since these original papers and are included here, together with an application to a hypothetical multistory building.

The Anomalies of Elasticity

Every elastic analysis of accurately recorded earthquake records conducted in the United States and New Zealand to date, regardless of any reasonable damping assumption or the number of masses involved, indicates that the theoretical responses are much greater than any static code or design procedure requires. The differences are so great as to negate reconciliation of the gap by safety factors or other conventional explanations. Fig. B-6 illustrates smoothed elastic spectral accelerations including a curve ($F = 1.83$) for the 1940 El Centro (N-S) earthquake. Numerical considerations of the energy-dissipation capacity of complex structures have been quite limited to date [16, 20, 148] as have inelastic spectral analyses of actual earthquake records. The latter have thus far been limited to elasto-plastic systems, a special case of inelasticity [8, 9, 10, 19, 149, 150]. The indications from these investigations are, however, that inelasticity is the most realistic approach to the earthquake problem. It can explain most, if not all, of the anomalies that elasticity presents, including why a certain weak building may have a good earthquake history and a strong building may not.

Current elastic design procedures and code requirements do not, directly at least, satisfactorily consider the following important items:

1. The deflections necessary to develop energy resistance to severe earthquakes.
2. The effect of these deflections on the structure—its unit stresses, yield excursions, cracking, permanent set, damage, or possible collapse.
3. Changes of natural period with change in stiffness.
4. The fact that for a majority of buildings the stiffness is not constant, per-

haps even at low amplitudes; that with severe earthquakes the characteristics change with not only deflection but the number of severe excursions
beyond design values.

5. Buildings have many and greatly different elements providing structural
   strength and energy resistance, including frames, walls, partitions, stairways, foundations, and the supporting soil.

6. There may be two or more basic plateaus of resistance depending upon
   the design, the construction, and the earthquake exposure.

7. In addition to stress, there are four other characteristics or indexes of
   measurement or comparison in earthquake resistance: (a) energy development, (b) maximum deflection or drift, (c) permanent set, and (d)
   damage (structural and nonstructural).

With the advent of buildings without traditional filler walls and heavy partitions that were either noncalculated elements [20] or were in whole or in part
considered structural, it becomes even more vital and urgent that the anomalies
of elastic design become recognized and that they be eliminated from design
procedures. The reserve energy technique and the earthquake rating system
are suggested as practical means of reconciling the anomalies listed above and
of improving understanding of inelasticity.

The Reserve Energy Technique—Basic Considerations

1. THE ENERGY DEMANDS of a vibrating or moving system must balance as
well as the static and dynamic forces. It is convenient to consider feed-in energy
or kinetic energy from the ground motion effect on the building, strain energy
(elastic), energy dissipation or work capacity (strain and/or damage), internal
energy loss (to heat) without damage, and energy feedback or radiation from
the structure back to the soil. At peak demands, feed-in kinetic energy less
energy feedback must equal strain energy plus energy lost to heat plus energy
dissipation in work or damage done. The strain energy is often a small part of
the total energy requirement or capacity. (See Figs. B-1 to B-4, inclusive.)

2. THE FORCE-DEFLECTION diagram of a structure or of a basic element of the
structure can be used graphically or numerically as a measure of strain energy
and work capacity, as well as a convenient means of adjusting the period, estimating the permanent yield or damage, and of visualizing the basic problem.
Figs. B-2 and B-3 illustrate the general construction and use of the diagram [20],
and Fig. B-4 shows some common types of inelasticity. The elastic strain energy
is often difficult to isolate in buildings due to the lack of a definite yield point.
Therefore, the design energy D up to force P_D, corresponding to a certain static
coefficient C' is used as a basis. The value U_i as shown in Fig. B-2 is total work
capacity on the initial application of severe force. In order to allow for deterioration or softening of the resistance under repeated excursions beyond the yield
point, factors H_i and γ are introduced to indicate the hump area and its deterioration, respectively. H_i is the area of the "hump" as shown in Fig. B-2 above a

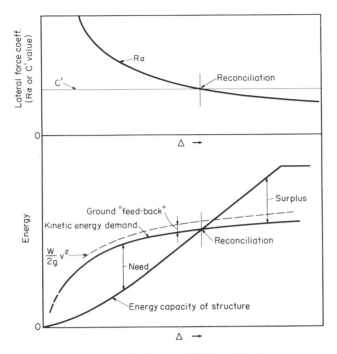

Fig. B-1. Energy development with shear deflection.

straight line from the origin of the P-Δ curve to any point on the curve at Δ_i. The deterioration factor γ, which is applied to H_i, is zero for elasto-plastic moment-resisting frames. For shear-wall-type structures or moment-resisting frames with integrally cast shear walls or masonry panel walls, γ is arbitrarily taken as 0.5 unless test data indicate other values. Jacobsen [148] has considered deterioration under repeated cycles based upon various tests by Japanese and American investigators.

The force-deflection diagrams of Figs. B-2 and B-3 are for the *initial loading* on a *static* (or slow-loading) basis. This is done for the practical reasons that (a) only such data are available today in reasonable quantities, and (b) this eliminates complications as to the various speeds of rapid loading and the history of prior cycles. In general, the additional values of rapid loading tend to compensate for the deterioration of initial excursions into the damaging or straining range. * It may be suggested that there are inadequate data to construct a force-deflection diagram for a complete story of a building, but on the other hand,

---

*A hypothetical example would be one of a composite material subject to moment with the unit stresses such that the dynamic values would be 15 per cent greater than the static values. However, the softening effect or loss of some resistance due to reversals and additional cycles under earthquake reversals might reduce the dynamic values by 13 per cent. Thus the effective values would be $(1 + 0.15) \times (1 - 0.13) = 1.00 =$ static value. Although these values are variable they do indicate the general order of magnitude.

unless the response characteristics of the building are known or can be estimated reasonably well up to failure, no method of design or analysis no matter how rigorous, mathematical, or involved can consistently or properly provide for economical and predictable earthquake resistance. Actually, considerable test data on members and elements are available [56, 59, 61, 63] and diagrams have been developed for very complex as well as simple structures [16, 20]. The procedure can be relatively simple for personnel experienced in structural design who have basic test data available.

3. EARTHQUAKE EXPOSURE. The reserve energy technique is based upon using the *elastic* acceleration spectral response for any specific earthquake or

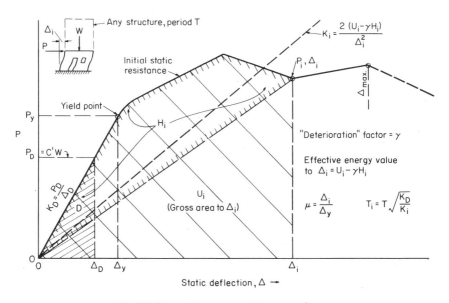

Fig. B-2. Reserve energy geometry—general case.

for a standard or averaged earthquake spectrum (see Fig. B-6). In some cases, two or more earthquakes may be applied to the same structure to predict results. Spectral diagrams are now available for many United States earthquakes [5, 18, 151] and it is hoped that many more will become available for various parts of the world. It is not necessary to have a spectral diagram or to become involved with their many peaks and valleys because simple formulas have been developed [18] to provide basic information approximating the spectral results made available thus far by Housner and others [151]. For 5 per cent of critical damping, the elastic spectral velocity v may be expressed as

$$v_i = F(T_i)^{\frac{1}{4}} \qquad \text{(B-1)}$$

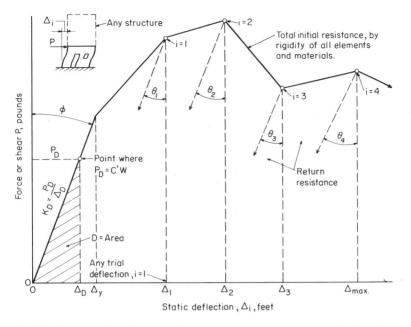

Fig. B-3. Force-deflection diagram in the reserve energy technique for inelastic seismic design.

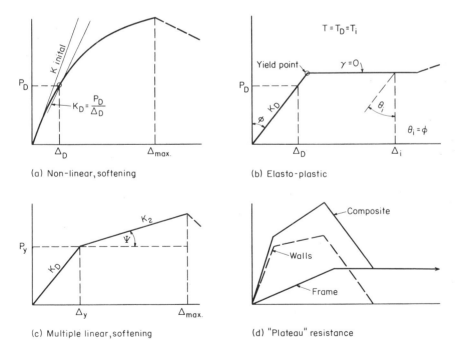

(a) Non-linear, softening

(b) Elasto-plastic

(c) Multiple linear, softening

(d) "Plateau" resistance

Fig. B-4. Common types of inelasticity.

for periods of 0.30 second and over, up to 3 seconds (see Fig. B-5). Although this equation would apply to much shorter periods, for reasons later to be discussed, a different relationship is used in the short period range. The elastic

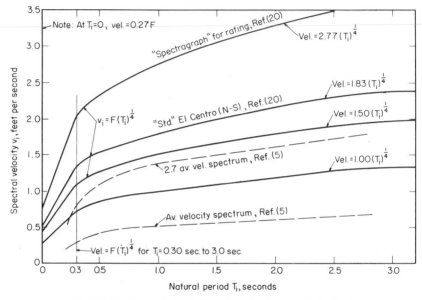

Fig. B-5. Elastic spectral velocities, damping 5 per cent of critical.

spectral acceleration α_i for the same period values may be expressed

$$\alpha_i = 0.194 \, F(T_i)^{-\frac{3}{4}} \tag{B-2}$$

Fig. B-6 indicates various acceleration values. Estimated values for F and the number of equal or greater occurrences somewhere in California per 100-year period* are:

	F	Occurrences*
"Spectragraph"	2.77	2
El Centro 1940 N-S	1.83	20
El Centro 1940, average of 2 components	1.50	32
El Centro 1934, average of 2 components	1.00	70

*Approximations only, by analogy to reference 151 data.

The range of periods shorter than 0.3 second was investigated in considerable detail in a recent research effort [16]. There are many low, rigid buildings of one or two stories in this range. A typical acceleration response vs. period plot such

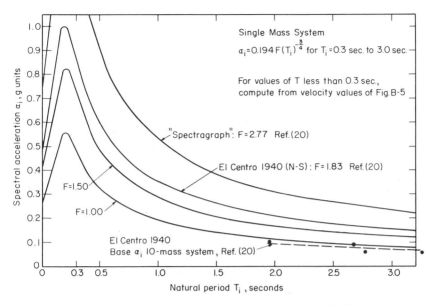

Fig. B-6. Elastic spectral accelerations, damping 5 per cent of critical.

as Fig. B-6 indicates some similarity with forced vibration resonance curves. An analogy can be drawn between magnification factor or transmissibility of forced vibration in the steady state to the spectral acceleration response. It can be argued that for the major earthquakes thus far recorded the period range of 0.2 to 0.3 second could be considered a resonant response band where the dominant ground motion for all practical purposes was close to that of the natural period of the system being forced into vibration. Thus in this range the structure would be expected to vibrate in or close to its own natural frequency during the worst part of the earthquake. For longer periods it would be expected that the structure would tend to move in or return to its own natural mode of vibration except when interrupted by severe ground disturbances of other periods. Accordingly, for the range of approximately 0.2 to 0.3 second up to 3.0 seconds, it seems proper to enter the spectral curves with the natural period of the structure. However, for periods below the 0.2 to 3.0 second range, it would be more logical to enter the spectrum with the period of the ground motion since the structure would be responding directly with such motion. Finite values of velocity and acceleration are thus maintained for design purposes, even at the situation where the structure's period is zero. Fig. B-6 has been constructed in accordance with equation (B-2) for T values over 0.3 second but with values in the short period range determined as follows. At $T = 0$, the velocity values are as noted on Fig. B-5. Between these points and the 0.3 second velocity values determined by equation (B-1), a straightline variation of velocity is arbitrarily assumed. The velocity and acceleration values for corresponding F factors in Fig. B-5 and Fig. B-6 may be determined by the equation

$$\alpha_i = \frac{2\pi v_i}{gT_i}$$

For the reasons discussed above, the value of T_i in this equation has been taken as the assumed ground period T_g for short periods; specifically, T_g has been assumed as 0.18 from 0 to 0.18 second for Fig. B-6 and as the true value of T_i above 0.18 second. Peak values on Fig. B-6 have been rounded.

There are some indications (Fig. B-6) that spectral values obtained by various investigators in the long period range may not agree even after allowances for the different responses of single and multimass systems. The results of the energy analysis for certain buildings also indicate that for periods of 2.5 seconds and over, some spectral values [151] provide greater energy demands than good buildings may have capacity to meet even with damping and energy considerations. Whether more energy is fed back to the ground than can now be assumed (about 10 per cent), whether some spectral data [151] are conservative, whether the buildings are inadequate, or whether the assumption of story participation proposed herein is conservative, remains to be demonstrated with future research. It seems logical, however, that velocity must approach zero for very long periods T. There must be a terminal point for ground energy and therefore the expression $v_i = F(T_i)^{\frac{1}{2}}$ should be considered applicable only for the period range shown. It may even be conservative for periods over 2 or 2.5 seconds. This expression, however, is independent of the reserve energy technique.

4. DAMPING. The reserve energy procedure can be used for any assumed damping value, but 5 per cent of critical damping is recommended because (a) it is considered a reasonable, nominal value of damping in the elastic range, (b) it is adequate to iron out many of the extreme peaks and valleys of spectral response for lesser damping, and (c) the use of more than 5 per cent would be considered unsafe in view of the fact that the reserve energy procedure provides otherwise for any greater values or types of damping that may be due to more than the normal hysteretic (heat loss) values in the elastic range for internal viscous damping. Determinations of damping in actual buildings to date reveal values under small amplitudes in the order of 5 to 10 per cent of critical with some less than 5 per cent [35] and average values closer to 5 per cent [16]. The question of response—transient or steady state—is also important in this consideration and will be discussed below. Contrary to some opinion, damping does not decrease response directly, although the response generally does decrease to some extent with an increased damping factor [16, 20]. However, there are indications that damping may be less effective in reducing response for close-epicenter shocks than for longer distances [151]. Fig. B-7 illustrates these relationships for several recorded earthquakes.

5. Lurches. The nature of inelastic response seems to be one of a few occasional lurches or excursions beyond elastic conditions rather than a steady-state vibration phenomenon. There is not only a transient condition but a chaotic one, not easily treated by mathematical formulas. There are somewhat limited but nonetheless consistent reasons for this theory, including (a) observations of the

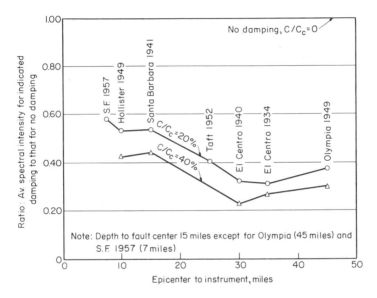

Fig. B-7. Effect of damping on spectral intensity.

type and degree of damage and permanent set, (b) observations of lack of damage and set, (c) sound and sensation in buildings during earthquakes, (d) study of earthquake records, (e) calculations of energy demand versus energy dissipation and strain, and (f) results to date from digital and analog research in elasto-plastic systems exposed to earthquake spectra [8, 9, 10, 19, 149, 150].

Work at the University of Illinois [8, 150] indicated only a few half-cycles of excursions beyond the yield. For the entire El Centro 1940 N-S record of some 30 seconds, only 5 half-cycle excursions were noted for one elasto-plastic system and another had only 3 excursions in the first 10 seconds of the record, the worst part. In spite of these few lurches, the response was greatly attenuated. Similar results were obtained at the New Zealand Dominion Physical Laboratory [10] where the total of all yield excursions at peak period values for El Centro 1940 N-S, if divided by an arbitrary two-thirds of the maximum yield excursion, provides an average of only four excursions beyond yield in the total earthquake.

It may thus be postulated that:

a. Only a few severe energy demands are required for a structure in a major earthquake. The condition is not steady-state or even a transient build-up; instead there are a few lurches preceded by and followed by elastic response.

b. The equivalent viscous damping concept [148] seems not as applicable to abrupt lurches as it is to steady-state vibration phenomena.

c. The balancing of peak kinetic energy demand with potential energy capacity, as in the reserve energy technique, seems appropriate in the inelastic problem without recourse to integration of the whole earthquake record.

d. The use of initial static resistance values with the hump deterioration factor for a few to several possible repeat cycles is also appropriate to the problem of inelastic behavior.

Procedure of the Reserve Energy Technique

Figs. B-2 and B-3 present the basic force-deflection diagram and certain equations for the reserve energy technique. The symbols and other equations are shown in the nomenclature (Appendix E) and in Fig. B-12. The general principles have been outlined above. The reserve energy reduction coefficient R is the basis of reconciling any elastic coefficient, C or C', with the elastic spectral earthquake response of a structure of initial elastic period T; stated another way, R is the factor that reduces an elastic spectral response acceleration value to an equivalent value for elastic design modified for the more realistic inelastic response of the structure in a severe earthquake. The technique is general for all types or combinations of inelasticity, framing or other resistance, and numbers of stories. For specialized cases such as single stories or elasto-plastic or other simple inelastic systems, the steps are greatly simplified.

The procedures are as follows:

1. Design the structure in accordance with the elastic seismic code in effect; if no other is legally applicable, the SEAOC code is recommended. For a structure already built, determine its P_D, C', and Δ_D values.

2. Plot the total resistance diagram as shown generally in Fig. B-3, on the basis of applicable static test data adjusted to the specific structural values; select the γ factor.

3. Determine the actual fundamental period of vibration T by measurement, computation, analogy, or approximate formula.

4. Calculate K_D and T_D.

5. For trial deflection Δ_i, compute U_i, H_i, K_i, and T_i; for each trial deflection let $i = 1$, $i = 2$, etc.

6. Compute R_{iz} by one of the formulas shown in Fig. B-12. For a single mass system $\mathcal{Z} = 1$ and only one $(U_i - \gamma H_i)$ value is involved.

7. Determine α_i for period T_i. This may be taken from an elastic spectral acceleration plot, may be converted from elastic spectral velocity, or may be taken from the smoothed curves of Fig. B-6. The degree of earthquake intensity F, or other criterion, is a matter of basic design criteria.

8. Compute $R_i\alpha_i$; if this value is equal to coefficient C', the structure (or

portion of it under consideration) is adequate (with no safety factor) at deflection Δ_i and with damage or yield as indicated by γH_i. If $R_i\alpha_i$ exceeds C', the structure is inadequate up to the deflection Δ_i for the specified earthquake intensity F and the corrective choices are:

a. Assume a greater deflection or deflections and repeat to obtain smaller $R_i\alpha_i$ values.

b. Add material to the structure and/or modify the design to obtain greater C' values.

c. Reduce α_i on the basis of any reliable data for energy feedback to the ground, or for greater (nondestructive) damping than 5 per cent; in no case reduce α_i more than 20 per cent total.

d. Combinations of (a), (b), and (c).

9. If $R_i\alpha_i$ is equal to or less than C' but the damage or deformation at Δ_i as indicated by γH_i is not acceptable, the procedure would be as in step 8 above except that lesser deflections would be tried, probably with a modified design.

Elasto-Plastic Behavior—a Special Case

Elasto-plastic systems are special cases of inelastic response and as such are also susceptible to reserve energy analysis. Whether or not a system or a structure truly behaves elasto-plastically is beyond the scope of this paper. However, many cases do occur where mild steel yields either alone or as the controlling element of reinforced concrete or reinforced masonry construction without the crushing of nonductile materials. Modern buildings without exterior walls have little participation of collateral elements and may approach elasto-plastic behavior. Elasto-plastic systems have been used experimentally because of their simplicity. The results of three investigations of such systems were compared [21] to those of reserve energy as shown on Fig. B-8. The reduction factor R_i reduces to the simple expression

$$R_i = \sqrt{\frac{D}{U_i}}$$

since the stiffness does not change and T_i is considered equal to T_D, and if it be postulated for comparative purposes that the elasto-plastic system is of such character as to allow γH_i to be zero; i.e., there is no deterioration under a repetition of cycles. From these comparisons (Fig. B-8) it is to be noted that for the limits of the available data (damping from 3 per cent to 20 per cent and period from 0.2 second to 0.6 second):

1. Period has little or no relationship in agreement to the R curve.

2. Damping seems to have little or no relationship in agreement to the R curve.

3. The agreement is so good, in this case at least, as compared to the many other uncertainties in practical earthquake design, as to suggest that the simple reserve energy procedure might be applied directly to elasto-

plastic energy design without the need for computer or analog analysis. More test data, however, are desirable.

4. An elastic acceleration response spectrum might be reduced to equivalent (inelastic) design values by simply multiplying α_i by R_i, determined for any limiting deflection ratio μ for an elasto-plastic system. (This is an inverse statement of 3 above.) For example, assume a single-mass design problem requires resistance to the smoothed 1940 El Centro N-S earthquake spectrum (Fig. B-6) at no safety factor, the limiting μ is 4, $\beta = 0.75$,

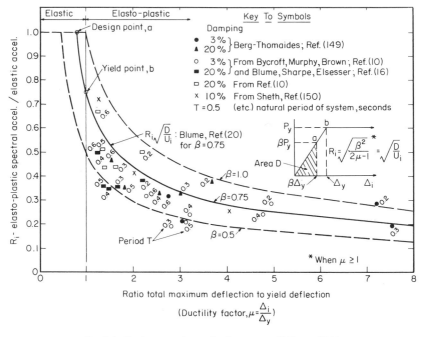

Fig. B-8. Single-mass elasto-plastic systems; El Centro 1940.

and T_D is 0.5 second. The R factor is then 0.29 and the acceleration value at the period of 0.5 second is $0.60g$ (Fig. B-6). Then the equivalent code or design value is simply 0.29 times $0.60g$ or $0.17g$, with no energy safety factor.

Multimass Systems

The procedure outlined on pages 260 and 261 is for a one-mass system such as a single-story building, a multistory building that can reasonably be represented by a single-mass system,* or any other structure that can be represented by the conventional lumped mass and spring analogy. A building of a few stories wherein the first story is much more flexible or vulnerable than the upper

---

*A yielding first-story condition makes this assumption reasonable for multistory buildings.

stories may be represented by a one-mass system in many cases, but with, of course, all the weight W considered.

Multistoried buildings that are better represented by many lumped masses and weightless springs acting in series require additional considerations in the reserve energy procedure as follows:

1. The fundamental elastic period of the entire structure, T, is determined by approximate (Appendix C), Rayleigh [27, 32, 34], or other [35] procedures.*

2. Multimass spectral analog or computer data for earthquake exposure that provide elastic shear values for all stories [20] should be used story by story (or for certain typical stories) if available; i.e., take the elastic shear for the eighth story and from it determine an equivalent α value for the analysis of the eighth story by the reserve energy procedure. Where only single-mass spectral values are available, shear determined from α corresponding to the fundamental period of the building may be greater than the probable multistory base shear. In such cases (a) the single mass α value may be slightly reduced but not to a value less than 90 per cent of the given spectral value, unless future research should justify a further reduction; and (b) an α diagram similar in shape to that for a building of similar stiffness and slenderness ratio should be drawn to provide approximate α values for the upper story analyses. Fig. 13 of reference 20 indicates α distributions for several conditions of a slender building.

3. Work done anywhere in the structure assists other parts by draining energy. However, because of mode shapes and structural values, all stories do not yield or participate in inelastic energy absorption simultaneously, or to their full capacity. The total energy capacity at and above a story has been assumed equal to the sum of all the story energy values (for consistent deflections as noted below) at and above the story, multiplied by the factor omega (Ω), which is a reduction factor applied to the summation of the energy capacity of multistory buildings. It is based on the probability of all stories above any level participating simultaneously to their maximum value during any one energy demand. An interim value of $\Omega = 1/\sqrt{Z}$ has been suggested [17, 20], pending further research, where Z is the reciprocal of the number of stories in the summation; however, values of the order of 0.3 to 0.5 are considered to be a more appropriate estimate for ductile moment-resisting frames except for the top four stories where $1/\sqrt{Z}$ is applicable. Additional research in the future will no doubt yield more data on probability relationships for this purpose.

For tall, slender units without floors or other massive discontinuities such as chimneys, arbitrarily assume Z = the number of 30-ft. units of height. In determining the $(U_i - \gamma H_i)$ value for each story or unit, the absolute positions of all units should be proportional to the mode shape of the structure. Only the *net* story deflection is used, however, to obtain U_i and H_i. Thus, Δ_i could vary between different stories for the same trial unless a straightline fundamental mode shape is assumed, as is often justified, and story heights are constant.

---

*See Chapter 2 for a detailed discussion of period determination.

$R_{iz}\alpha_i$ is compared to the story design coefficient C_z', in a manner similar to that for the single-mass procedure. In all cases C_z' is the coefficient used to determine shear, not force, at any level (shear $= C_z'W$). It is basic to check the lowest story and several typical upper stories as well.

4. When constructing P-Δ diagrams for multistory buildings, the possibility of progressive hinge development rather than the simultaneous yielding of all the columns in a story should be considered. In fact, the design might well foster this progression in order to increase the total energy capacity. Some columns, for example, would tend to remain elastic for greater deflections than others because they have less rigidity or less restraint from the intersecting girders. The story energy diagram could thus be of the multiple-linear softening type of Fig. B-4(c) even though the framing members might have elasto-plastic characteristics.

5. If multimass story-by-story spectral values are not available, important tall or slender buildings should be checked also for second and third mode response, which, with the fundamental mode, are generally adequate for all but very tall or very slender structures. These mode periods can be calculated [34, 35] or can be estimated as ratios of the fundamental period, and the spectral curve entered at each period. Each particular mode shape must be used as a basis for obtaining $(U_i - \gamma H_i)$ values. The results for each mode can be weighted [36] or combined by root mean square or other indicated probability values [152, 153].

Example of Reserve Energy Analysis

Fig. B-9 and Table B-1 illustrate the analysis for a hypothetical one-story building that has a C' value of 0.19. Since this structure has the resistance and reserve energy capacity of nonstructural partitions as shown in Fig. B-9, the deterioration factor γ has been assumed to be 0.5 to allow for major loss of this capacity under severe distortion. Fig. B-9 indicates the results for several F factors or "smoothed earthquakes" to illustrate their various effects on deflec-

TABLE B-1   Reserve Energy Analysis of One-Story Building, $F=1.83$

See Figs. B-3, B-12, and text for basis and Fig. B-9 for data. $P_D=54$ kips; $\Delta_D=0.05$ in.; $K_D=13\times10^6$ lb. per ft.; $D=112$ ft.-lb.; $T=0.156$ sec.; $C'=0.19$; $\gamma=0.5$

Trial No. i	Δ_i inch	U_i ft.-lb.	H_i ft.-lb.	$K_i=\dfrac{2U_i-H_i}{\Delta^2}$ lb. per ft.	$T_i=T\sqrt{\dfrac{K_D}{K_i}}$ sec.	R_i	α_i	$R_i\alpha_i$ for $F=1.83$
1	0.4	2,900	736	4.56×10^6	0.262	0.340	0.95	0.322
2	0.8	8,180	2,070	3.22×10^6	0.328	0.250	0.82	0.205
3	1.2	14,750	3,420	2.61×10^6	0.365	0.206	0.77	0.160
4	1.6	22,000	7,440	2.05×10^6	0.412	0.197	0.70	0.138
5	2.0	30,400	10,890	1.80×10^6	0.440	0.180	0.66	0.119
6	2.4	38,400	14,400	1.56×10^6	0.474	0.173	0.62	0.108

tion and damage. The crossings of the C' line on Fig. B-9(b) indicate the points of reconciliation or deflections each earthquake would be expected to cause under the most severe lurches or excursions. Table B-1 indicates the tabular form of computation to obtain the $R_i\alpha_i$ values for the $F = 1.83$ El Centro 1940 idealized earthquake; these values are plotted on Fig. B-9.

For this example building, it is assumed that the actual static elastic value C' has been determined to be 0.19 at allowable code unit stresses. This value is greater than normal code values of C and has been determined by computing the strength actually provided in the building. P_D is 54 kips and $W = 54/0.19 = 285$ kips. Δ_D is 0.05 in., D is computed to be 112 ft.-lb. (see Figs. B-3 and B-12), and $K_D = 13 \times 10^6$ lb. per foot. The energy and other terms are all converted to foot and pound units for the analysis.

From the above values and either formula (see nomenclature) for T_D, the hypothetical period for a single-mass system of weight W and spring factor K_D is computed to be 0.164 second. Since the building is not a true lumped-mass system with a weightless spring, its actual period could be different from T_D. This is especially true for one-story or few-story buildings, which do not simulate lumped-mass systems as well as do multistory buildings. Assume that

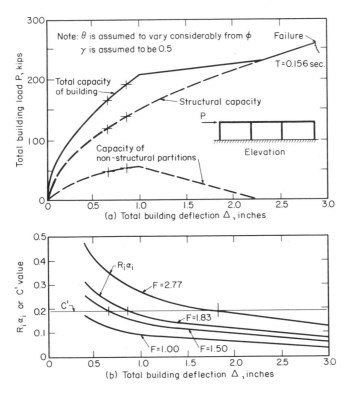

Fig. B-9. Reserve energy analysis for one-story building

the actual period T in this case has either been measured or has been determined by an empirical formula to be 0.156 second under elastic, pre-earthquake conditions.

The first trial deflection ($i = 1$) is arbitrarily taken as 0.4 in. and U_i, H_i, K_i, and T_i are computed and entered in Table B-1. Note that since this is *not* an elasto-plastic system, T_i varies with deflection. R_i is computed from equations (g), (h), or (i) in Fig. B-12. Since this is a one-story building, $Z = 1$ and only one value of ($U_i - \gamma H_i$) need be considered for each trial deflection. R_i is calculated to be 0.34 and is entered in the table. The α_i determination in this case is more complex than for taller buildings with longer periods, since the period is close to the peak of the acceleration curve. α_i can be read directly from Fig. B-6 or computed by the formula shown on Fig. B-6 or B-5, as applicable. Where velocity is first determined, it is converted to acceleration by the formula

$$\alpha_i = \frac{2\pi v_i}{g T_i}$$

No allowance for energy feedback to the ground, as noted in Fig. B-1, has been made in this example.

$R_i \alpha_i$ is 0.322, greater than C' which is 0.19, so additional deflection is indicated for energy balance. Other deflections are tried and the process repeated, with results as shown in Table B-1. It is normally not necessary to compute more than a few trial values nor to plot the results as in Fig. B-9(b). The reconciliation can be interpolated in the last column of the table.

The solution for this example is that the building would require about 0.85 in. deflection for the $F = 1.83$ earthquake. The corresponding condition of the building elements can be readily estimated from Fig. B-9(a).

Fig. B-10 indicates for six buildings the amount of $H_i/2U_i$, which is one of the rating indexes discussed below (actually a function of half of the hump area to the total energy capacity as an indication of the amount of damage or yield that might be expected), plotted against the drift index, which is the story slope from vertical at maximum deflection. The figure illustrates the con-

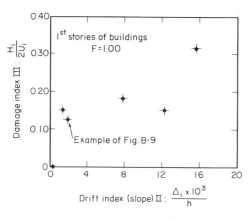

Fig. B-10. Comparison of damage and drift when energy demand is reconciled.

siderable variation in damage and drift for buildings having different dimensions and other characteristics when resisting an earthquake. The capacities shown are not necessarily the ultimate for the buildings, all of which merely meet the energy demands in this figure. Of course, secondary or buckling failures must be considered as limiting values when the drift is appreciable.

Symbol	Rating Name and Deflection Position	Index Consideration		
		I. Energy $= \dfrac{\Sigma(U_i-0.5H_i)}{0.014\,WF^2\sqrt{T_iZ}}$ *	II. Drift $= \dfrac{\Delta_i \times 10^3}{h}$	III. Damage $= \dfrac{H_i}{2U_i}$
"BN" (i=n)	"No damage" Δ_n at the first peak or Δ beyond which $H_n > 0.1U_n$	$\dfrac{\Sigma(U_n-0.5H_n)}{0.014WF^2\sqrt{T_nZ}}$	$\dfrac{\Delta_n \times 10^3}{h}$	$\dfrac{H_n}{2U_n}$
"BD" (i=d)	"Drift"-(slope) Δ_d at 0.004h	$\dfrac{\Sigma(U_d-0.5H_d)}{0.014WF^2\sqrt{T_dZ}}$	$\dfrac{\Delta_d \times 10^3}{h}$ (=4)**	$\dfrac{H_d}{2U_d}$
"BE" (i=e)	Energy Δ_e such that BEI=1.0	$\dfrac{\Sigma(U_e-0.5H_e)}{0.014WF^2\sqrt{T_eZ}}$ (=1.00)**	$\dfrac{\Delta_e \times 10^3}{h}$	$\dfrac{H_e}{2U_e}$
"BF" (i=f)	Failure $\Delta_f = \Delta_{max}$	$\dfrac{\Sigma(U_f-0.5H_f)}{0.014WF^2\sqrt{T_fZ}}$	$\dfrac{\Delta_f \times 10^3}{h}$	$\dfrac{H_f}{2U_f}$

* For $T_i = 0.30$ to 3.0 sec.; For other values the general form is applicable
$$I = \frac{2.72\,\Sigma(U_i-0.5H_i)}{W a_i^2 T_i^2 \sqrt{Z}}\;; \quad 10\% \text{ allowance for } G$$
F shall be reported in three values; 2.77, 1.83 and 1.00

** By definition

Sample Report:
Building X - 1st story (N-S) (10 stories total)
Analysis by _____ Date _____

	I			II	III
	2.77	1.83	1.00		
BN	0.67	1.53	5.17	3.2	0.10
BD	0.94	2.15	7.23	4.0	0.20
BE	1.00	–	–	4.8	0.30
	–	1.00	–	2.3	0.06
	–	–	1.00	0.6	0
BF	1.22	2.79	9.40	7.0	0.40

Fig. B-11. Earthquake rating system for structures.

The fact that various types of structures can have considerable difference in energy-based capacity even though designed for the same or similar static capacities illustrates that the static approach does not include all of the basic parameters of the problem. It is not feasible to attempt to generalize these results between types of buildings or between their basic materials, since the problem is too involved and can best be approached by individual consideration of the various factors that are brought out in the reserve energy analysis.

Moreover, it is undesirable to examine a particular structure only on the basis of safety factor since the amount of damage that might be entailed in reaching these safety factors could vary tremendously between structures.

A Proposed Earthquake Rating System for Structures

A basic requirement in scientific and engineering endeavor is to have a standard means of measurement or comparison. This is very difficult in the earthquake field because of the many and complex parameters and the lack of adequate data. There are many comparisons of earthquakes *per se* but none for structures except static lateral coefficients, which do not include important factors. A

Fig. B-12

I. General Case – for Reserve Energy Analysis with any spectral accelerations, α, and any type of inelastic behavior :

Let $R_{iz}\alpha_i$ = the equivalent "static" design coefficient, then the safety margin

for coefficient $= B = \dfrac{C'}{R_{iz}\alpha_i}$ — — — — — — — — — — — — — — — — (a)*

Assume story total strain energy and energy dissipation value $= U_i - \gamma H_i$ — — — (b)

and $K_i = \dfrac{2(U_i - \gamma H_i)}{\Delta_i^2}$ — — — — — — — — — — — — — — — — (c)

Kinetic energy (gross) $= E = \dfrac{W}{2g}v_i^2 = \dfrac{Wg}{8\pi^2}\alpha_i^2 T_i^2$ — — — — — — — — — (d)*

Assume C' and $R_{iz}\alpha_i$ vary as $\sqrt{\Sigma(U_i - \gamma H_i)\Omega}$, then

$B = \sqrt{\dfrac{\text{Energy capacity}}{\text{Energy demand}}} = \sqrt{\dfrac{\Sigma(U_i - \gamma H_i)\Omega}{E}}$ — — — — — — (e)

or $B = \sqrt{\dfrac{2.44\,\Sigma(U_i - \gamma H_i)\Omega}{W\alpha_i^2 T_i^2}}$ — — — — — — — — — — — — —(f)*

From above, and geometry of Fig. B-3, three alternate equations for R_{iz}, the reserve energy reduction coefficient, are obtained:

Eq. (1): $R_{iz} = T_i C' \sqrt{\dfrac{W}{2.44\,\Sigma(U_i - \gamma H_i)\Omega}}$ — — — — — — — (g)

Eq. (2): $R_{iz} = T_i \sqrt{\dfrac{C'}{\Delta_D}} \times \sqrt{\dfrac{D_z}{1.22\,\Sigma(U_i - \gamma H_i)\Omega}}$ — — — — — — (h)

Eq. (3): $R_{iz} = \rho\,\dfrac{T_i}{T} \sqrt{\dfrac{D_z}{\Sigma(U_i - \gamma H_i)\Omega}}$ — — — — — — — — — (i)

$\rho = 1$ if $T = 2\pi\sqrt{\dfrac{W}{gK_D}}$: otherwise $\rho = 0.90T\sqrt{\dfrac{C'}{\Delta_D}}$ — — (j)

All units in feet, pounds, seconds.

* Where the gross energy demand may be reduced an amount G for ground feedback (Fig. B-1 and Nomenclature), substitute $\overline{\alpha}_i$ for α_i and $\overline{v}_i$ for v_i determined as follows

$\overline{\alpha}_i = \alpha_i\sqrt{\dfrac{E - G}{E}}$ — — — — (k) $\overline{v}_i = v_i\sqrt{\dfrac{E - G}{E}}$ — — — — — (l)

Fig. B-12 (continued)

II. Special Case – for analysis with earthquake spectral values from Figs. B-5 or B-6, for T = 0.3 to 3.0 seconds : G = 0 :

$$E' = \frac{W}{2g} \times F^2 \sqrt{T_i} \quad \text{---------} \quad (m)$$

III. Special Case – Elasto-plastic behavior with no deterioration

For θ_i (Fig. B-3) between 0.9ϕ and 1.1ϕ let stiffness factor $K_i = K_D$

If the system is single-mass, elasto-plastic with no deterioration anticipated under the expected distortion, then $\gamma = 0$, and

$$R_i = \sqrt{\frac{D}{U_i}} \quad \text{---------------} \quad (n)$$

$$\text{or } R_i = \sqrt{\frac{\beta^2}{2\mu - 1}} = \frac{\beta}{\sqrt{2\mu - 1}} \quad \text{-------------} \quad (o)$$

IV. Special Case – for standard (index) rating system for structures -- see Fig. B-11 equations.

Fig. B-12. Principal equations (refer also to nomenclature and figures).

system has been proposed based upon the reserve energy technique [20]. It is shown here in slightly revised form to include the earthquake characteristic F and with 10 per cent reduction in energy demand for ground feedback.

In order to provide a standard reference basis, it is necessary to assume arbitrary values for some of the many parameters involved in earthquake resistance. In addition to the selected earthquake spectral characteristics, damping and energy feedback, the deterioration factor of $\gamma = 0.5$ has been selected and also the factor of $1/\sqrt{Z}$ for Ω, the multistory reduction factor for total energy capacity (Fig. B-12). Any exceptional deviations from these sometimes conservative values can be noted on the report form, but the values are to be used as shown in order to provide the necessary standard means of reference.

Fig. B-11 illustrates the method of rating and the manner of reporting. From a total resistance curve for the lower story as shown in Fig. B-3 (and for another typical story if more than four stories), the ratings are determined according to the formulas shown. The weakest direction for the lower story and same direction for the other story should be reported.

Three proposed F values are shown. (See Figs. B-5 and B-6 for the velocities and accelerations.) When the energy index is determined for one F value, the others are inversely proportional to the respective squares of the F values and are easily obtained. In general terms these F values may be considered to represent catastrophic, severe (El Centro 1940), and mild earthquakes, respectively—with California probability of occurrence as shown on page 256. They may also be severe for long periods, as discussed under the subject of Earthquake Exposure beginning on page 254, but they have the advantage of being a definite basis for comparison.

The ratings consider three types of earthquakes, four key conditions of structural deflection, and the three important indexes: energy capacities compared to demand, drift (slope), and damage. The reported numbers alone, which can easily be typed or recorded by nontechnical personnel, give a vast amount of information for those who consider their significance. High $BF(I)$ values indicate good relative energy capacity for the corresponding conditions of drift or slope of the structure from the vertical (II), and of damage and/or permanent set (III). Not to consider *all* these various factors leads to inadequate comparisons and evaluations of risk and poor statistical history.

For the 10-story building X example reported, the El Centro 1940 N-S ($F = 1.83$) energy requirement would be met ($BE = 1.00$) at a slope of $0.0023h$ from the vertical (II) and only 6 per cent damage (III). The mild shock ($F = 1.00$) has no appreciable effect. The catastrophic ($F = 2.77$) earthquake could be resisted with 30 per cent damage, a slope of $0.0048h$, and with an ultimate safety factor $BF(I)$ of 1.22. This is a good building.

Conclusions and Recommendations

It is hoped that the reserve energy technique and the proposed earthquake rating system for structures will provide convenient and simple devices for the urgently needed design consideration of inelastic response to earthquake motion. Some empirical and judgment factors have been combined with theoretical considerations. However, such has been done with care and the consideration of many factors too numerous for inclusion in this manual. Further research is needed, particularly to provide a library of more lateral force test data up to complete failure. There is no danger or harm (and it is believed, a great deal of good) to be done, however, in using the method as a check and refinement of design for special structures first designed under current codes, or for the research analysis of existing structures and parameters related to inelastic behavior.

Several subjects have been discussed in this section. Some are general in nature, such as the reserve energy technique, the earthquake rating system, and the expressions for spectral velocity and acceleration. These are independent items and each can be utilized without regard to the others. However, the various common terms and relationships are useful. Also presented were several specific situations or special cases of the general procedures, such as the elastoplastic system analysis or direct inelastic design with the use of the R factor and the deflection or ductility factor. Other special matters have to do with the specific F values proposed for various types of earthquakes. The recommended values and the 5 per cent recommended damping factor are believed reasonable and consistent for California conditions shown to date, especially up to 2- or 2.5-second periods. If these spectral values should be found to change in the future, or in areas where the conditions are basically different, naturally the proper values of α should be used in the general equations for the procedures of energy analysis.

With the procedure outlined, the anomalies of a great deal of apparently baffling earthquake history can be explained as can the gap between elastic spectral data and the capacity to resist earthquakes. The advantages of ductility, indeterminate construction, plateaus of resistance, period change, damping, energy loss due to cracking, friction, yield, etc., can be approached numerically as well as philosophically—and in terms familiar to designers conversant only with static procedures who are even now producing great numbers of structures for future earthquake exposure. Although many of the buildings analyzed thus far have adequate resistance, all do not, and the amount of drift and damage seem to be highly variable for different building types even though meeting static code requirements. A more realistic approach to earthquake-resistant design is indicated, at least for important and unusual structures.

Although the rating system for structures is not a part of the design analysis technique, it is considered an important device for better communication and recording as well as rating of structures on the important parameters of inelastic resistance, extreme deflection, and damage, if any, necessary to develop the resistance. Unfortunately, it is unrealistic to speak of earthquake resistance without also considering the results, if any, of developing this resistance in the form of drift and damage or permanent set.

It is not intended that the reserve energy technique should replace modern codes or the judgment of structural engineers thoroughly familiar with the earthquake problem in all of its important aspects. It is felt, however, that the technique would sharpen the judgment of engineers and designers, stimulate the research worker, and perhaps lead to code improvements. One of its basic objectives, of course, is to help to bridge the gap between earthquake history and research and practical structural design.

B.2 Reserve Energy Analysis of a 24-Story Building

The hypothetical building designed in Chapter 7 has been subjected to modal analysis and the results are presented in Appendix A. The shears resulting from the assumption of a completely elastic shear-type structure subjected to the idealized earthquake spectrum of Fig. A-1 are shown in Table A-6 for the transverse direction of six selected stories. It is to be noted that these shears are considerably in excess of the design shears required by the SEAOC code or, for that matter, any existing design code. This would be true irrespective of the construction material.

This section presents an analysis of the structure by the reserve energy technique discussed in Section B.1. Instead of utilizing the 5 per cent damping spectral accelerations of Fig. B-6 and modifying them for energy feedback to the ground or for multistory spectral response as outlined in Section B.1 under Multimass Systems, the available elastic response accelerations from Appendix A will be used directly together with the computed fundamental mode period of 1.91 seconds.

Special Considerations

There are many parameters involved in the reconciliation of theoretical elastic shears and code design shears. In addition to ductile energy absorption and the differences in behavior of idealized single-mass systems compared with actual systems, there are factors such as the following that assume importance, especially in connection with multistory buildings: energy return or feedback to the ground; possible period change under severe motion; the relative participation of various members and stories in energy absorption; the conversion of member ductility to story work or reserve energy capacity; interrelationships of strength, ductility, and energy; and others.

Although these factors have been investigated in considerable degree, more knowledge and experience are desirable to further evaluate them for multistory buildings of all types and materials. The reserve energy technique has been developed to facilitate the inelastic analysis of complex structures. Before applying the reserve energy procedures to the building under consideration, certain questions should be considered.

1. Does yielding occur only in the lowest story so that the building can be considered to be essentially a single-mass system? In the design example of Chapter 7, the ratio of computed shears to the design shears is essentially constant for all but the upper stories, as shown in Table A-6. It therefore seems likely that all of the lower stories have about the same probability of yielding, and plastic yielding may occur in several stories at once. It is probable that the upper stories will yield before the lower stories.

2. Is the story behavior elasto-plastic, with or without deterioration of resistance, even though all the individual frame members and joints may not develop elasto-plastic behavior? The answer depends upon the frame analysis under severe loading and yielding conditions and the resulting force-deflection diagrams. Generally, an indeterminate structure will develop hinges progressively rather than simultaneously. It is possible for the girders to develop hinges, for example, while the columns remain elastic so the story as a whole has ductile characteristics. The story stiffness varies in two or more steps similar to Figs. B-2, B-3, or B-4(c) and the energy capacity may thus be increased over that of the same design assumed to become elasto-plastic at the first point of yielding. Deterioration under severe and repeated lurches into the plastic range has been discussed in Section B.1 wherein a deterioration factor γ of 0.5 has been proposed, pending further research, especially for shear walls and frames stiffened by

shear walls. This value would be quite conservative where the members of a frame behave in an elasto-plastic manner even though they may yield at various stages; in this case, γ would be nearly 0. Therefore, in the review of the design example that was detailed in accordance with the recommendations of Chapter 6, values of $\gamma = 0$ and $\gamma = 0.2$ will be used to explore the range of results and the story P-Δ characteristics, based upon the individual member characteristics as inferred from tests.

3. Does the natural period lengthen under severe earthquake motion, and if so, how is the lengthening computed for a multistory building? The nature of the P-Δ diagrams and especially a comparison of the unloading slope (angle θ_1) to the initial loading angle ϕ (Fig. B-3) is a key to the answer to this question. If the behavior of all members strained beyond yield is essentially elasto-plastic, as defined in Section B.1 by this angle relationship, the period is assumed constant. If, however, the stiffness decreases with excursions beyond yield value at one or more stories, the period lengthens and the building may be subject to less spectral acceleration on subsequent earthquake cycles. Stiffness changes in lower stories have more effect on period than those in upper stories. It is of course possible to compute T_i based upon whatever changed story stiffness factors may be involved or, more simply, to assume that all story stiffnesses change simultaneously and in the same degree as the one under consideration so that the procedure shown in Fig. B-2 and Table B-1 would apply to the multistory building. Another approach that has logic as well as simplicity is to determine a new building period T_i for each set of trial story deflections and based upon the probable average story stiffness

$$T_i = T \sqrt{\frac{(\text{Ave. } K_D)\Omega}{\text{Ave. } K_i}}$$

However, in no case would T_i be less than T. This T_i basis will be used herein with Ω taken as the particular value for the midheight, or 12th story, of the building.

4. How do stories other than the one under consideration contribute to energy absorption? This has been discussed in paragraph 3, page 263, under multimass systems. The range of permissible assumptions of Ω for this 24-story building is estimated to be from 0.5 to $1/\sqrt{Z}$ or essentially from 0.5 to 0.2 for the lowest story. The mode shape also is important in this connection and will be discussed under Procedures.

Judgment is essential to the solution of many problems in structural engineering when there are no simple, well-defined answers. It is often an aid to judgment to assume extreme conditions for parameters that are difficult to isolate and to study the effect of these boundary values on the results. This will be done herein for the design problem of Chapter 7.

Data for Analysis

The values of "probable" elastic shears shown in line (d) of Table B-2 are taken from Table A-6. These are the root-mean-square values of the first five modes of vibration.

The procedure for obtaining the values in line (f) is to enter Fig. B-6 with $F = 1.83$ and $T = 1.91$ seconds, and apply a 10 per cent deduction to the values taken from the figure to account for energy feedback to the ground. Moreover, the α values could be further adjusted for multimode behavior as discussed on page 263, paragraph 2. With an assumed system A-5 as shown in Fig. 10 of reference 20, α values as shown in line (f) of Table B-2 would be obtained. The differences between the values of lines (e) and (f) in Table B-2 (which would be slightly greater if a corresponding 10 per cent were deducted from line (e) values for energy feedback) are due to several factors, including the use of slightly different smoothed spectra. The differences are not great except in the top stories where, for reasons previously noted, this building has unusual response characteristics. The α values of line (e) will be used in the analysis. Changes in α with T_i will be obtained by proportion to the slope of the curve for $F = 1.83$ in Fig. B-6.

The penthouse story 24–25 will be assumed to be a 25th story for this analysis, although it will not be considered in detail since its severe modal accelerations result from a unique dynamic situation that could readily be corrected by simple design revisions such as stiffening the penthouse to shorten its natural period.

Story G-1 is different from the others in that it has different boundary conditions. There is a solid shear wall from the ground level to the basement of the building. The G-1 and basement story framing, although subject to less computed moment and shear from lateral forces (because of the ground resistance and the shear walls), is generally designed by virtue of gravity loads and engineering judgment to have no smaller members, regardless of moments from lateral design forces, than those of the story immediately above. The problem can be treated in several ways in the reserve energy analysis. For this example, it will be assumed that story G-1 has the same member sizes as story 1-2 and that all

TABLE B-2 Comparison of Spectral Accelerations

	Story between floors				
	G-1	1–2	9–10	16–17	23–24
(a) Code design shear, kips	2,120	2,100	1,750	1,120	180
(b) Superimposed weight, kips	85,600	80,900	49,900	26,200	3,570
(c) $C = \dfrac{(a)}{(b)}$	0.025	0.026	0.035	0.043	0.050
(d) "Probable" elastic shears Table A-6, kips	12,200	12,000	9,130	6,700	1,930
(e) $\alpha = \dfrac{(d)}{(b)}$, for $T=1.91$	0.14	0.15	0.18	0.25	0.54
(f) α from Fig. B-6, $F=1.83$, $T=1.91$, adjusted	0.17	0.18	0.19	0.26	0.34

stories deflect in proportion to their deflections in the first or fundamental mode shape (see Fig. B-13).

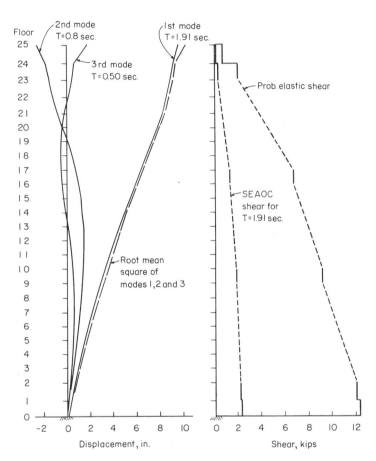

Fig. B-13. Elastic modal shears and displacements.

Assumptions for Analysis

Three sets of assumed parameters will be considered in order to explore their effects on the results as discussed under Special Considerations above.

CASE A   1. $\gamma = 0.2$

2. Ω in the R_{iz} equation (g) of Fig. B-12 equals $1/\sqrt{Z}$

3. $T_i = T\sqrt{\dfrac{(\text{Ave. } K_D)\Omega}{\text{Ave. } K_i}}$ where Ave.K_D and Ave.K_i refer to average story stiffnesses of the building under elastic and trial

inelastic deflections, respectively; however, T_i shall not be less than T
4. Story distortions proportional to fundamental mode shape (Fig. B-13)

CASE B
1. $\gamma = 0$
2. Assume Ω in equation (g) of Fig. B-12 equals the constant 0.5 at all levels except the upper four for which $\Omega = 1/\sqrt{Z}$
3. $T_i = T = 1.91$, a constant
4. Story distortions as for Case A

CASE C
1. $\gamma = 0.2$
2. As for Case B
3. T_i as for Case A
4. Story distortions increased from the fundamental mode shape by the factor $\dfrac{T_i}{T}\sqrt{\dfrac{R_{iz}\alpha_i}{C'}}$ with data from Case A values

Discussion of Case Assumptions and Procedures

There are various mode shapes that could be assumed for the purpose of computing energy development at the different stories. Fig. B-13 shows that the root-mean-square envelope of modes 1, 2, and 3 is closely similar to that of the fundamental mode except at the top. The root-mean-square envelope of the first five modes (not shown) is very close to that for the first three modes. For simplicity therefore, in Cases A and B the fundamental mode shape is used here to determine the relative story distortions Δ_i. It would be possible, of course, to use any other mode shape in the energy procedure to check for reaction to motion in that mode. Where mode shapes or root-mean-square envelopes are not known specifically, a straightline fundamental mode displacement may be used for tall buildings with little error for this purpose.

For Case C, a different mode shape will be investigated on the basis that unsatisfied energy demands would lead to increased story distortions, yielding and, further, that the stories having the lowest energy factor B would tend to yield the most. A somewhat arbitrary modal adjustment factor as shown under Case C has been adopted to explore this parameter. It is also of interest that if cantilever-type flexural deflections (column axial deformation) had also been included in the modal analysis, the upper stories would have moved a greater amount in relation to the lower stories, although this increased motion would be primarily due to distortions in the lower stories.

For each trial deflection, an arbitrary Δ_i value will be assumed for story G-1. Corresponding net deflections for the other stories under Cases A and B will be more or less than that for the G-1 story, depending upon the fundamental mode shape. The cases are shown in Table B-3 with some of their trial story deflections. The story load-deformation or P-Δ diagrams were developed for the stories

TABLE B-3   Certain Trial Story Net Deflections, Inches

Story between floors	Case A and B $i=1$ Δ_1	Case A and B $i=2$ Δ_2	Case C $i=3$ Δ_3
23-24	0.56	1.01	3.50
16-17	1.19	2.14	2.23
9-10	1.11	2.00	1.85
1-2	0.81	1.46	1.77
G-1	1.00	1.80	1.70

shown in Table B-3 in accordance with Section B.1 procedures. It was found for this building as initially designed in Chapter 7 under the SEAOC code that the girders started to hinge at and subsequently above or below each story under consideration as the assumed story shear was increased. The floors were not assumed to be locked plates but as elastic and, finally, as inelastic elements. It was assumed that the applied shear was constant over several adjacent stories as well, so that as one level of girders hinged, the adjacent level would participate elastically until it also developed hinges. It was further assumed that only one story region became inelastic at any one instant and all other stories were elastic, i.e., that there was a spread of hinges *outward* from the story involved but no overlapping spread of hinges from below or above into the story area under consideration. For each step, as a complete level of girder hinges developed at a floor line, the columns became "longer columns" with the partial restraint of hinge-value applied moments at intermediate levels.

Beam test data were studied in detail for the determination of the girder hinge characteristics. For the reinforcing details as set forth in Chapter 6, the hinge proper has a ductility, as shown by Fig. 5-14, greater than a μ value of 28. The action involved in story deformation, however, is first an elastic stage where both girders and columns remain elastic up to a yield point and then, in the case of this hypothetical building, the girders hinge adjacent to the columns under increasing assumed story shears. The hinge is a relatively small proportion of the total concrete mass. The ultimate moment value of the girders is such that for this particular example the columns remain elastic at all stages of inelastic story action. The second stage of deformation involves rotation of the hinge together with an additional amount of elastic deformation as the shear is increased up to ultimate values.

Calculations were made of the story P-Δ characteristics based upon empirical data, M/EI diagrams, and slope-deflection equations. It was assumed, based upon test results, that the maximum shear value was 40 per cent greater than the yield shear and, further, that the girder hinge ductility was limited to the lower values obtained from tests of similar members. Whichever of these factors controlled in each case determined the ultimate girder contribution shown in the diagrams. Typical procedures are illustrated below.

STORY BETWEEN FLOORS 9-10

Story deflection

Girder: Let E'_c = an equivalent modulus of elasticity between yield and ultimate. From various test data $E'_c = E_c/20$ is selected as an appropriate value. Let M_y and M_u be the yield and ultimate moment values of the girder.

$$\text{Ultimate } \Theta_A = \Theta_B = \frac{0.153 M_y L}{E'_c I_g}$$

Column: From the slope-deflection equation,

$$R = \Theta_A + \frac{1}{12}\left(\frac{2.8 M_y h}{E_c I_c}\right) = \Theta_A + 0.0117\frac{M_y h}{E'_c I_c}$$

Ultimate story $\Delta_u = Rh$

For $M_y = 437$ ft.kips, $h = 12$ ft.,

$I_g = bd^3/12 = 29{,}400$ in.^{4}, $I_c = bt^3/12 = 112{,}000$ in.^{4}

$\therefore \Delta_u = 3.35$ in.

Ratio of ϕ/ϕ_y for girder

$$\Theta_u = \frac{0.153 M_y L}{E'_c I_g} = 22.9 \times 10^{-3}$$

For $\Delta = 1.70$ in., $\Theta \cong \frac{\Theta_u}{\Delta_u}\Delta = 11.6 \times 10^{-3}$

$p = 0.0136$, $p' = 0.0102$, $d'/d = 2.5/27.5 = 0.09$, $k \cong 0.275$

$$\therefore \phi_y = \frac{\epsilon_y}{d(1-k)} = \frac{0.0015}{(27.5)(1-0.275)} = 7.55 \times 10^{-5}$$

But $\Theta = d(\phi - \phi_y)$

$$\therefore \phi = \Theta/d + \phi_y = 50.0 \times 10^{-5}$$

$$\phi/\phi_y = 6.6$$

Figs. B-14, B-15, and B-16 are the P-Δ diagrams for stories G-1, 9-10, and 23-24, respectively, in the design example. The trial deflections corresponding to Table B-3 are indicated.

Figs. B-14, B-15, and B-16 and this analysis are for motion and forces to be resisted by the narrow, transverse framing of the building or parallel to bents A, B, C, etc., as shown in the plan, Fig. 7-2. The column-line beams or girders in this direction are larger than the adjacent parallel floor beams because of their lateral force resistant function. Although these girders together with the columns are the only resisting elements assumed in Chapter 7 for the static lateral force (code) requirements, it was assumed for the purpose of computing story stiffnesses and inelastic energy values that there is some participation of the two adjacent parallel beams. With allowance for the torsional value and deflections of the longitudinal girders and the participation of the floor slabs, 50 per cent of the stiffness and 50 per cent of the energy value of the two adjacent beams has been considered as effective. It was also assumed that beam yield and beam failure would occur at the same story deflections as for girder yield and failure. The relatively small amount of this beam energy value as compared to that of the transverse column-line girder can be estimated by the respective lines on Figs. B-14, B-15, and B-16.

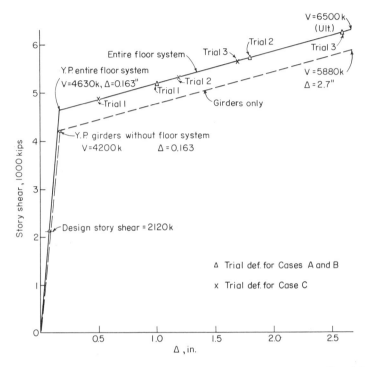

Fig. B-14. Story shear-deflection relationship for story between floors G and 1.

In accordance with the recommendations of Chapter 6, the minimum positive moment capacity of the girders adjacent to columns has been held to three-quarters of the negative moment capacity. This has slightly increased the bottom (positive moment) steel area over the amount that would be required by the SEAOC code. The difference in lateral force coefficient value for the code requirement, C, and that actually provided, C', can be seen in Fig. B-18.

With the P-Δ diagrams for the five stories, trial deflection values of U_i and H_i were computed in accordance with the modal deflection criteria and the procedures of Section B.1. Fig. B-17 shows the U_i and $(U_i - \gamma H_i)$ values obtained for certain trial deflections. Intermediate values for stories not computed were interpolated in this figure for the purpose of taking summations.

Table B-4 shows the analysis for Case A. The procedures, equations, and nomenclature are described in Section B.1 except that the α_i values in Table B-4 have been determined as described above in subsection Data for Analysis.

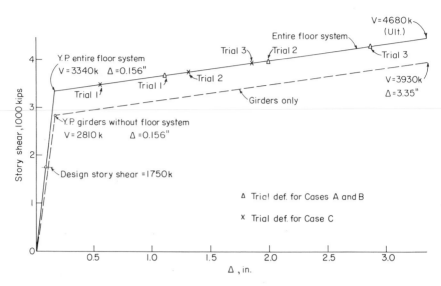

Fig. B-15. Story shear-deflection relationship for story between floors 9 and 10.

Fig. B-18 shows the reserve energy technique results for stories G-1, 9-10, and 16-17 for Cases A, B, and C. The crossings of the $R_i \alpha_i$ lines and the C' lines indicate energy reconciliation or points where the energy safety factor $B = 1$ [equation (a) of Fig. B-12] for the corresponding story deflections. There is little difference between the results for Cases B and C. Case A does not obtain energy balance within the deflection range considered except at G-1. The upper stories have less energy capacity as compared to their energy demands than the lower stories. It is to be noted that *all* stories would not deflect to the amounts found; the probability relationships would not permit this. A general word of caution seems desirable, however, against the use of very large story deflections or large ductility assumptions without the careful consideration of secondary-type failures from eccentricity of loading or buckling

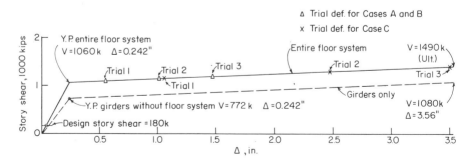

Fig. B-16. Story shear-deflection relationship for story between floors 23 and 24.

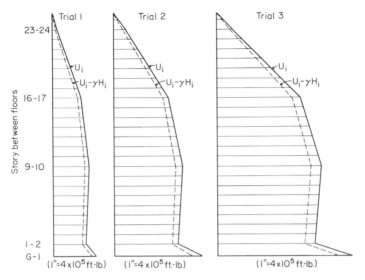

Fig. B-17. Values of U_i and $(U_i - \gamma H_i)$ for three trial deflections—Cases A and B. For Case A, $\gamma = 0.2$ and for Case B, $\gamma = 0$.

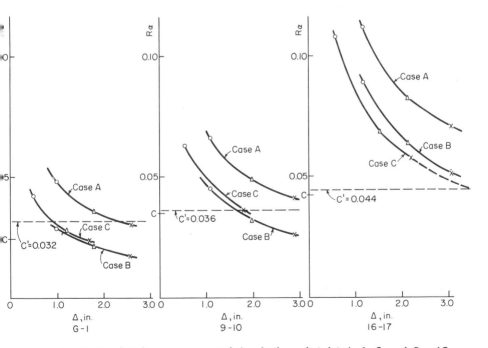

Fig. B-18. Results of analysis by reserve energy technique for three selected stories for Cases A, B, and C

TABLE B-4   Analysis for Case A

$\gamma = 0.2$ $\Omega = 1/\sqrt{Z}$ $T = 1.91$ sec.

Trial No.	Story between floors	Δ_i in	U_i ft.-kips	H_i ft.-kips	$U_i - \gamma H_i$ ft.-kips	$\Sigma(U_i - \gamma H_i)$ ft.-kips	K_i k/ft.	K_D k/ft.	T_i sec.	Z	W kips	$\frac{W}{\Omega}$	$2.44\Sigma(U_i-\gamma H_i)$	$\sqrt{\dfrac{W/\Omega}{2.44\Sigma(U_i-\gamma H_i)}}$	C'	T_iC'	R_{iz}	a_{iz}	$R_{iz}a_{iz}$
1	23-24	0.56	40	13	37	47	34,000	53,000	1.98	2	3,570	5,060	115	6.62	0.051	0.101	0.670	0.515	0.344
	16-17	1.19	239	100	219	1,029	44,500	160,000	1.98	9	26,200	78,600	2,550	5.55	0.044	0.0872	0.484	0.235	0.113
	9-10	1.11	302	131	276	2,795	64,500	252,000	1.98	16	49,900	199,000	6,840	5.39	0.036	0.0715	0.385	0.172	0.0662
	1-2	0.81	277	121	253	4,909	111,000	508,000	1.98	24	80,900	396,000	12,000	5.74	0.032	0.0635	0.365	0.143	0.0521
	G-1	1.00	376	158	344	5,253	99,000	337,000	1.98	25	85,600	428,000	12,800	5.78	0.032	0.0635	0.367	0.133	0.0488
2	23-24	1.01	83	34	76	106	21,400	53,000	2.54	2	3,570	5,060	259	4.42	0.051	0.130	0.572	0.415	0.237
	16-17	2.14	467	204	426	2,033	26,800	160,000	2.54	9	26,200	78,600	4,950	3.99	0.044	0.112	0.447	0.192	0.0858
	9-10	2.00	588	255	537	5,460	38,800	252,000	2.54	16	49,900	199,000	13,300	3.87	0.036	0.0915	0.354	0.138	0.0488
	1-2	1.46	538	228	492	9,592	66,500	508,000	2.54	24	80,900	396,000	23,400	4.11	0.032	0.0815	0.334	0.115	0.0385
	G-1	1.80	745	310	683	10,275	60,500	337,000	2.54	25	85,600	428,000	25,100	4.13	0.032	0.0815	0.336	0.107	0.036
3	23-24	1.46	128	55	117	157	15,800	53,000	2.97	2	3,570	5,060	383	3.64	0.051	0.151	0.550	0.376	0.206
	16-17	3.10	713	301	653	3,161	19,600	160,000	2.97	9	26,200	78,600	7,720	3.19	0.044	0.131	0.418	0.174	0.073
	9-10	2.88	892	376	817	8,413	28,400	252,000	2.97	16	49,900	199,000	20,500	3.11	0.036	0.107	0.333	0.125	0.0416
	1-2	2.10	824	334	757	14,680	49,400	508,000	2.97	24	80,900	396,000	35,800	3.32	0.032	0.095	0.315	0.104	0.0327
	G-1	2.60	1,151	456	1,040	15,720	44,400	337,000	2.97	25	85,600	428,000	38,400	3.33	0.032	0.095	0.316	0.0975	0.0308

$$K_i = \frac{2(U_i - \gamma H_i)}{\Delta_i^2}$$

$$R_{iz} = T_i C' \sqrt{\frac{W/\Omega}{2.44\Sigma(U_i - \gamma H_i)}}$$

$$\text{where } T_i = T\sqrt{\frac{(Ave.\ K_D)\Omega}{Ave.\ K_i}}$$

of local elements. The massive columns of this building have great stability against local buckling effects. Adequate shear resistance has to be provided in accordance with Chapter 6 and ductility should be provided in design even though the columns do remain elastic.

The following considerations in total or in any combination could explain the situation shown graphically in Fig. B-18:

a. The "probable" elastic shears from Table A-6 may be conservative.

b. Energy feedback to the ground should be considered. (If the α values were reduced for this phenomenon, the $R\alpha$ curves would fall correspondingly closer to the C' lines on Fig. B-18. Unless and until research indicates otherwise, however, a reduction of over 10 per cent for this factor does not seem justified.)

c. Any walls or elements other than the bare frame should have been included in the reserve energy capacities. (Even buildings with no external walls generally have *some* interior walls or partitions that add to the energy capacity of the structure.)

d. The assumptions for the analysis are conservative. In this connection Case A could be considered conservative for this building example, but it may not be in all other situations. Case B cannot be considered conservative since, with $\Omega = 0.5$, one-half of the total story energy capacity at any trial deflection is considered effective at one time and since there is no deterioration γ. Case C, which is essentially a progressive development of Case A under severe earthquake motion, seems reasonable. In criteria A and C, the γ factor is the same as is the treatment of period lengthening T_i. The probability factor Ω is generally greater for Case C than for A, not without logic, since the greater story distortions would involve greater overall energy development. The difference in the inelastic displacement shape is such that the greater story distortions occur where the energy capacity to energy demand ratio is initially less under the elastic mode shape. This also has logic since the weakest elements would tend to distort further into the inelastic range than elastic theory would indicate. It would, of course, be possible to try another case or "energy closure" wherein the data developed for Case C would form the basis for further adjusting the inelastic deformations. Moreover, since the lower stories apparently undergo smaller distortions, a γ factor of 0 could be applied for these and the 0.2 value for the upper levels. By trial, the probable "spectrum" of the building's complete response to the earthquake can be developed as well as its condition following the earthquake. If three-dimensional deformations were introduced, some additional reserve energy could, of course, be found due to the torsional resistance of members and/or to twisting of the building as a whole under progressive yielding. Moreover, actual reinforcing bar selections rather than net area design requirements as used herein would add some measure of additional capacity.

e. Any weak points exposed by the analysis, or items that could be improved at nominal additional construction cost should be corrected or adjusted as indicated.

f. If account is not taken of items (a) through (e) above, tall building frames, regardless of material or ductility, as initially designed for the inverted triangular loading without modification, would undergo large deflections at the higher levels for the earthquake exposure selected in Appendix A.

Items (a) and (b) will not be altered herein since the elastic values of Table A-6 are assumed to be specified for this hypothetical case. The walls, stairs, etc., of item (c) will also be ignored herein except as a judgment factor. Item (d) is a matter of engineering judgment along with item (e), which should be a basic consideration in all circumstances. The design engineer must determine the story deflections that can be tolerated for each particular structure and risk situation. These deflections may vary from story to story. He also has to select his factors γ and Ω to suit the conditions, and in practice determine not two or three, but generally one basic design case or criterion.

For the building example at hand it shall be assumed that Case C applies and that the story deflections and hinge rotations are as shown in Table B-5.

It is apparent from a comparison of the story deflections and ductility factors at compliance (when $R_i \alpha_i = C'$) to the ultimate values that the lower stories have greater reserve values than the upper stories. Although none of the stories shown reach the ultimate values of ductility or strength under Case C, the designer would no doubt carefully consider the upper stories with reference to any limiting deflections that should be imposed for secondary effects, column stability, or the effects on nonstructural materials and elements. He could quite readily provide some additional girder reinforcement at the upper levels to increase the reserve energy values, with no change in concrete dimensions. This would also increase the lower story values and in general provide resistance at even lower ductility values. The procedures will be discussed generally.

The design criterion for energy compliance is

$$B = \frac{C'}{R_i \alpha_i} = 1$$

However, consideration of the parameters in B by substitution of equation (g) for R_{iz} in equation (a) of Fig. B-12 shows that

$$B = \frac{1}{T_i \alpha_i} \sqrt{\frac{2.44 \sum (U_i - \gamma H_i)\Omega}{W}}$$

TABLE B-5   Story Deflections and Hinge Rotations—Case C

Story between floors	C'	When $R_i a = C'$			Story ultimate	
		Story Δ_i, in.	Story μ	Girder ϕ/ϕ_y	Δ_{max}, in.	Story μ
16-17	0.044	3+	16+	10.9	3.1	17
9-10	0.036	1.80	11.5	7.0	3.4	22
G-1	0.032	0.85	5.2	3.3	2.7	17

and C' does not affect B except as changes in C' may indirectly affect the energy capacity $\sum(U_i - \gamma H_i)$ or the period T_i. However, to obtain more energy capacity, the net effective areas $(U_i - \gamma H_i)$ must be increased. This can be done by increasing the story yield shear and/or the deflection Δ_i. Where Δ_i is limited for any reason, the strength coefficient C' must be increased. In most cases, with positive and negative reinforcing, C' can be increased considerably without sacrificing ductility or changing concrete dimensions. Additional steel area is provided at the critical points in the girders adjacent to the columns. Shear and concrete crushing values must be checked, of course, to have values at safe margins above the ultimate girder hinge (moment) values.

For example, the initial design for story 16-17 provides reinforcement of only 1.2 per cent at the top of the girder ends near the columns. If this were increased to 2 per cent, the story C' value would increase proportionately at a relatively insignificant increase in cost. This would appreciably improve the energy values for a given ductility. Additional value could also be obtained by increasing girder sizes as well as the reinforcing steel.

The proper procedure would be to take trial increases and then recompute the period T (which incidentally would not be too sensitive to any stiffness changes at the upper levels), compute revised U_i and H_i values and try a new reserve energy analysis. The lower stories would benefit to some extent from the increased values of the upper stories and their reconciliation deflections would be somewhat less.

It should be noted in conclusion that this example has not included the several possible energy-absorbing elements such as walls, stairs, partitions, etc., which can materially add to the energy capacity of a building, even where not considered as basic parts of the structural system. Further, even though such elements, by stiffening the building, tend to decrease the period and invite greater accelerations, the velocity and thus the energy demand may be less at these shorter periods. (See Figs. B-5 and B-6.) In any event, *all* elements that tend to resist movement should be considered, both as to their energy capacity and their possible damage due to movement. This can be done as outlined in Section B.1 with detailed procedures as indicated in this example so as to economically reconcile design shears with the much greater elastic spectral shears.

A reinforced concrete frame building with its design in accordance with the recommendations of Chapter 6 to avoid shear or crushing failures and to have ductility in girders, beams, and columns, has great energy-absorption value as well as strength and resistance to local secondary-type failures. The reserve energy technique together with sound engineering judgment can be utilized to design, analyze, and adjust strength and energy values of the frame alone or of the frame in combination with other building elements such as walls and partitions so as to obtain economy of construction and optimum earthquake resistance.

RECOMMENDED
LATERAL FORCE REQUIREMENTS

Seismology Committee
Structural Engineers Association of California

July, 1959*
417 Market St.
San Francisco 5
California

---

*Subsequent to the version of July 1959, of the *Recommended Lateral Force Requirements*, the Seismology Committee and the Board of Directors of the Structural Engineers Association of California adopted and approved, in December 1959, revisions in certain sections and portions of the above lateral force code that have been incorporated in this authorized reprint in bold-face type.

INTRODUCTION

to

RECOMMENDED LATERAL FORCE REQUIREMENTS
SEISMOLOGY COMMITTEE
STRUCTURAL ENGINEERS ASSOCIATION OF CALIFORNIA

In 1957 the Structural Engineers Association of California Seismology Committee, at the direction of its Board of Directors, began developing a uniform seismic code which would resolve the important differences in the several codes used in seismic areas of the United States, and California in particular. A sixteen member committee was selected on a statewide basis with members from each of the Central, Northern and Southern California local Associations. The committee members worked for more than two years, pooling their knowledge and experience in seismic matters, to develop a uniform code.

Prior to development of the first draft of the proposed seismic code, the committee held several statewide meetings. Separate studies were made by study groups on the subjects of Base Shear, Shear Distribution, Structural Frames, Diaphragms, Torsion, Overturning, Setbacks, Drift, and Foundations. The general committee served as a coordinating group to evaluate the results and considerations of the study groups. The major objective of the general committee and the study groups was to consider the dynamic response of structures, giving due consideration to all available research and damage studies. Since the code is developed on the basis of broad considerations, items of detail are to be presented in a manual of practice currently under development.

Although the concepts of the Base Shear formula as presented are not new, a new method of application of two variables has been introduced. One variable directly introduces the fundamental period of the structure and defines a method of determining the period where it cannot be accurately predetermined. A second variable is dependent on the *type* of *structural system* to be used. Based on research, experience and damage studies, certain types of construction are assigned bonus considerations for the seismic factors. It should be noted that the code is based on seismic experience in the United States.

Like any progressive building code, this is an interim code. The committee realizes there is much work still to be done as the results of research and further study become available. However, the committee believes this code represents a major contribution by the Structural Engineers Association of California in the field of design for lateral forces due to earthquakes.

Members of Seismology Committee

Structural Engineers Association of California

S. B. Barnes	Roy G. Johnston
R. W. Binder	Harold S. Kellam
John A. Blume	J. F. Meehan
Henry J. Degenkolb	Harald Omsted
Murray Erick	Henry C. Powers
Herman F. Finch	John E. Rinne
Norman B. Green	G. A. Sedgwick
Harold B. Hammill	William T. Wheeler, Chairman

Secretaries to Committee

Herman F. Finch   Harald Omsted

Sub-Committee Members for Study Groups

J. S. Barrish	Ernest Maag
R. W. Brandley	Frank E. McClure
A. H. Brownfield	William W. Moore
LeRoy Crandall	W. D. Rumberger
M. A. Ewing	A. A. Sauer
G. M. Hart	M. J. Skinner
M. T. Knox	John Steinbrugge
Ed Lindskog	

Code Consultants

Walter Brugger   Truland Carter

Liaison Members to the Committee

R. W. Binder, SEAOSC   G. A. Sedgwick, SEAONC
J. F. Meehan, SEAOCC

RECOMMENDED LATERAL FORCE REQUIREMENTS

SEISMOLOGY COMMITTEE

STRUCTURAL ENGINEERS ASSOCIATION OF CALIFORNIA

Refer to Section 2312. The following provisions are suggested for inclusion in the Uniform Building Code by cities located within an area subject to earthquake shocks:

Sec. 2312. (a) *General.* These lateral force requirements are intended to provide minimum standards as design criteria toward making buildings and other structures earthquake-resistive. The provisions of this Section apply to the structure as a unit and also to all parts thereof, including the structural frame or walls, floor and roof systems, and other structural features.

The provisions incorporated in this Section are general and, in specific cases, may be interpreted as to detail by rulings of the Building Official in order that the intent shall be fulfilled.

Every building or structure and every portion thereof, except Type V buildings of Group I occupancy which are less than twenty-five feet (25') in height, and minor accessory buildings, shall be designed and constructed to resist stresses produced by lateral forces as provided in this Section. Stresses shall be calculated as the effect of a force applied horizontally at each floor or roof level above the foundation. The force shall be assumed to come from any horizontal direction.

(b) *Definitions.* The following Definitions apply only to the provisions of this section.

SPACE FRAME is a three dimensional structural system composed of interconnected members, other than shear or bearing walls, laterally supported so as to function as a complete self-contained unit with or without the aid of horizontal diaphragms or floor bracing systems.

SPACE FRAME—VERTICAL LOAD-CARRYING: a space frame designed to carry all vertical loads.

SPACE FRAME—MOMENT RESISTING: a vertical load-carrying space frame in which the members and joints are capable of resisting design lateral forces by bending moments. This system may or may not be enclosed by or adjoined by more rigid elements which would tend to prevent the space frame from resisting lateral forces.

BOX SYSTEM is a structural system without a complete vertical load-carrying space frame. In this system the required lateral forces are resisted by shear walls as hereinafter defined.

SHEAR WALL is a wall designed to resist lateral forces parallel to the wall. Braced frames subjected primarily to axial stresses shall be considered as shear walls for the purpose of this definition.

(c) *Symbols and Notations.* The following symbols and notations apply only to the provisions of this Section.

C = Numerical coefficient for base shear as defined in Section 2312(d)1.

C_p = Numerical coefficient as defined in Section 2312(d)2 and as set forth in Table No. 23-D.

D = The dimension of the building in feet in a direction parallel to the applied forces.

F_a = Allowable axial stress.

f_a = Computed axial stress.

F_b = Allowable bending stress.

f_b = Computed bending stress.

F_p = Lateral forces on the part of the structure and in the direction under consideration.

F_x = Lateral force applied to a level designated as x.

H = The height of the main portion of the building in feet above the base.

h_x = Height in feet above the base to the level designated as x.

J = Numerical coefficient for base moment as defined in Section 2312(h).

K = Numerical coefficient as set forth in Table 23-C.

$\sum wh$ = Summation of the products of all $w_x \cdot h_x$ for the building.

M = Overturning moment at the base of the building or structure.

N = Total number of stories above exterior grade.

T = Fundamental period of vibration of the building or structure in seconds in the direction under consideration.

V = Total lateral load or shear at the base.

W = Total dead load.

EXCEPTION: W shall be equal to the total dead load plus 25 per cent of the floor live load in storage and warehouse occupancies.

W_p = The weight of a part or portion of a structure.

w_x = That portion of W which is **located at or is assigned** to the level designated as x.

(d) *Minimum Earthquake Forces for Buildings.* 1. *Total lateral force and distribution of lateral force.* Every building shall be designed and constructed to withstand minimum total lateral seismic forces assumed to act non-concurrently in the direction of each of the main axes of the building in accordance with the following formula:

$$V = KCW$$

The value of K shall be not less than that exhibited in Table 23-C. The value C shall be determined in accordance with the following formula:

$$C = \frac{0.05}{\sqrt[3]{T}}$$

EXCEPTION: $C = 0.10$ for all one and two story buildings.

T is the fundamental period of vibration of the structure in seconds in the direction considered. Properly substantiated technical data for establishing the period T for the contemplated structure may be submitted.

In the absence of such data, the value of T shall be determined by the following formula:

$$T = \frac{0.05H}{\sqrt{D}}$$

EXCEPTION: $T = 0.10N$ in all buildings in which the lateral resisting system consists of a moment-resisting space frame which resists 100% of the required lateral forces and which frame is not enclosed by or adjoined by more rigid elements which would tend to prevent the frame from resisting lateral forces.

For the purpose of computing C the value of T need not be less than 0.10 seconds.

The total lateral force "V" shall be distributed over the height of the building in accordance with the following formula:

$$F_x = \frac{Vw_x h_x}{\sum wh}$$

EXCEPTION 1: One and two story buildings shall have uniform distribution.

EXCEPTION 2: Where the height to depth ratio of a lateral force resisting system is equal to or greater than five to one, 10 per cent of the total force "V" shall be considered as concentrated at the top story. The remaining 90 per cent shall be distributed as provided for in the above formula.

At each level designated as x, the force F_x shall be applied over the area of the building in accordance with the mass distribution on that level.

2. *Lateral force on parts or portions of buildings or other structures.* Parts or portions of buildings or structures and their anchorage shall be designed for lateral forces in accordance with the following formula:

$$F_p = C_p W_p$$

The values of C_p are in Table 23-D. The distribution of these forces shall be according to the gravity loads pertaining thereto.

3. *Pile foundations.* Individual pile footings of every building or structure shall be so interconnected by ties each of which can carry by tension and compression a horizontal force equal to 10% of the larger pile cap loading unless it can be demonstrated that equivalent restraint can be provided by other means.

(e) *Distribution of Horizontal Shear.* Total shear in any horizontal plane shall be distributed to the various resisting elements in proportion to their rigidities considering the rigidity of the horizontal bracing system or diaphragm as well as the rigidities of the vertical resisting elements.

291

(f) *Drift*. Lateral deflections or drift of a story relative to its adjacent stories shall be considered in accordance with accepted engineering practice.

(g) *Horizontal Torsional Moments*. Provisions shall be made for the increase in shear resulting from the horizontal torsion due to an eccentricity between the center of mass and the center of rigidity. Negative torsional shears shall be neglected. In addition, where the vertical resisting elements depend on diaphragm action for shear distribution at any level, the shear resisting elements shall be capable of resisting a torsional moment assumed to be equivalent to the story shear acting with an eccentricity of not less than five per cent of the maximum building dimension at that level.

(h) *Overturning*. Every building or structure shall be designed to resist the overturning effects caused by the wind forces and related requirements set forth in Section 2307, or the earthquake forces specified in this section, whichever governs.

EXCEPTION: The axial loads from earthquake force on vertical elements and footings in every building or structure may be modified in accordance with the following provisions:

(1) The overturning moment (M) at the base of the building or structure shall be determined in accordance with the following formula:

$$M = \bar{J}\sum F_x h_x$$
$$\text{WHERE} \quad \bar{J} = \frac{0.5}{\sqrt[3]{T^2}}$$

The required value of $\bar{J}$ shall be not less than 0.33 nor more than 1.00.

(2) The overturning moment (M_x) at any level designated as x shall be determined in accordance with the following formula:

$$M_x = \frac{H - h_x}{H} M$$

At any level the overturning moments shall be distributed to the various resisting elements in the same proportion as the distribution of the shears in the resisting system. Where other vertical members are provided which are capable of partially resisting the overturning moments, a redistribution may be made to these members if framing members of sufficient strength and stiffness to transmit the required loads are provided.

Where a vertical resisting element is discontinuous, the overturning moment carried by the lowest story of that element shall be carried down as loads to the foundation.

(i) *Set-Backs*. Buildings having set-backs wherein the plan dimension of the tower in each direction is at least 75 per cent of the corresponding plan dimension of the lower part may be considered as a uniform building without set-backs for the purpose of determining seismic forces.

For other conditions of set-backs the tower shall be designed as a separate building using the larger of the seismic coefficients at the base of the tower determined by considering the tower as either a separate building for its own height or as part of the overall structure. The resulting total shear from the tower shall be applied at the top of the lower part of the building which shall be otherwise considered separately for its own height.

(j) *Structural Frame.* Buildings more than 13 stories or one hundred and sixty feet (160') in height shall have a complete moment resisting space frame capable of resisting not less than 25 per cent of the required seismic load for the structure as a whole. The frame shall be made of a ductile material or a ductile combination of materials. The necessary ductility shall be considered to be provided by a steel frame with moment resistant connections or by other systems proven by tests and studies to provide equivalent energy absorption.

(k) *Design Requirements.* 1. *Combined axial and bending stresses in columns forming a part of a space frame.* Maximum allowable extreme fiber stress in columns at intersection of columns with floor beams or girders for combined axial and bending stresses shall be the allowable bending stress for the material used. Within the center one-half of the unsupported length of the column, the combined axial and bending stresses shall be such that

$$\frac{f_a}{F_a} + \frac{f_b}{F_b} \text{ is equal to or less than 1.}$$

When stresses are due to a combination of vertical and lateral loads, the allowable unit stresses may be increased as specified in Section 2302.

2. *Building separations.* All portions of structures shall be designed and constructed to act as an integral unit in resisting horizontal forces unless separated structurally by a distance sufficient to avoid contact under deflection from seismic action or wind forces.

3. *Minor alterations.* Minor structural alterations may be made in existing buildings and other structures, but the resistance to lateral forces shall be not less than that before such alterations were made, unless the building as altered meets the requirements of this section of the Code.

4. *Unreinforced masonry.* All elements within the structure which are of masonry or concrete and which resist seismic forces or movement shall be reinforced so as to qualify as reinforced masonry or concrete under the provisions of Chapters 24 and 26.

5. *Combined vertical and horizontal forces.* In computing the effect of seismic force in combination with vertical loads, gravity load stresses in-

duced in members by dead load plus design live load, except roof live load, shall be considered.

TABLE 23-C

HORIZONTAL FORCE FACTOR "K" FOR BUILDINGS OR OTHER STRUCTURES[2]

Type or Arrangement of Resisting Elements	Value of K^1
All building framing systems except as hereinafter classified.	1.00
Buildings with a box system as defined in Section 2312(b).	1.33
Buildings with a complete horizontal bracing system capable of resisting all lateral forces, which system includes a moment resisting space frame which, when assumed to act independently, is capable of resisting a minimum of 25% of the total required lateral force.	0.80
Buildings with a moment resisting space frame which when assumed to act independently of any other more rigid elements is capable of resisting 100% of the total required lateral forces in the frame alone.	0.67
Structures other than buildings and other than those listed in Table 23-D.	1.50

[1]The coefficients determined here are for use in the State of California and in other areas of similar earthquake activity. For areas of different activity, the coefficient may be modified by the building official upon advice of seismologists and structural engineers specializing in aseismic design.

[2]Where wind load as set forth in Section 2307 would produce higher stresses, this load shall be used in lieu of the loads resulting from earthquake forces.

TABLE 23-D

HORIZONTAL FORCE FACTOR "C_p" FOR PARTS OR PORTIONS
OF BUILDINGS OR OTHER STRUCTURES

PART OR PORTION OF BUILDINGS	Direction of Force	Value of C_p
Exterior bearing and nonbearing walls, interior bearing walls and partitions, interior nonbearing walls and partitions over ten feet (10') in height, masonry fences over six feet (6') in height.	Normal to flat surface	0.20
Cantilever parapet and other cantilever walls, except retaining walls.	Normal to flat surface	1.00
Exterior and interior ornamentations and appendages.	Any direction	1.00
When connected to or a part of a building: towers, tanks, towers and tanks plus contents, chimneys, smokestacks, and penthouses. Elevated tanks plus contents not supported by a building.	**Any direction**	**0.20[1]**
When resting on the ground: tank plus effective mass of its contents.	**Any direction**	**0.10**
Floors and roofs acting as diaphragms[2].	Any direction	

[1]When H/D of any building is equal to or greater than 5 to 1 increase value by 50%.

[2]Floors and roofs acting as diaphragms shall be designed for a minimum value of C_p of 10% applied to loads tributary from that story unless a greater value of C_p is required by the basic seismic formula $V = KCW$.

References

1. U.S. Coast and Geodetic Survey, *United States Earthquakes*, U.S. Government Printing Office, Washington, D.C., various years.
2. M. A. Biot, "Analytical and Experimental Methods in Engineering Seismology," *Transactions*, American Society of Civil Engineers, Vol. 108, 1943, pages 365–408.
3. D. E. Hudson, "Response Spectrum Techniques in Engineering Seismology," *Proceedings*, World Conference on Earthquake Engineering, Earthquake Engineering Research Institute, Berkeley, Calif., 1956, pages 4-1 to 4-12.
4. E. Rosenblueth, "Some Applications of Probability Theory in Aseismic Design," *Proceedings*, World Conference on Earthquake Engineering, Earthquake Engineering Research Institute, Berkeley, Calif., 1956, pages 8-1 to 8-18.
5. G. W. Housner, "Behavior of Structures During Earthquakes," *Journal*, Engineering Mechanics Division, ASCE, Vol. 85, No. EM4, October 1959, pages 109–129.
6. R. W. Clough, "Dynamic Effects of Earthquakes," *Journal*, Structural Division, ASCE, Vol. 86, No. ST4, April 1960, pages 49–65.
7. N. M. Newmark, "A Method of Computation for Structural Dynamics," *Journal*, Engineering Mechanics Division, ASCE, Vol. 85, No. EM3, July 1959, pages 67–94.
8. A. S. Veletsos and N. M. Newmark, "Effect of Inelastic Behavior on the Response of Simple Systems to Earthquake Motions," *Proceedings*, Second

World Conference on Earthquake Engineering, Tokyo, 1960, Vol. II, pages 895–912.

9. G. V. Berg and S. S. Thomaides, *Energy Consumption by Structures in Strong-Motion Earthquakes*, University of Michigan, College of Engineering, Progress Report on UMRI Project 2881, March 1960.

10. G. N. Bycroft, M. J. Murphy, and K. J. Brown, "Electrical Analog for Earthquake Yield Spectra," *Journal*, Engineering Mechanics Division, ASCE, Vol. 85, No. EM4, October 1959, pages 43–64.

11. G. W. Housner, "Earthquake Resistant Design Based on Dynamic Properties of Earthquakes," *Proceedings*, American Concrete Institute, Vol. 53, 1956–57, pages 85–98.

12. J. A. Cheney, "Structural Analysis by Dynamic Load Parameters," *Proceedings*, ACI, Vol. 53, 1956–57, pages 99–111.

13. J. E. Rinne, "Earthquake Design Criteria for Stack-Like Structures," *Journal*, Structural Division, ASCE, Vol. 84, No. ST4, July 1958, pages 1696-1 to 1696-25.

14. G. W. Housner, "Limit Design of Structures to Resist Earthquakes," *Proceedings*, World Conference on Earthquake Engineering, Earthquake Engineering Research Institute, Berkeley, Calif., 1956, pages 5-1 to 5-13.

15. D. E. Hudson and G. W. Housner, "Structural Vibrations Produced by Ground Motion," *Transactions*, ASCE, Vol. 122, 1957, pages 705–721.

16. J. A. Blume, R. L. Sharpe, and E. Elsesser, *A Structural-Dynamic Investigation of Fifteen School Buildings Subjected to Simulated Earthquake Motion*, Printing Division, Documents Section, State of California, Sacramento.

17. J. A. Blume, "A Reserve Energy Technique for the Earthquake Design and Rating of Structures in the Inelastic Range," *Proceedings*, Second World Conference on Earthquake Engineering, Tokyo, 1960, Vol. II, pages 1061–1084.

18. J. A. Blume, discussion of "Behavior of Structures During Earthquakes," *Journal*, Engineering Mechanics Division, ASCE, Vol. 86, No. EM3, June 1960, pages 197–201.

19. J. Penzien, "Elasto-plastic Response of Idealized Multi-Story Structures Subjected to a Strong Motion Earthquake," *Proceedings*, Second World Conference on Earthquake Engineering, Tokyo, 1960, Vol. II, pages 739–760.

20. J. A. Blume, "Structural Dynamics in Earthquake-Resistant Design," *Transactions*, ASCE, Vol. 125, 1960, pages 1088–1139.

21. J. A. Blume, discussion of "Electrical Analog for Earthquake Yield Spectra," *Journal*, Engineering Mechanics Division, ASCE, Vol. 86, No. EM3, June 1960, pages 177–184.

22. U.S. Atomic Energy Commission, *The Effects of Nuclear Weapons*, Superintendent of Documents, U.S. Government Printing Office, Washington, D.C., June 1957, especially Chapters IV and XII.

23. G. W. Housner, R. R. Martel, and J. L. Alford, *Spectrum Analysis of Strong Motion Earthquakes*, Bulletin of Seismological Society of America, Vol. 43, April 1953, pages 97–119.

24. L. Zeevaert and N. M. Newmark, "Aseismic Design of Latino Americana Tower in Mexico City," *Proceedings*, World Conference on Earthquake Engineering, Earthquake Engineering Research Institute, Berkeley, Calif., 1956, pages 35-1 to 35-11.

25. T. P. Tung and N. M. Newmark, "Shears in a Tall Building Subjected to Strong Motion Earthquakes," *Proceedings*, World Conference on Earthquake Engineering, Earthquake Engineering Research Institute, Berkeley, Calif., 1956, pages 10-1 to 10-11.

26. R. L. Jennings and N. M. Newmark, "Elastic Response of Multi-Story Shear Beam Type Structures Subjected to Strong Ground Motion," *Proceedings*, Second World Conference on Earthquake Engineering, Tokyo, 1960, Vol. II, pages 699–718.

27. L. S. Jacobsen and R. S. Ayre, *Engineering Vibrations*, McGraw-Hill Book Co., Inc., New York, 1958, especially Chapters 8 and 9.

28. W. T. Thomson, *Mechanical Vibrations* (Second Edition), Prentice-Hall, Inc., Englewood Cliffs, N.J., 1953.

29. L. E. Goodman, E. Rosenblueth, and N. M. Newmark, "Aseismic Design of Firmly Founded Elastic Structure," *Transactions*, ASCE, Vol. 120, 1955, pages 782–802.

30. N. O. Myklestad, *Fundamentals of Vibration Analysis*, McGraw-Hill Book Co., Inc., New York, 1956, especially Chapters 5 and 8.

31. C. H. Norris, R. J. Hansen, M. J. Holley, Jr., J. M. Biggs, S. Namyet, and J. K. Minami, *Structural Design for Dynamic Loads*, McGraw-Hill Book Co., Inc., New York, 1959, especially Chapters 4 and 5.

32. S. Timoshenko, *Vibration Problems in Engineering* (Third Edition), D. Van Nostrand Co., Inc., Princeton, N.J., 1955, especially Chapter 4.

33. M. G. Salvadori, "Earthquake Stresses in Shear Buildings," *Transactions*, ASCE, Vol. 119, 1954, pages 171–193.

34. J. A. Blume, discussion of "Earthquake Stresses in Shear Buildings," *Transactions*, ASCE, Vol. 119, 1954, pages 194–201.

35. J. A. Blume, "Period Determinations and Other Earthquake Studies of a Fifteen-Story Building," *Proceedings*, World Conference on Earthquake Engineering, Earthquake Engineering Research Institute, Berkeley, Calif., 1956, pages 11-1 to 11-27.

36. A. W. Anderson, J. A. Blume, H. J. Degenkolb, H. B. Hammill, E. M. Knapik, H. L. Marchand, H. C. Powers, J. E. Rinne, G. A. Sedgwick, and H. O. Sjoberg, "Lateral Forces of Earthquake and Wind," *Transactions*, ASCE, Vol. 117, 1952, pages 716–780.

37. J. K. Minami, "Designing for Earthquakes in Japan," *Modern Designing with Steel*, Kaiser Steel Corp., June 1956.

38. P. M. Ferguson, *Reinforced Concrete Fundamentals*, John Wiley and Sons, New York, 1959.

39. J. I. Parcel and R. B. B. Moorman, *Analysis of Statically Indeterminate Structures*, John Wiley and Sons, New York, 1955, pages 391–397.

40. A. H. Mattock, "The Strength of Singly Reinforced Beams in Bending," *Proceedings of a Symposium on the Strength of Concrete Structures*, Cement and Concrete Association, London, 1956, pages 77–100.

41. J. Warwaruk, *Strength and Behavior in Flexure of Prestressed Concrete Beams*, Doctoral Thesis, Civil Engineering Department, University of Illinois, Urbana, June 1960.

42. E. Hognestad, N. W. Hanson, and D. McHenry, "Concrete Stress Distribution in Ultimate Strength Design," Portland Cement Association, Development Department Bulletin D6 (Reprint from *Journal*, ACI, December 1955, pages 455–479).

43. H. Rüsch, "Versuche zur Festigkeit der Biegedruckzone," *Deutscher Ausschuss für Stahlbeton*, Heft 120, Berlin, 1955.

44. E. Hognestad, "A Study of Combined Bending and Axial Load in Reinforced Concrete Members," University of Illinois Engineering Experiment Station Bulletin No. 399, Urbana, November 1951 (Reprinted as Bulletin No. 1, Reinforced Concrete Research Council).

45. R. F. Blanks and D. McHenry, "Plastic Flow of Concrete at High Loads Relieves Stress Concentrations," *Civil Engineering*, Vol. 19, No. 5, May 1949, pages 320–322.

46. E. Hognestad, "Confirmation of Inelastic Stress Distribution in Concrete," PCA, Development Department Bulletin D15 (Reprint from *Journal*, Structural Division, ASCE, Vol. 83, No. ST2, March 1957, pages 1189-1 to 1189-17).

47. F. E. Richart, A. Brandtzaeg, and R. L. Brown, "A Study of the Failure of Concrete Under Combined Compressive Stresses," University of Illinois Engineering Experiment Station Bulletin No. 185, Urbana, November 1928.

48. F. E. Richart, A. Brandtzaeg, and R. L. Brown, "The Failure of Plain and Spirally Reinforced Concrete in Compression," University of Illinois Engineering Experiment Station Bulletin No. 190, Urbana, April 1929.

49. W. W. L. Chan, "The Ultimate Strength and Deformation of Plastic Hinges in Reinforced Concrete Frameworks," *Magazine of Concrete Research* (London), Vol. 7, No. 21, November 1955, pages 121–132.

50. *Reinforced Concrete Design Handbook* (Second Edition), 1955, ACI 317 (available from PCA).

51. C. S. Whitney and E. Cohen, "Guide for Ultimate Strength Design of Reinforced Concrete," *Journal*, ACI, Vol. 28, No. 5, November 1956, pages 456–490.

52. Joint ASCE-ACI Committee on Shear and Diagonal Tension, Report

presented at 1960 Annual Meeting of American Concrete Institute in New York City.

53. JoDean Morrow and I. M. Viest, "Shear Strength of Reinforced Concrete Frame Members Without Web Reinforcement," *Proceedings*, ACI, Vol. 53, 1956–57, pages 833–870 (Reprinted as Bulletin No. 10, Reinforced Concrete Research Council).

54. J. W. Baldwin, Jr., and I. M. Viest, "Effect of Axial Compression on Shear Strength of Reinforced Concrete Frame Members," *Proceedings*, ACI, Vol. 55, 1958–59, pages 635–654.

55. R. D. de Cossio and C. P. Siess, "Behavior and Strength in Shear of Beams and Frames Without Web Reinforcement," *Journal*, ACI, Vol. 31, No. 8, February 1960, pages 695–735.

56. H. M. McCollister, C. P. Siess, and N. M. Newmark, *Load-Deformation Characteristics of Simulated Beam-Column Connections in Reinforced Concrete*, Civil Engineering Studies, Structural Research Series No. 76, University of Illinois, Urbana, June 1954.

57. G. C. Ernst, "Plastic Hinging at the Intersection of Beams and Columns," *Proceedings*, ACI, Vol. 53, 1956–57, pages 1119–1144.

58. G. C. Ernst, *Reinforced Concrete in the Plastic Range, Part II—Knee Connections*, Report on a Research Project Conducted Under a Grant from the National Science Foundation, University of Nebraska, Lincoln, July 1956.

59. J. R. Gaston, C. P. Siess, and N. M. Newmark, *An Investigation of the Load-Deformation Characteristics of Reinforced Concrete Beams up to the Point of Failure*, Civil Engineering Studies, Structural Research Series No. 40, University of Illinois, Urbana, December 1952.

60. J. R. Benjamin and H. A. Williams, "The Behavior of One-Story Brick Shear Walls," *Journal*, Structural Division, ASCE, Vol. 84, No. ST4, July 1958, pages 1723-1 to 1723-30.

61. J. R. Benjamin and H. A. Williams, "Behavior of Reinforced Concrete Shear Walls," *Transactions*, ASCE, Vol. 124, 1959, pages 669–702.

62. A. J. Ockleston, "Tests on the Old Dental Hospital, Johannesburg; Paper No. 3; The Effect of Floors and Walls on the Behavior of Reinforced Concrete Frameworks Subject to Horizontal Loading," The Concrete Association of South Africa, Johannesburg, South Africa, November 1956, 20 pages.

63. J. R. Benjamin and H. A. Williams, "Behavior of One-Story Reinforced Concrete Shear Walls Containing Openings," *Proceedings*, ACI, Vol. 55, 1958–59, pages 605–618.

64. W. A. Slater, A. R. Lord, and R. R. Zipprodt, "Shear Tests of Reinforced Concrete Beams," *Technological Papers*, Bureau of Standards, Vol. 20, No. 314, U.S. Government Printing Office, Washington, D.C., April 1926, 495 pages.

65. *Analysis of Small Reinforced Concrete Buildings for Earthquake Forces* (Fourth Edition), PCA, 1955.

66. J. R. Benjamin, *Statically Indeterminate Structures*, McGraw-Hill Book Co., Inc., New York, 1959.

67. J. R. Allgood and W. A. Shaw, *Elasto-Plastic Response of Beams to Dynamic Loads*, Technical Memorandum M-130, U.S. Naval Civil Engineering Research and Evaluation Laboratory, Port Hueneme, Calif., March 1958.

68. F. T. Mavis and S. A. Richards, "Impulse Testing of Reinforced Concrete Beams," *Proceedings*, ACI, Vol. 52, 1955–56, pages 93–102.

69. F. T. Mavis and M. J. Greaves, "Destructive Impulse Loading of Reinforced Concrete Beams," *Proceedings*, ACI, Vol. 54, 1957–58, pages 233–252.

70. R. J. Hansen and others, *Behavior of Structural Elements under Impulsive Loads, Parts I, II, and III*, Department of Civil and Sanitary Engineering, Massachusetts Institute of Technology, Cambridge, April and November 1950, and July 1951.

71. A. Feldman, *Resistance and Behavior of Reinforced Concrete Beams under Rapid Loading*, Doctoral Thesis, Civil Engineering Department, University of Illinois, Urbana, October 1960.

72. W. H. Munse, *Impact Tests of Reinforced Concrete Beams*, Master's Thesis, Civil Engineering Department, University of Illinois, Urbana, June 1944.

73. L. G. Simms, "Actual and Estimated Impact Resistance of Some Reinforced Concrete Units Failing in Bending," *Journal of the Institution of Civil Engineers* (London), Vol. 23, 1945, pages 163–179.

74. W. A. Keenan, *The Yield Strength of Intermediate Grade Reinforcing Bars under Rapid Loading*, Master's Thesis, Civil Engineering Department, University of Illinois, Urbana, June 1959.

75. M. J. Manjoine, "Influence of Rate of Strain and Temperature on Yield Stresses of Mild Steel," Journal of Applied Mechanics, *Transactions*, American Society of Mechanical Engineers, Vol. 66, 1944, pages A.211–A.218.

76. Building Code Requirements for Reinforced Concrete, ACI 318–56.

77. Manual of Standard Practice for Detailing Reinforced Concrete Structures, ACI 315–57.

78. Recommended Practice for Placing Reinforcing Bars, Concrete Reinforcing Steel Institute, 1959.

79. *Building Design Handbook*, Wire Reinforcement Institute, 1960.

80. Methods of Test and Inspection for Manual Weld Splicing of Steel Reinforcing Bars (Test Method No. Calif. 601-C), California Division of Highways, January 1959, Part IX, pages 29–32.

81. Welding Qualification Tests and Procedures (Reinforcing Bars), Schoolhouse Section, Circular No. 6, California State Division of Architecture, Part IV, pages 11–15.

82. Uniform Building Code, 1958, International Conference of Building Officials.

83. *Continuity in Concrete Building Frames* (Fourth Edition), PCA.

84. H. J. Degenkolb, "Structural Observations of the Kern County Earthquake," *Transactions*, ASCE, Vol. 120, 1955, pages 1280–1294.

85. *Inspector's Manual, Earthquake Resistant Construction*, Earthquake Engineering Research Institute, 1959.
86. *Manual of Concrete Inspection* (Fourth Edition), 1957, ACI 611.
87. *Design and Control of Concrete Mixtures* (Tenth Edition), PCA.
88. *Concrete Manual* (Sixth Edition), U.S. Bureau of Reclamation.
89. *Forms for Architectural Concrete* (Third Edition), PCA.
90. *Design of Wood Formwork for Concrete Structures*, Wood Construction Data, No. 3, National Lumber Manufacturers Association.
91. *Control of Quality of Ready-Mixed Concrete*, Publication No. 44, National Ready Mixed Concrete Association.
92. Specifications and Test Methods for Ready-Mixed Concrete, Publication No. 47, NRMCA.
93. Specifications for Ready-Mixed Concrete, American Society for Testing Materials C 94.
94. Methods of Verification of Testing Machines, ASTM E 4.
95. Recommended Practice for Selecting Proportions for Concrete (ACI 613–54), *Proceedings*, ACI, Vol. 51, 1954–55, pages 49–64. (Also included in *ACI Standards 1959*.)
96. Recommended Practice for Evaluation of Compression Test Results of Field Concrete (ACI 214–57), *Proceedings*, ACI, Vol. 54, 1957–58, pages 1–20. (Also included in *ACI Standards 1959*.)
97. Sampling Fresh Concrete, ASTM C 172.
98. Making and Curing Concrete Compression and Flexure Test Specimens in the Field, ASTM C 31.
99. Test for Compressive Strength of Molded Concrete Cylinders, ASTM C 39.
100. Specifications for Portland Cement, ASTM C 150.
101. Specifications for Air-Entraining Portland Cement, ASTM C 175.
102. Specifications for Portland Blast-Furnace Slag Cement, ASTM C 205.
103. Specifications for Portland-Pozzolan Cement, ASTM C 340.
104. Specifications for Concrete Aggregates, ASTM C 33.
105. Specifications for Lightweight Aggregates for Structural Concrete, ASTM C 330.
106. Recommended Practice for Petrographic Examination of Aggregates for Concrete, ASTM C 295.
107. Test for Potential Reactivity of Aggregates (Chemical Method), ASTM C 289.
108. Test for Potential Alkali Reactivity of Cement-Aggregate Combinations, ASTM C 227.
109. Test for Potential Volume Change of Cement-Aggregate Combinations, ASTM C 342.
110. Test for Slump of Portland Cement Concrete, ASTM C 143.
111. Recommended Practice for Selecting Proportions for Structural Lightweight Concrete (ACI 613A–59), *Proceedings*, ACI, Vol. 55, 1958–59, pages 305–314. (Also included in *ACI Standards 1959*.)

112. Test for Specific Gravity and Absorption of Coarse Aggregate, ASTM C 127.
113. J. J. Shideler, "Lightweight Aggregate Concrete for Structural Use," PCA, Development Department Bulletin D17 (Reprint from *Journal*, ACI, Vol. 29, No. 4, October 1957, pages 299–328).
114. J. A. Hanson, "Shear Strength of Lightweight Reinforced Concrete Beams," PCA, Development Department Bulletin D22 (Reprint from *Journal*, ACI, Vol. 30, No. 3, September 1958, pages 387–403).
115. Recommended Practice for Hot Weather Concreting (ACI 605–59), *Proceedings*, ACI, Vol. 55, 1958–59, pages 525–534. (Also included in *ACI Standards 1959*.)
116. P. Klieger, "Effect of Mixing and Curing Temperature on Concrete Strength," PCA, Research Department Bulletin 103 (Reprint from *Journal*, ACI, Vol. 29, No. 12, June 1958, pages 1063–1081).
117. "Effect of Initial Curing Temperatures on the Compressive Strength and Durability of Concrete," U.S. Bureau of Reclamation, Concrete Laboratory Report No. C-625, July 29, 1952.
118. *Prevention of Plastic Cracking in Concrete*, PCA.
119. Recommended Practice for Winter Concreting (ACI 604–56), *Proceedings*, ACI, Vol. 52, 1955–56, pages 1025–1047. (Also included in *ACI Standards 1959*.)
120. Test for Weight per Cubic Foot, Yield, and Air Content (Gravimetric) of Concrete, ASTM C 138.
121. Test for Air Content of Freshly Mixed Concrete by the Volumetric Method, ASTM C 173.
122. Test for Air Content of Freshly Mixed Concrete by the Pressure Method, ASTM C 231.
123. Specifications for Air-Entraining Admixtures for Concrete, ASTM C 260.
124. Specifications for Calcium Chloride, ASTM D 98.
125. Testing Air-Entraining Admixtures for Concrete, ASTM C 233.
126. Test for Autoclave Expansion of Portland Cement, ASTM C 151.
127. Test for Time of Setting of Hydraulic Cement by Vicat Needle, ASTM C 191.
128. Test for Time of Setting of Hydraulic Cement by Gillmore Needles, ASTM C 266.
129. Test for Air Content of Hydraulic Cement Mortar, ASTM C 185.
130. Test for Tensile Strength of Hydraulic Cement Mortars, ASTM C 190.
131. Test for Compressive Strength of Hydraulic Cement Mortars, ASTM C 109.
132. Recommended Practice for Measuring, Mixing and Placing Concrete (ACI 614–59), *Proceedings*, ACI, Vol. 55, 1958–59, pages 535–565. (Also included in *ACI Standards 1959*.)
133. H. S. Meissner, "Compacting Concrete by Vibration," *Proceedings*, ACI, Vol. 49, 1953, pages 885–892.

134. *Vibration for Quality Concrete*, PCA.

135. "Curing Concrete," ACI Committee 612, *Proceedings*, ACI, Vol. 55, 1958–59, pages 161–172.

136. R. F. Blanks and L. H. Tuthill, "Horizontal Construction Joints," U.S. Bureau of Reclamation, Technical Memorandum No. 622, October 28, 1941

137. J. W. Robinson, "Tests of 6-in. Diameter Construction Joint Cores, Shasta Dam, Central Valley Project," U.S. Bureau of Reclamation, Technical Laboratory Report No. C-285, September 10, 1945.

138. "Pressures on Formwork," ACI Committee 622, *Proceedings*, ACI, Vol. 55, 1958–59, pages 173–190.

139. Specifications for Billet-Steel Bars for Concrete Reinforcement, ASTM A 15.

140. Specifications for Rail-Steel Bars for Concrete Reinforcement, ASTM A 16.

141. Specifications for Special Large Size Deformed Billet Steel Bars for Concrete Reinforcement, ASTM A408.

142. Specifications for High-Strength Billet Steel Bars for Concrete Reinforcement, ASTM A431.

143. Specifications for Deformed Billet Steel Bars for Concrete Reinforcement with 60,000 psi Minimum Yield Point, ASTM A432.

144. Specifications for Minimum Requirements for the Deformations of Deformed Steel Bars for Concrete Reinforcement, ASTM A305.

145. Specifications for Welded Steel Wire Fabric for Concrete Reinforcement, ASTM A185.

146. Specifications for Fabricated Steel Bar or Rod Mats for Concrete Reinforcement, ASTM A184.

147. A. C. Bianchini, R. E. Woods, and C. E. Kesler, "Effect of Floor Concrete Strength on Column Strength," *Proceedings*, ACI, Vol. 56, 1959–60, pages 1149–1169 (Reprinted as Bulletin No. 13, Reinforced Concrete Research Council).

148. L. S. Jacobsen, *Frictional Effects in Composite Structures Subjected to Earthquake Vibrations*, Stanford University, March 9, 1959 (California State Division of Architecture, Sponsor).

149. G. V. Berg and S. S. Thomaides, discussion of "Electrical Analog for Earthquake Yield Spectra," *Journal*, Engineering Mechanics Division, ASCE, Vol. 86, No. EM2, April 1960.

150. R. M. Sheth, *Effect of Inelastic Action on the Response of Simple Structures to Earthquake Motions*, Master's Thesis, Civil Engineering Department, University of Illinois, Urbana, 1959.

151. G. W. Housner, *Intensity of Ground Motion During Strong Earthquakes*, Office of Naval Research, Contract N60NR-244, August 1952.

152. D. E. Hudson, "A Comparison of Theoretical and Experimental Determinations of Building Response to Earthquakes," *Proceedings*, Second World

Conference on Earthquake Engineering, Tokyo, 1960, Vol. II, pages 1105–1120.

153. R. W. Clough, "On the Importance of Higher Modes of Vibration in the Earthquake Response of a Tall Building," *Bulletin*, Seismology Society of America, Vol. 45, October 1955.

154. L. Chow, H. D. Conway, and G. Winter, "Stresses in Deep Beams," *Transactions*, ASCE, Vol. 118, 1953, pages 686–708.

155. *Design of Deep Girders*, PCA.

156. P. H. Kaar, "Stresses in Centrally Loaded Deep Beams," PCA, Development Department Bulletin D18 (Reprint from *Proceedings*, Society for Experimental Stress Analysis, Vol. 15, No. 1, 1957, pages 77–84).

157. J. A. Blume, discussion of "Dynamic Effects of Earthquakes," *Journal*, Structural Division, ASCE, Vol. 86, No. ST12, December 1960, pages 123–125.

158. "Formwork for Concrete," ACI Committee 622, *Journal*, ACI, Vol. 32, No. 9, March 1961.

159. National Design Specifications for Stress-Grade Lumber and Its Fastenings (1960 Edition), National Lumber Manufacturers' Association.

160. *Wood Structural Design Data* (Third Edition), Vol. 1, NLMA.

APPENDIX **E**

Notation

(For Appendix B notation, see page 311)

A = area of cross-section.

A_c = area of core of a spirally reinforced column; also rectangular section confined by rectangular hoops.

A_g = gross area of concrete section.

A_s = area of tensile reinforcement or of column bars.

A_s' = area of compressive reinforcement.

A_s'' = cross-sectional area of spiral reinforcement.

A_{sh}'' = cross-sectional area of transverse, rectangular hoop reinforcement.

A_{tr} = transformed area of uncracked cross-section.

A_v = total area of web reinforcement within a distance s (for column ties used as web reinforcement, see Chapter 6).

C = coefficient in formula for base shear (SEAOC).

$\bar{C}$ = coefficient of modal deflection component.

C_p = shear coefficient for portion of a structure (SEAOC).

D = dimension of the building in feet in a direction parallel to the applied force (SEAOC); also diameter of reinforcing bar.

$\bar{D}$ = diameter of confined concrete core.

E_c = Young's modulus of elasticity of concrete; also specifically of concrete in columns.

E_g = Young's modulus of elasticity of concrete in girders.

E_s = Young's modulus of elasticity of steel.

F = general designation of force; also $bd^2/12{,}000$ used in determination of resisting moment of concrete sections.

F_z = lateral force at level z (F_x in SEAOC report).

$G = 0.4E_c$ = modulus of elasticity of concrete in shear.

H = height of the main portion of the building in feet above the base (SEAOC).

H' = clear story height.

H_s = story height.

I = moment of inertia of a member.

I_c = moment of inertia of a column.

I_g = moment of inertia of a girder.

I_p = total rotational stiffness about center of rigidity.

$J = \dfrac{0.5}{\sqrt[3]{T^2}}$ = coefficient of overturning moment at base (SEAOC).

K = numerical coefficient in formula for base shear (SEAOC).

K_c = stiffness at top of a column or column stiffness.

K'_c = stiffness at base of a column.

K_g = girder stiffness.

L = length or span.

M = bending moment; also overturning moment at the base of a building (SEAOC).

M_B = moment at the base of a column.

M_b = maximum sum of the ultimate positive moment and ultimate negative moment of the two beams framing at a joint.

M_c = column moment.

M_c^B = ultimate moment at base of column.

M_c^T = ultimate moment at top of column.

M_{cr} = flexural cracking moment.

$\bar{M}_{cr}$ = torsional moment of mass about the center of rigidity of a frame.

M_F = fixed end moment.

M_g = sum of yield end moment capacities of the two girders connected to a joint.

M_s = smaller of the two quantities M_g or ($M_B + M_T$) at a joint.

M_T = moment at the top of a column.

M_u = ultimate moment.

M_y = yield moment, moment corresponding to yielding of tensile reinforcement.

M_z = overturning moment at level z (M_x in SEAOC report).

N = total number of stories above exterior grade (SEAOC).

$\bar{N}$ = number of stories above the story under consideration or number of stories counting down from the top.

P = column axial compressive force.

P_t = column axial tensile force.

P_u = ultimate column axial compressive force.

$\bar{Q}$ = inertial force.

$\bar{R}$ = average range of strength of groups of companion concrete cylinder specimens.

R_n = residual force.

S = spectral value of displacement relative to the ground.

$S_a = \omega^2 S$ = spectral value of acceleration.

$S_v = \omega S$ = spectral value of velocity.

$T = 1/f = 2\pi/\omega$ = period of vibration or fundamental period (SEAOC).

$\bar{T}$ = temperature of concrete as placed.

U = internal stored energy or energy absorbed.

U_c = ultimate-strength capacity of a column.

V = shear or lateral force at base of building (SEAOC); also story shear; also total shear carried by a member due to vertical loads.

$\bar{V}$ = coefficient of variation.

V_c = shear carried by concrete; also cracking shear in shear walls.

$\bar{V}_o$ = within-test coefficient of variation.

V_u = total ultimate shear carried by concrete and web reinforcing.

V_x = shear due to torsion on a column line.

V_x' = torsional shear at a column.

V_y = story shear at yielding; also shear due to torsion on a column line.

V_y' = torsional shear at a column.

V_z = story shear at level z.

W = total dead load (SEAOC). (For warehouses, W shall be equal to the total dead load plus a portion of the live load in accordance with the applicable code.)

$\bar{X}$ = average strength of all concrete test cylinders.

X_{cr} = distance of assumed origin from center of rigidity cr.

$\bar{X}_{cr}$ = distance to a column or wall from the center of rigidity.

X_o = distance to a column or wall from an assumed origin; also the length over which yielding occurs in a flexural member.

Y_{cr} = distance of assumed origin from center of rigidity cr.

$\bar{Y}_{cr}$ = distance to a column or wall from the center of rigidity.

Y_o = distance to a column or wall from an assumed origin.

a = pitch or spacing of transverse reinforcement.

b = width of rectangular beam or width of flanges of T- and I-sections; also width of column or shear wall.

b' = minimum width of a section (web of I-shaped sections, stem of T-beams, etc.).

b'' = width of concrete confined by hoops or ties.

c = distance from neutral axis to extreme fiber in tension.

$\bar{c}$ = constant—see Table 8-2.

d = effective depth of flexural member or distance from the compression face to centroid of longitudinal tensile reinforcement.

d' = distance from compression face to centroid of longitudinal compressive reinforcement.

e = eccentricity—distance between center of rigidity and center of gravity or mass of a building.

e' = eccentricity of axial load measured from centroid of section.

$f = 1/T$ = natural frequency of vibration.

f_c = concrete stress.

f_c' = concrete cylinder compressive strength at 28 days.

f_{cu} = average flexural compressive stress of unconfined concrete at ultimate.

f_{cu}'' = effective strength of confined concrete.

f_r' = required average concrete cylinder compressive strength.

f_s = stress in tensile reinforcement.

f_s'' = stress in transverse spiral reinforcement.

f_{sh}'' = stress in transverse rectangular hoop reinforcement.

f_{su} = stress in tensile reinforcement at ultimate.

f_{su}' = stress in compressive reinforcement at ultimate.

f_y = yield stress of tensile reinforcement.

f_y' = yield stress of compressive reinforcement.

f_y'' = yield stress of transverse spiral reinforcement.

f_{yh}'' = yield stress of transverse rectangular hoop reinforcement.

g = acceleration of gravity.

h = total depth of member.

h'' = length of effective side of transverse rectangular hoop.

h_z = height in feet above the base to the level designated as z (h_x in SEAOC report).

$j = 1 - k/3$ = ratio of distance between centroids of compressive and tensile stresses to effective depth d.

k = ratio of distance between extreme compressive fiber and neutral axis to effective depth d.

k_u = value of k at ultimate.

k_u'' = value of k_u for beams with confined core.

m = mass; also $f_y/0.85f_c'$

$n = E_s/E_c$ = modular ratio.

$p = A_s/bd$ = ratio of area of tensile reinforcement to area of concrete.

$p' = A_s'/bd$ = ratio of area of compressive reinforcement to area of concrete.

$$p'' = 0.45\left(\frac{A_g}{A_c} - 1\right)\frac{f_c'}{f_y''}$$

p_l = maximum lateral pressure of concrete as placed.

$q = pf_y/f_c'$ = reinforcement index.

$$q'' = \frac{A_{sh}''f_{yh}''}{ah''f_c'}$$

$q_u = pf_y/f_{cu}$ = useful limit of q for tensile reinforcement.

$q'_u = p'f'_y/f_{cu}$ = useful limit of q for compressive reinforcement.
$\bar{r}$ = rate of placing concrete.
s = spacing of web reinforcing.
t = time; also overall dimension of column.
$\bar{t}$ = constant—see Table 8-1.
$u = y - x$ = displacement of mass relative to ground or story displacement.
$\dot{u}$ = first derivative of u with respect to time, velocity of a point relative to the ground.
$\ddot{u} = \ddot{y} - \ddot{x}$ = second derivative of u with respect to time, acceleration of a point relative to the ground.
u_{na} = assumed deflection of mass n.
u_{nb} = computed deflection of mass n due to inertial forces.
$\bar{u}_{nb} = u_{nb}/\omega^2$
u_m = maximum displacement of an elasto-plastic system for a given T.
u_o = maximum displacement of an elastic system for a given T.
$u(t)$ = relative displacement as a function of time.
u_y = displacement of mass relative to ground at yielding.
u_z = total displacement at any level.
v_c = unit shear stress carried by concrete.
w_z = that portion of w that is located or is assigned to the level designated as z (w_x in SEAOC report).
x = displacement of ground.
$\ddot{x}$ = second derivative of x with respect to time, ground acceleration.
y = displacement of mass or structure in space.
$\ddot{y}$ = second derivative of y with respect to time, acceleration at a point on the structure.
z = level (x in SEAOC report).

Δ = displacement or deflection.
$\sum$ = summation.
$\sum K_j$ = sum of all stiffnesses at the joint at top of a column.
$\sum K'_j$ = sum of all stiffnesses at the joint at base of column.
$\sum wh$ = sum of all weights w_z multiplied by their respective height h_z above the base (SEAOC).
$\sum \lambda$ = sum of all λ's in a story of a frame or building.

α = a particular quantity (displacement, shear, acceleration, etc.) in modal response computations.
$\alpha(t) = \alpha$ as a function of time.
$\beta = (\eta/2m\omega)$ = damping coefficient expressed as a percentage of the critical damping value.

γ = modal participation factor.
δ = increment in story displacement.
ϵ_c = concrete strain.
ϵ_{cu} = concrete strain at ultimate.
ϵ_h = reinforcing steel strain at the beginning of strain hardening following yielding.
ϵ_s = strain in reinforcing steel.
ϵ_{su} = strain in reinforcing steel at ultimate.
ϵ'_{su} = strain in compressive reinforcing steel at ultimate.
ϵ''_{su} = strain in transverse spiral reinforcement at maximum stress.
ϵ_y = yield strain of reinforcing steel.
ϵ''_y = yield strain of transverse spiral reinforcement.
η = damping coefficient.
λ = spring constant, ratio of spring force to deformation.
λ_{inf} = spring constant of a column or story with infinite floor stiffness.
μ = ductility factor, ratio of maximum deformation to yield deformation.
σ = standard deviation.
σ_a = axial strength of confined concrete.
σ_l = lateral confining pressure.
σ_o = within-test standard deviation.
ϕ = curvature of a member due to an applied moment.
ϕ_u = curvature at ultimate.
ϕ_y = curvature at yield.
$\omega = 2\pi f$ = circular frequency of vibration.

Subscripts not defined in preceding notation:
f = due to flexure.
j = mode designation.
k = mode designation.
m = maximum value.
n = story designation above ground (0 = ground). For displacement of the nth story in the jth mode, use y_{nj} (absolute) or u_{nj} (relative to ground).
v = due to shear.

Notation Pertaining to Appendix B

B = a safety factor based upon reserve energy (see Fig. B-12).

$\left.\begin{array}{l} BD \\ BE \\ BF \\ BN \end{array}\right\}$ = earthquake rating symbols (see Fig. B-11).

C = the design coefficient of story shear.

C' = the actual value of coefficient C for the structure as designed and detailed.

D = area under force-deflection curve for the force P_D (see Figs. B-2 and B-3).

E = energy requirement or kinetic energy (see Fig. B-12).

E' = energy requirement—special value of E (see Fig. B-12).

F = a factor to express spectral values (see Figs. B-5 and B-6).

G = energy assumed fed back to the ground (see Fig. B-12).

H_i = the "hump" area (see Fig. B-2 and page 252).

K_D = initial (elastic) stiffness (see Fig. B-2).

K_i = stiffness at or after having reached deflection Δ_i (see Figs. B-2 and B-12).

P = lateral force or story shear.

P_D = the design shear (see Fig. B-2).

R = the reserve energy reduction coefficient (see Fig. B-12).

T = natural period of vibration of entire structure.

T_D = a hypothetical period = $1.11\sqrt{W/K_D}$ = $1.11\sqrt{\Delta_D/C'}$

T_i = assumed natural period after reaching deflection Δ_i (see Figs. B-2 and B-4).

T_g = ground period.

U_i = total work capacity (see Fig. B-2).

W = the total weight at and above the story or level under consideration.

Z = total number of stories, panels, or units above and including the one under consideration.

g = acceleration of gravity.

h = story height in feet.

v = velocity.

Δ = deflection of the story or unit under consideration (see Figs. B-2 and B-3).

Δ_{max} = the deflection beyond which the force-deflection curve slopes downward or deflection at point of collapse, whichever is less (see Figs. B-2, B-3, B-11).

Ω = energy capacity reduction factor for multistory buildings (see page 263).

a_i = spectral or analog response acceleration at period T_i, normally for 5 per cent of critical damping (see Figs. B-6 and B-12).

β = ratio of design force to yield force.

γ = deterioration factor for H_i (see page 252).

θ = angles as in Fig. B-3.

μ = ductility factor for elasto-plastic system, or the ratio of total deflection Δ_i to yield deflection Δ_y.

ρ = a factor as in Fig. B-12.

ϕ = angles as in Fig. B-3.

Subscripts:

D = design or initial elastic condition.

$\left.\begin{array}{l} d \\ e \\ f \end{array}\right\}$ = specific values of i (see Fig. B-11).

i = a trial deflection.

n = specific value of i (see Fig. B-11).

y = yield-point condition.

z = story or mass designation starting from top of building.

Index

Acceleration
   ground, 1
   spectral, 7–14
Aggregates, 207, 211–215

Base shear, *see* seismic shear
Beams, *see* concrete members, curvature, ductility, moments, reinforcement, shear, stiffness, ultimate curvature, ultimate strength

Columns, *see* concrete members, curvature, ductility, moments, reinforcement, shear, stiffness, ultimate curvature, ultimate strength
Concrete
   admixtures, 224
   aggregates, 207, 211–215
   air entrainment, 222–224
   cold-weather concreting, 220–222
   construction joints, 166, 231–234
   curing, 218, 222, 230
   handling, transporting, and placing, 225–230
   hot-weather concreting, 215–220
   lightweight-aggregate, 214
   quality control, general, 206–214
   recommended strength, 147
   strength of confined, 96–101, 109–112
   strength of unconfined, 94–96

   stress-strain relationship, 94–101
Concrete members
   reversal of loading, 141–144, 150
   ultimate capacity—bending, 101–112, 194, 195
   ultimate capacity—bending and axial load, 113–117, 190–194, 197
   ultimate capacity—bending, axial load, and shear, 117–121, 194–200
Construction joints, 166, 231–234
Curvature
   and energy absorption, 137–141, 196, 199
   at ultimate, 101–117, 121–125
   at yield, 101–104
   distribution at ultimate, 121–125
   measured in tests, 123–125

Damping
   critical, 4
   effect on spectral values, 8–14, 45, 258–261
   per cent of critical, 4, 7
   velocity, 4
Deflection
   earthquake, 60–62, 200–202, 259
   lurches, 259
   reversal of loading, 141–144, 150
   tests of concrete members, 125–131
   wind, 61, 62

Index

Diagonal tension, *see* shear
Displacement
  ground, 1–3
  spectral, 5–15
  yield, 3–5
Ductility, 46, 73–75, 96, 112, 114–117,
    also see curvature
  design and details, 194–200
  of frames, 15, 125
  relation to energy absorption, 137–141,
    250–285
  reversal of loading, 141–144
Ductility factor
  definition, 5
  effect on spectral values, 11–15
  minimum required for structures, 15, 42,
    46, 146

Eccentricity
  accidental, 71, 182
  frame torsion, 71–73
Elastic
  displacement, 5
  response, 5, 251
  response, multimass systems, 17–25, 32–
    37, 241–249
Elasto-plastic
  displacement, 5, 61, 200–202
  energy absorption, 90
  reserve energy technique, 90, 249, 261,
    272
  response, 5
  reversal of loading, 141–144
  shear vs. displacement, 3
  spectral response, 11–14
El Centro earthquake
  accelerogram, 1–3
  spectra, 3–10
Energy
  absorption, 15, 45, 46, 73–75, 90, 137–
    141, 196, 250–285
  elastic, 7
  feedback to ground, 15, 38, 45, 252, 261,
    272, 274
  maximum, 7
Expansion joints, *see* construction joints

Flexibility, *see* stiffness
Forms, 229, 234–236
Foundation
  effects of, 38, 252, 261, 272, 274
Frame
  analysis for lateral loads, 73–88, 173–187

box-system, 74
design of members, 145–166, 187–194
detailing of members, 145–166, 194–200
ductility, 194–200
limit design, 86–88
moment-resisting, 73–75
vertical load carrying, 74
Frequency
  circular, 4, 19–25
  natural, 4, 22
  higher modes, 25–30, 241
  Rayleigh's method, 20–25
  step-by-step or Holzer method, 28–30
  successive approximations (Stodola), 20–
    25
  "sweeping" process, 25–28, 241

Gravity, center of, 71
Ground motion
  acceleration, 1–3
  displacement, 1–3
  duration, 1–3
  dynamic response to, 3–7
  idealized, 8–14, 244
  maximum dynamic response to, *see* spec-
    tral values
  velocity, 1–3

Hammering, 60

Inelastic
  energy absorption, 252, 260, 261
  force-deflection relation, 252–254, 278–
    280
Inspection
  general, 203–206
  concrete, 206–233
  forms, 234–236
  reinforcement, 236–240
  building separations, 240

Lightweight-aggregate concrete, 214
Loads
  dead, 49, 50, 54, 169
  live, 49, 50, 54, 169
  reversal of, 141–144
  wind, 50, 53, 169
Lurches, *see* deflection

Materials
  admixtures, 224
  aggregates, 213–215
  cement, 207, 208, 213
  reinforcement, 147, 148, 238

Modal analysis, 32–37, 241–249

Modal participation factors, 30–32

Modal response
in the inelastic range, 37, 38, 246–249
maximum possible, 17, 18, 33, 34, 37, 244–249
probable maximum, 19, 36, 37, 244–249

Mode
fundamental, 19–25, 49, 58–60, 241–244
higher modes, 25–30, 59, 60, 241–244
Rayleigh's method, 20–25
step-by-step or Holzer method, 28–30
successive approximations (Stodola), 20–25
"sweeping" process, 25–28
torsional, 71

Moment-curvature relations, *see* curvature

Moments
reversal of loading, 141–144
ultimate in bending, 101–112, 194–196
ultimate in bending and axial load, 113–117, 190–194
yield, 86–88, 103

Moments due to lateral forces
beam, 79–86, 177–182
column, 79–86, 177–183
overturning, 62–64, 172, 173
yield, 86–88

Overturning moment
earthquake, 62–64, 172, 173, 183
wind, 63, 186

Period of vibration
estimated, 44, 58–60, 171, 273
fundamental, 4, 5, 19–25
higher modes, 25–30
Rayleigh's method, 20–25
step-by-step or Holzer method, 28–30
successive approximations (Stodola), 20–25
"sweeping" process, 25–28

Reinforcement
compression, 108
for confinement, 96–101, 109–112, 114–117
grades or type, 147, 148
placing, 236–240
strain at ultimate, 104–107
stress-strain relationship, 93
transverse shear, 119
yield stress, 93, 94
yielding in concrete members, 103

Reinforcement, design requirements
anchorage, 153–155, 162
beams, 149–153, 187–190, 194–196
bond, 153–155, 162
columns, 156–162, 190–194, 196–200
compression, 149–153, 194, 195
construction joints, 164, 165
flat plate, 156
floor openings, 155
hoops, 156–161, 196, 197
slabs, 155
spiral, 156, 157
splices, 153, 154, 162, 164
stirrups, 150, 151, 196
stirrup-ties, 151, 152, 154, 196
walls, 163–166
wall intersections, 163, 164
wall openings, 164
welding, 148, 154, 162

Reserve energy technique, 90, 249, 250–285
earthquake rating, 268, 269
general, 16, 250–260
multimass systems, 262–264, 272–285
procedure, 260–268
single-mass systems, 260–268

Rigidity, *see* stiffness
centroid of, 71

Seismic lateral forces
building parts, 88–90
code, 48, 54–58, 171, 172
modal analysis, 34–37, 241–249

Seismic shear
distribution to frame members, 72, 73, 75–79, 84, 179–183
from modal analysis
inelastic range, 37, 38, 241–247
maximum possible base, 17, 18, 33, 34, 37, 244–249
probable maximum base, 19, 36, 37, 244–249
story, 32–37, 244–249
reserve energy technique, 254–268
specified by code
base, 42–44, 51–58, 74, 170–172
story, 54, 55, 172, 177, 178
torsional, 71–73, 182

Seismic zoning, 51–53

Separation between buildings, 60–62, 240

Shear
combined with bending, 117–120
combined with bending and axial load, 120, 121
reinforcement requirements, 150, 151, 160, 164–166, 195–200
resisted by concrete, 119–121
resisted by web reinforcement, 119

Shear walls, 66–71, 74, 131–137
  behavior, 131–137
  reinforcement, 163–166
  stiffness, 136
  tests, 132–136
Soil, effects of, 38, 51–53
Spectral values
  acceleration, 7–14, 251, 254, 256–260, 262
  applied to multimass systems, 32–37
  displacement, 7–14
  velocity, 7–14, 256–260
Spectrum
  design, 14, 244, 245, 254–258
  elastic, 7–10
  elasto-plastic, 11–14
  idealized, 42
Spring constant, 3–5, 21–25, 241
Stiffness
  beams, 77–86, 173–175
  columns, 77–86, 173–177
  effect on frame moments, 77–86, 177–182
  floors, 70, 71
  members in parallel, 66
  members in series, 66
  of frame in torsion, 71–73, 182–185
  story, 64–71, 75–79, 173–177
  walls, 67–71, 136
Strain
  concrete, confined, 96–101
  concrete, unconfined, 94–96
  elastic, 93
  hardening, 94
  reinforcement at ultimate, 104–108
  useful limit in confined concrete, 109, 110, 114–117
  useful limit in unconfined concrete, 102, 104, 108
  yield, 93, 94, 101–104
Stress
  allowable, 49–51
  unconfined concrete at ultimate, 104, 105
  yield, 93, 94

Stress-strain relationship, 93–101
  concrete, confined, 96–101
  concrete, unconfined, 93–96
  reinforcement, 93
Supervision, 204–206

Torsion
  accidental, 71, 182–185
  frame, 71–73, 173, 182–185

Ultimate curvature of members
  concrete, confined, 111, 112, 114–117
  concrete, unconfined, 105, 111–115
  measured, 123–125
  relation to energy absorption, 137–141
Ultimate strength
  bending, 101–112
  bending and axial load, 112–117
  bending, axial load, and shear, 117–121
  design, 146
  moment computation — beams, 150, 151, 194–196
  moment computation — columns, 190–193
  reversal of moment, 141–144

Velocity
  ground, 1–3
  spectral, 7–14
Vibration, *see* period of vibration

Wind
  analysis, 186
  deflection, 61, 62
  forces, 50, 169

Yield moment, 103

Zoning, 53